D1096367

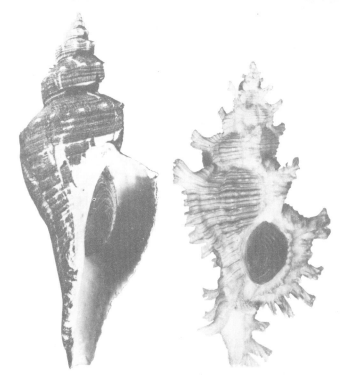

SHELLS OF THE WESTERN PACIFIC IN COLOR

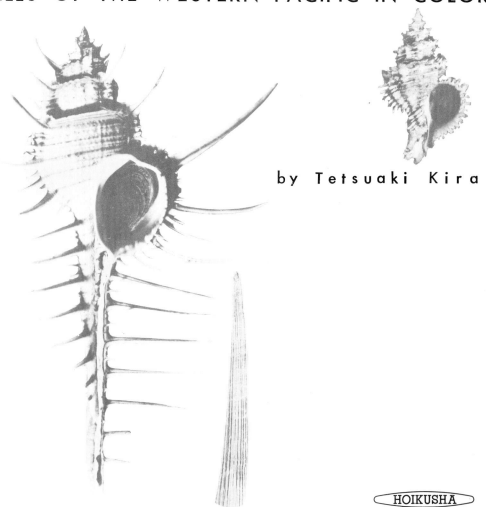

by Tetsuaki Kira

HOIKUSHA

SHELLS OF THE WESTERN PACIFIC IN COLOR

by Tetsuaki Kira

Copyright © 1962
HOIKUSHA PUBLISHING CO., LTD.
20, 1-chome Uchikyuhoji-machi, Higashi-ku, Osaka, Japan
Printed in Japan

PREFACE TO THE ENGLISH EDITION

Shells are found everywhere around us. Not to speak of marine shells crowding the seaside, we will surely find some land snails in our gardens, and a lot of freshwater shells in wayside streams and ponds. Although the molluscs are next to the insect in the number of species, they are perhaps the most widespread group of animals found on the earth. They inhabit almost all corners of land and water, from the very bottom of the deepest trench of the Pacific to 14,000 feet height of the Himalayan Range, and from the polar seas to the heart of a continent where little water is available.

Unlike the plants, insects, and many other animals, the beauty of shells is very easily and almost permanently preserved in dried specimens. A vast amount of waste shells, that supplied an important food for prehistoric people, still remains as shell-mounds, surviving thousands of years of weathering and offering a valuable material for archaeological study. The unequalled importance of fossil shells in the geological science may need no further explanation.

Since the permanent beauty and familiarity of shells first fascinated the author in his youth, he has been an amateur collector for almost fifty years during his life as an educator. Being an outsider of the shell science, he does not intend this book to be a comprehensive work on Japanese shells. He only hopes that this will be a handy guide for junior students, for amateur collectors, and for all people who loves the beauty of nature.

Japan is rightly proud of its wealth of shells. About five thousand species of marine shells live in the seas around the Japanese Archipelago, from the Kuriles as far south to the Ryukyus. Both warm and cold currents bring characteristic faunas with them to the islands, where the animals thrive, favored by the diversified topography of coasts and bottoms. It may seem rather surprising to add that nearly seven hundred species and many subspecies of land snails are known on these islands, no more than 150,000 square miles in total area.

Out of this ample shell fauna, only some 1,300 species are illustrated here, almost exclusively based on the author's own collection. Minute-sized shells are mostly omitted because of the difficulty in printing. A considerable number of these minute species are shown as magnified photographs in another volume by Dr. T. Habe, which is now being translated into English.

Besides the brief description of each species, approximate ranges of horizontal and vertical distribution are noted in the text. The northeastern, central and southern Japan (or Honshû), as frequently used in describing the horizontal distribution, respectively indicate the areas, north of the Bôsô Peninsula, between the Bôsô Peninsula and Shikoku, and between the Kii Peninsula and Kyûshû. The vertical range given in fathoms is not accurate enough, since the figures are mainly based on the experience of fishermen.

The families are not always arranged in the order of the systematic classification. The readers should consult the table at the beginning of the book for the exact systematic position of the families.

In publishing this book, the author wishes to express his deepest appreciation to Dr. Tokubei Kuroda, the president of the Malacological Society of Japan, for the kind guidance given to the author throughout many years of friendship, and for the critical review of the manuscript. He also owes much to Drs. Tadashige Habe and Tatuo Kira in the English translation. Dr. Habe took the trouble of revising the Latin names into the latest and authorized way of use, which the author is pleased to acknowledge.

July 1962

Tetsuaki Kira

CONTENTS

Parts of the gastropod and bivalve shells

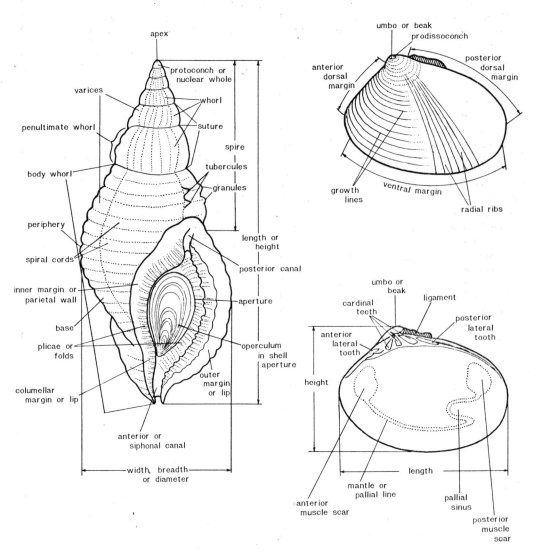

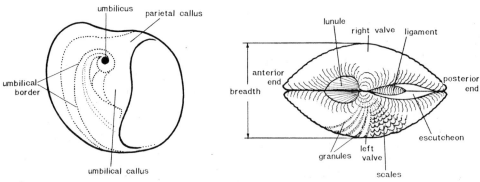

Parts of the scallop, chiton and tusk shells

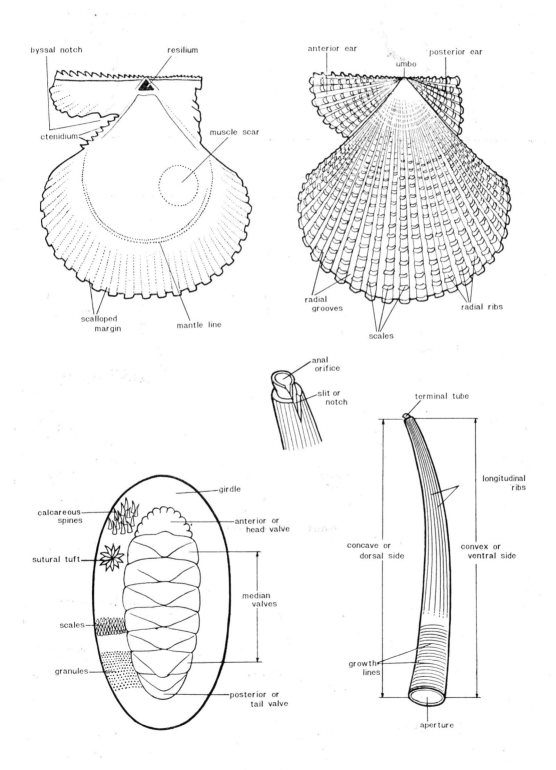

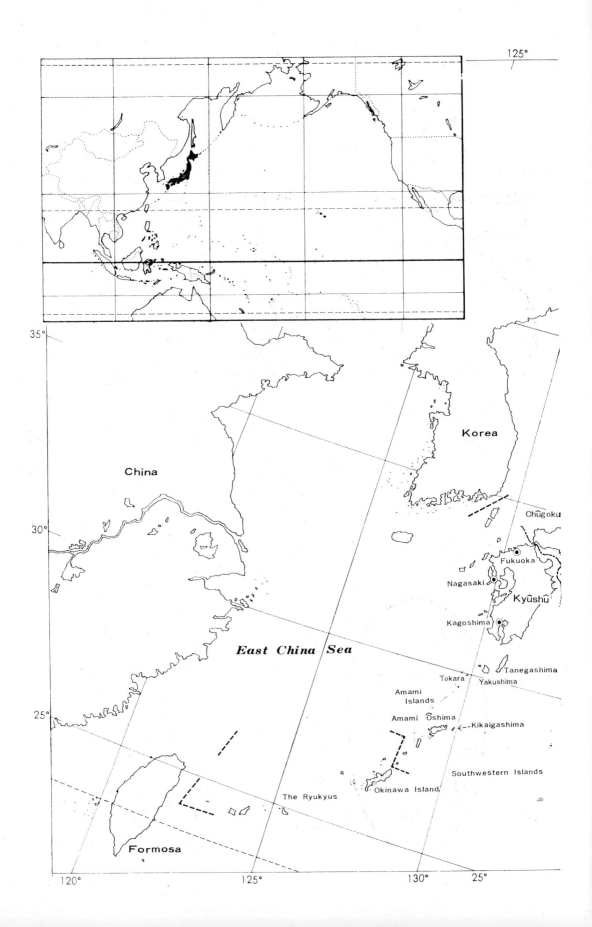

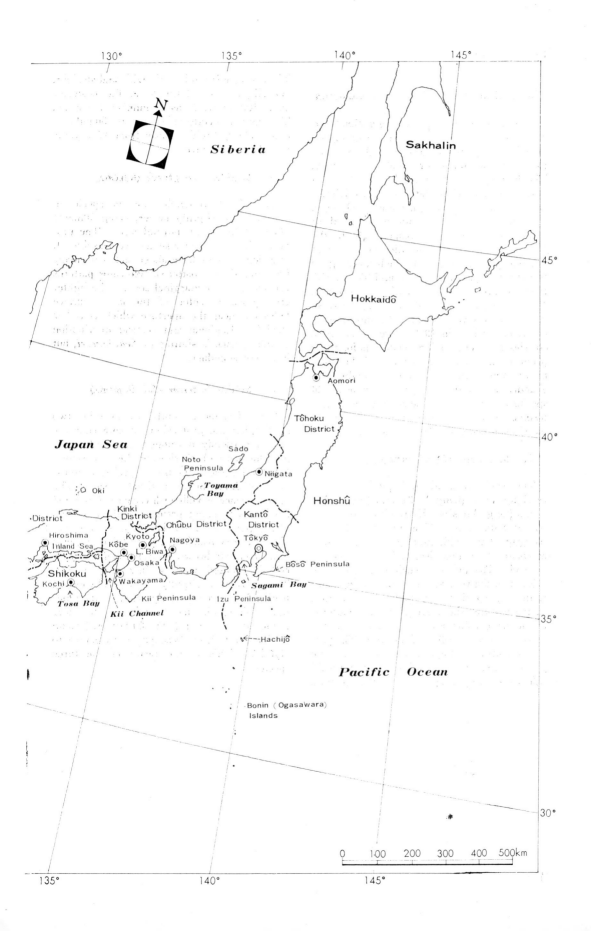

[PLATE 1]

Three Celebrated Japanese Cowries

Three cowries, *Schilderia hirasei*, *Sch. langfordi*, and *Sch. teramachii* are most highly prized among shell collectors of Japan, due to their beautiful colors and their rarity. The first species was named by Roberts in 1913 in honor of the late Yoichiro Hirase, an eminent pioneer of Japanese conchology. The names of the second and the third species were dedicated respectively to the late D. B. Langford, who did an important but *poorly* known service to the Malacological Society of Japan, and to Akifumi Teramachi, the most prominent shell collecter in Japan. *Sch. hirasei* was first discovered by Dr. Tokubei Kuroda in his youth, while the others were described by him in 1938. Names of these cowries form everlasting memorials for these persons who have been leaders of Japanese malacology. *Sch. hirasei* is relatively the most abundant among the three, and perhaps 20–30 specimens have hitherto been collected. *Sch. teramachii* is by far the rarest, only several individuals being known to science.

1. *Schilderia hirasei* (ROBERTS)

The shell is solid and piriform, often reaching 48mm (length) × 31.5mm (breadth) × 21mm (height) in size. Extremities are drawn out at both ends. The upper surface is strongly inflated with the highest part situated at about 1/3 of total length from the posterior end. The polished surface is pale-rose colored on the ventral side with a large quadrilateral purplish brown spot at the center. In the matured shell, irregular small patterns of the same color are also found near the margin and in the hollow of the apex. The protruded ends are colored in darker rose. The ground color becomes lighter on the ventral side and entirely disappears near the aperture.

The aperture is moderately wide and straight, but slightly bent leftward at the posterior end. Rather weak teeth number about 20. This species is collected from 100–150 fathoms depth along Pacific coasts from Wakayama to Kôchi Prefecture.

2. *Schilderia langfordi* (KURODA)

This closely resembles the first species in shape, but is slightly larger, being 50mm × 26mm × 26mm in normal size. The proboscis-like ends are also less remarkable. It is reddish brown from above and bears many irregular darker patterns. No color patterns are found in the marginal zone. The lighter creamy-orange color of the under surface fades out near the aperture which is rather straight. Regional and vertical distribution of this species is similar to *Sch. hirasei*, but it is less abundant.

3. *Schilderia teramachii* (KURODA)

General shape is similar to the other two species, but the protrusions at both ends are most remarkably developed into wide margins formed on both sides of the proboscides. It is the largest of the three species, 78mm × 47mm × 39mm in approximate size. The upper surface is yellowish cream colored and marked with cloud patterns of light brown. Three purplish brown lateral bands are visible on the sub-surface layer. The margins bear irregular brown patterns, and posterior end is marked with a dark reddish spot. The aperture is slightly curved and contains teeth which are especially weak on the inner lip. This species has been known to occur in the bathyal region (100–200 fathoms) along Pacific coasts from Wakayama Prefecture to Kyûshû. This is the rarest of the three species.

PLATE **1**

1

$\times\ 1\frac{1}{5}$

2

$\times\ 1\frac{1}{5}$

3

$\times\ 1\frac{1}{5}$

PLATE **2**

1

× 1⅕

2

× 1⅕

[PLATE 2]

Class Gastropoda

Class Gastropoda or snail-like molluscs is the largest group next to the insects in the animal world. Most of the animals of this class are characterized by a single spirally built shell, but it may be conical, shield-like, or even absent in certain species. Spiral shells are largely dextral or coiled clockwise ; species with sinistral shells are rather few in number. The body possesses a well developed head with tentacles, eyes and a mouth containing radula. Underside of the body forms a broad flat foot with which the animal slides along. Total body can usually be retreated within the shell when the animal stands still, but in some species small degenerate shells are entirely or half buried in the flesh. The animals are often hermaphrodite and generally oviparous, but some viviparous species are known. They are found everywhere in aquatic environments and groups with a kind of lung in their body are also widely distributed all over the land surface. Beautifully colored shells of marine Gastropoda are valuable for ornamental use. Many species have also been one of the important food sources of mankind since prehistoric times.

Family Pleurotomariidae

This family is one of the so-called living fossils, and had once thrived in the remote geologic past, but is now represented by only eight living species in tropical and subtropical waters. Five of them, *Mikadotrochus beyrichii*, *M. hirasei*, *M. salmiana*, *M. teramachii*, and *Entemnotrochus rumphii*, are known from Japan.

1. *Mikadotrochus beyrichii* (HILGENDORF)

The shell is moderately large, conical and thick with inflated whorls. A remarkable slit, characteristic to the family, is found at the center of the outer lip of aperture, and leaves behind it a peculiar spiral band with the growth of shell. The outer surface is sparsely sculptured with spiral lines on which granules are formed where the lines are crossed by oblique growth striae. The shell is beautifully colored with irregular, red and yellow radial patterns. The basal surface is rather flat, with a moderate depression at the center, without umbilicus, and white with traces of color patterns. The inner side is splendidly covered with a pearly layer. The shell is collected from middle depths (20–100 fathoms) along the coasts of Kantô District.

The species was first described by Hilgendorf in 1877, a German lecturer in the medical school of the Tokyo University, who obtained a specimen from a shellwork shop at Enoshima in 1875. But it was later known that a Japanese naturalist, Sekiju Musashi, had illustrated this shell as early as in 1843 in his book 'Mokuhachi-fu' or Illustration of Shells. Species of Pleurotomariidae are sometimes called the 'millionaire shell' by Japanese fishermen because of the high price among collectors of earlier days.

2. *Mikadotrochus hirasei* (PILSBRY)

This shell is larger than the former species, having a taller and more pointed spire, and less inflated whorls. The outer surface is more finely sculptured, the slit band is situated somewhat higher, and the slit itself is 1.5 times as long as that of *P. beyrichii*. This species inhabits the bathyal regions (70–100 fathoms) along Pacific coasts of southwestern Japan.

[PLATE 3]   Haliotidae

Family Haliotidae (1)

The shells of this family are characteristically flat and saucer-shaped, resembling human ear in outline. The spire is very small, low and situated near the anterior end of shell. The body whorl is so extremely expanded that the aperture, with which the animal clings to the rock surface, occupies most of the total shell base. The inner lip of aperture is remarkably thickened. Several small perforations are found in a row along the inner lip; new holes are successively formed, while older ones are closed as the shell grows, leaving a constant number of open perforations. The flesh of certain species is a favorite food of the Japanese and the Chinese. Its dried slice has been a sacred offering to the gods in the Shinto ceremony. Pearly inside layer is widely used for ornamental use, especially for inlaid works of Japanese lacquer art.

1. Haliotis asinina LINNÉ

The shell is oblong and will reach 120mm in length, but about one half as wide. The apex is at the foremost end of the shell. The outer surface is smooth, lustrous and dark-brown with irregular greenish patterns. Perforations are 5–7 in number. This species is found on rocky shores of southernmost islands of Japan and farther south.

2. Ovinotis ovina (GMELIN)

The outline of the shell is round and oval. The apex is only somewhat shifted from the center toward the front end. Coarse outer surface is scattered with irregular tubercles formed by the intersection of spiral lines and radial folds. The ground color is rather light, but greenish brown spots and white vortical stripes cover the outer surface. Perforations are 5–6 in number. Distribution: southwestern islands of Japan.

3. Sulculus supertexta (LISCHKE)

The shell resembles immature specimens of the larger species belonging to the genus *Notohaliotis*, but is easily discriminated from them by the larger number of perforations (6–9). Dorsal side of perforation does not form a tube-like protrusion as in *Notohaliotis*. This edible species is widely distributed in shallow waters of Japanese coasts, reaching as far north as southern Hokkaidô. The animals are known for their rapid movement in water.

4. Sanhaliotis varia (LINNÉ)

The shell is elliptic in outline and rather tall. Irregular knobs on the spiral lines are characteristic. The number of perforations is 5–6. Distribution: southern Honshû and southwards, in subtidal zone.

PLATE **3**

1

× 1⅓

2

× 1⅓

3

× 1⅓

4

× 1⅓

PLATE 4

1

× ½

2

× ½

3

× ½

Family Haliotidae (2)

1. *Notohaliotis sieboldi* (Reeve)

The shell is large, oval in outline, flatter than the following two species, and reddish brown in color. Spiral ribs are distinct and thick. The margin of the outer lip is remarkably expanded. The apex is situated nearly on the longitudinal axis. This shell is usually found at an intermediate depth (about 10 fathoms) between the zones inhabited by the other two species.

2. *Notohaliotis discus* (Reeve)

More oblong and more inflated than *H. sieboldi*, and colored in dark greenish brown on the outer surface. Ribs are flat and very indistinct. The outer lip is less expanded with a more or less straight margin. This species prefers the shallowest habitat among the three, usually less than 10 fathoms below the surface.

3. *Notohaliotis gigantea* (Gmelin)

This is the largest species among Japanese *Notohaliotis*, with a thick, inflated shell reaching $205mm \times 175mm \times 75mm$ in size. The margin of its aperture is well expanded on inner and outer side into a round elliptic outline. The dorsal side bears distinct ribs and remarkable tubercular processes around each perforation. It is found in the deepest zone between 10 and 20 fathoms.

These species are widely distributed along the rocky coasts from Honshû to southern Kyûshû and are valued as food. *N. discus hannai* Ino inhabits the cooler waters of northern Japan. These three types had long been recognized by Japanese fishermen, but the specific differences were only recently established on anatomical and embryological bases.

[PLATE 5]   Fissurellidae

Family   Fissurellidae

This family is characterized by the presence of a slit-like opening in the shell. In *Emarginula*, a deep slit is found at the anterior end, while the slit is very shallow in *Montfortula*. *Macroschisma* has a remarkable opening at the apex. In *Puncturella*, a similar slit occurs on the posterior side of apex, but is often closed in adult shells. There are however other groups that lack apparent openings. The family includes many species which are generally small in shell size.

1.   Emarginula crassicostata SOWERBY

A white cone-shaped shell with an elliptical base, about 12mm × 9mm × 6.5mm in size. The apex is placed posterior to the center. The outer surface is marked by radial and concentric lines. A narrow slit, 1.0–1.5mm long, is found at the foot of the convex anterior slope. Distribution: southern half of Japan, in subtidal zone.

2.   Tugali decussata A. ADAMS

This shell is flat and elliptical at the base, having radial and concentric ribs on the upper surface. It is white in color, and the anterior slope is slightly concave. Distribution: southern half of Japan, in subtidal zone.

3.   Macroschisma dilatata A. ADAMS

An oblong ellipse in basal outline, with a moderately large foramen cut perpendicularly at the apex. The animal is so large compared with its shell size that the latter only partly covers the body. Distribution: all over Japan, in subtidal zone.

4.   Macroschisma sinensis A. ADAMS

This resembles the preceding species in general shape, but is larger. The central foramen is obliquely cut with posterior location and narrowing somewhat toward the anterior end. Distribution: the same with the preceding species.

5.   Montfortula pulchra (A. ADAMS)

The tall conical shell is sculptured by radiating ribs and concentric lines intersecting with each other. A small notch at the anterior end of shell is characteristic of the species which inhabits exposed rocky surfaces of the intertidal zone. Distribution: Honshû and southwards.

6.   Puncturella (Rimulanax) dorcas KIRA et HABE

Flat and circular in outline. This species is ornamented by fine concentric striae and radiating ribs on the external surface. The apex is somewhat shifted toward the posterior. There is a faint slit on the anterior side of the apex, partly closed and having a septum on the inner side. This occurs in the bathyal region (100–150 fathoms) of Tosa Bay, Shikoku.

7.   Montfortia oldhamiana (NEVILL)

This shell has a distorted cone shape. The apex of the shell is situated somewhat left of center. Five or six strong ribs run radially on the upper surface. The notch at the foremost end is similar to that of *Montfortula*. Distribution: central Japan, in subtidal zone.

8.   Puncturella nobilis A. ADAMS

The shell is tall and conical. A half-closed slit resembles that of *P. dorcas* in structure, but this contains a distinct foramen at its center. Rather rough radial ribs are crossed by concentric growth lines on the upper surface. Distribution: central Honshû and northwards, in subtidal zone.

9.   Scutus (Aviscutum) sinensis (BLAINVILLE)

A flat shell, elongated ellipse in outline, with the apex placed to the posterior, and the outer surface bearing fine growth lines surrounding the apex. The shell is entirely covered by the mantle of the large animal body. Distribution: Honshû and southwards, in subtidal zone.

PLATE **5**

PLATE 6

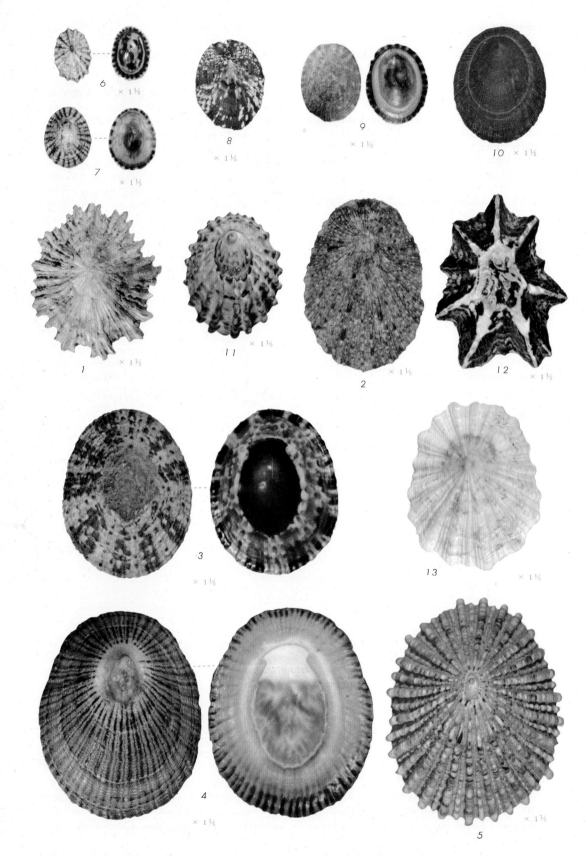

10. *Diodora suprapunicea* OTUKA

This is one of the largest species of *Diodora*. Like the crater of a volcano, an oblong foramen opens at the top of the low conical shell. Fine radiating and concentric striae cover the surface, which is also regularly fasciated by brown lines. Distribution: central Honshû and farther south in shallow waters.

11. *Diodora (Elegidion) quadriradiata* (REEVE)

A conical shell with an elliptical base and a central foramen small and dumb-bell shaped. The outer surface is covered by decussate sculptures. Distribution: Honshû and southwards, below the tide line.

12. *Diodora mus* (REEVE)

Somewhat elongated in outline, and flatter than the preceding species. The foramen is more anteriorly situated and the decussate relief is less deeply sculptured. Distribution: the same with *D. quadriradiata*.

13. *Tugali (Tugalina) vadososinuata* YOKOYAMA

This is the recent type of the fossil species originally described, and is found in deep seas (150–200 fathoms) off Iwate Prefecture. The shell is oval in outline and taller than *T. gigas*. The slit band on the anterior slope is entirely closed and swollen, ending in a remarkable sinuation of the most anterior part of the shell margin. The upper surface bears close and fine radial ribs and growth lines.

14. *Tugali (Tugalina) gigas* (VON MARTENS)

This species has the largest shell found in this family. Outline of the shell is elongated and elliptic. Radial ribs are strongly developed with occasional tubercles on the posterior half of the upper surface, while they are weakened on the anterior half. Distribution: northeastern Honshû and Hokkaidô, in shallow seas.

[PLATE 6]

Family Patellidae (1–5)
Family Acmaeidae (6–13)

These two families include limpet snails with non-spiral, conical shells. They are commonly found on rocky surfaces between the tides. Besides anatomical differences, the two families can be distinguished from each other by the coloration of inner shell surface. The shells of Patellidae are covered inside by silver white layer and without distinct peripheral area, while those of Acmaeidae are colored in other tones than silver white, and

[PLATE 6]

characterized by a distinct dark-colored peripheral zone along the outer margin of the inner surface, though a muscle scar of horseshoe shape at the center is common to both families.

1. Penepatella stellaeformis (REEVE)

The shell is flat; the basal outline is irregularly ragged, owing to the protruding ends of many unequal radial ribs, but the general outline is more or less polygonal. It is flesh-colored outside bearing heterogeneous dark patterns, and dull white inside. The muscle scar is indistinct. Distribution: Honshû and southwards.

2. Cellana toreuma (REEVE)

The shell is flattened, often reaching 70mm or more in the length of elliptic base. The upper surface is ornamented by fine, unequal ribs, pale blue, and irregularly spotted by dark colors. Sculpture, color and pattern are variable in different individuals, but the inside surface is always of glistening silvery color through which the patterns of upper surface are visible. Distribution: abundant everywhere in Japan.

3. Cellana dorsuosa (GOULD)

The shell is tall cone-shaped, and bears well-developed radial ribs and granules upon them. Matured shells are mostly eroded into dirty color, but younger specimens are dark brown. The inner surface is covered by a thin pearly layer and with a large central callus almost black in color. Distribution: throughout Japan.

4. Cellana nigrolineata (REEVE)

The shell reaches 70mm in length and is the second largest species of Japanese limpets next to C. testudinaria (LINNÉ). There are two types of surface coloration; one with radiating black and fine brown lines, and another with wavy concentric lines also brown and black in color. The inner side is always silverly colored, with a large cinnabar-brown callus in the center, usually covered partly by white layer on its anterior part. Distribution: common in Japan.

5. Cellana nigrisquamata (REEVE)

The shell is no smaller than C. nigrolineata, but is taller. The upper surface is deeply sculptured by strong radial ribs, on which develop remarkable granules. It is light brown on both sides. The outer surface is with fine black dots, while the inside is covered by a shining silvery layer. The muscle scar is apparent. Distribution: Ogasawara (Bonin) Islands and farther south.

6. Collisella (Kikukozara) langfordi HABE

The small shell is conical with an elliptic base, and sculptured with white radial ribs over the upper surface. The lower surface is chocolate brown. Distribution: all over Japan.

7. Collisella (Conoidacmea) heroldi (DUNKER)

A small conical shell bearing fine radiating ribs and greenish dark-brown fasciations on the outer surface. The inner side is milky white around a brown spot in the center. Peripheral area is darker in color. Distribution: throughout Japan, more or less prefering inland bays.

8. Notoacmea gloriosa HABE

The shell is flat cone-shaped with an elliptic base. The upper surface is covered by fine radial striae bearing granules. White and reddish spots beautifully alternate on the sur face. It is milky white inside, without bluish color. Distribution: southern half of Japan.

9. Notoacmea concinna fuscoviridis TERAMACHI

The base of the shell is elliptic. Radial ribs are slender and bear fine granules. The coloration is greenish brown with scattered white spots on the upper side, and yellowish green inside. Distribution: Honshû and southwards.

10. Notoacmea concinna (LISCHKE)

The shell is larger than the former species,

and round elliptic at the base. Inside of the shell is indigo blue. This species is found

N. *schrenckii*   N. *concinna*

everywhere on Japanese coasts together with another common species, *N. schrenckii* (LISCHKE). As shown by the attached drawings, *N. schrenckii* is more flat, more oblong in basal outline, and with apex more posteriorly situated than *N. concinna*. The outer shell surface of *N. concinna* is almost devoid of any color patterns, whereas that of *N. schrenckii* is spotted with white. The former is also separated from subsp. *fuscoviridis* by the color of inner surface.

11. Collisella grata (GOULD)

A tall conical shell having the apex remarkably shifted toward the front. Some 20 strong ribs bearing remarkable knobs radiate from the apex. The basal margin is serrate owing to the protruding ends of ribs. The shell is bluish milky white inside, with a brown scar at the center. Distribution : all over Japan, sometimes found high above the tide line hardly reached by the spray of surf.

12. Patelloida (Collisellina) saccharina lanx (REEVE)

The shell is more or less flat and star-shaped at the base. It appears like a web-foot, consisting of several radiating ribs and interspaces between them. The main ribs are about 7 in number ; minor intervening ribs are few. The inner side is milky white, surrounded by a black marginal zone. Distribution : common throughout Japan.

13. Acmaea (Niveotectura) pallida (GOULD)

The white shell surface is sculptured by unequal radial ribs. The base is elliptic with the irregularly waved outline. It is also white all over the lower surface. The species is distributed in cooler waters of Japan north of Tôhoku District.

[PLATE 7]   Trochidae

Family Trochidae (1)

More than one hundred species of this large family are found in Japan. Several subfamilies are included. These top shells are mostly small or medium in size; species with large shells are few in number. Shining pearly layer beautifully covers the inner side of shell, and also the outer side in some species. The operculum is horny, round and multi-spiral, with a nucleus at the center. Animals are dioecious.

1. Turcica coreensis PEASE

The conical shell is tall with 8–9 whorls. Each whorl bears granulated spiral striae, of which two on the periphery are especially strong. The suture forms a distinct furrow. The outer surface is brown or reddish brown with scattered spots of darker color, while the inside of aperture is decorated with fine pearly lustre. Two knobs on the collumella are characteristic. Distribution: from Hokkaidô to northern Kyûshû, 30–50 fathoms in depth.

2. Lischkeia alwinae (LISCHKE)

This resembles the former species in shape, but is white in color and lacks the suture furrow. The whorls are surrounded by rows of spiny tubercles of various sizes along the shoulder, suture line and basal edge, and by fine granuled threads between them. The callus layer on the inner lip of aperture is expanded, and there is a slit-like umbilicus. The base of shell is rather flat. Distribution: central Honshû and southwards, 30–50 fathoms deep.

3. Bathybembix crumpii (PILSBRY)

The shell is more or less similar to the last species in shape and color, but differs in the following characters. The shell surface is silvery white, suture deeper, rows of spiny tubercles more in number, without spiral threads between the rows, base remarkably convex, and umbilicus absent. Distribution: Honshû and Kyûshû, 30–50 fathoms deep.

4. Bathybembix aeola (WATSON)

The outer surface of the shell is covered with a greenish yellow epiderm. The whorls and base are well inflated and encircled by several rows of small granules, which are crossed by oblique radial folds. The aperture is round and wide. The umbilicus is lacking. Distribution: northern Kantô District and northwards, 30–50 fathoms.

5. Bathybembix (Ginebis) argenteonitens hirasei (IS. TAKI et OTUKA)

Distribution: Kantô District and northwards, 30–50 fathoms.

6. Bathybembix (Ginebis) argenteonitens (LISCHKE)

Distribution: Kantô District and south-westwards, 30–50 fathoms.

This original form and subsp. *hirasei* are similar in general character of shells. The shells bear splendid pearly layers on both sides, but are coated with a thin epiderm of dirty brown color on the external surface. The latter type is characterized by a single spiral row of blunt tubercles on the shoulder which disappears on earlier whorls, whereas in the former subspecies the tubercles are somewhat smaller, more or less spiny and continue up to the vertex.

Bembix convexiusclum

The two forms are separated in their geographical distribution by the Miura Peninsula at the mouth of Tôkyô Bay. Toward the east and north of this Peninsula, subsp. *hirasei* is exclusively found, but, on closer observations, a small number of specimens belonging to the original species type is found mixed in populations of northeastern regions, and vice versa. This suggests that both forms are the geographical races of the same species, which is probably the descendant of *Bembix convexiusclum* YOKOYAMA, a Pleistocene fossil species that entirely lacks row of tubercles. It is interesting that *B. convexiusclum* is rarely found alive in Tosa Bay, Shikoku.

PLATE **7**

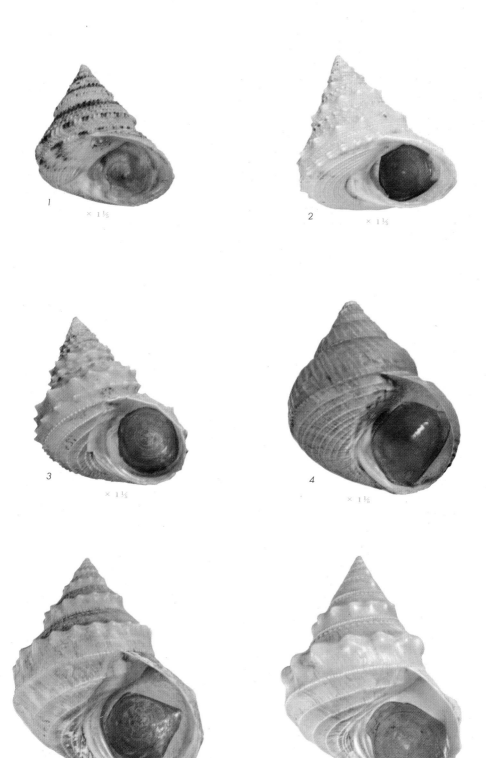

1   × 1⅕

2   × 1⅕

3   × 1⅕

4   × 1⅕

5   × 1⅕

6   × 1⅕

PLATE **8**

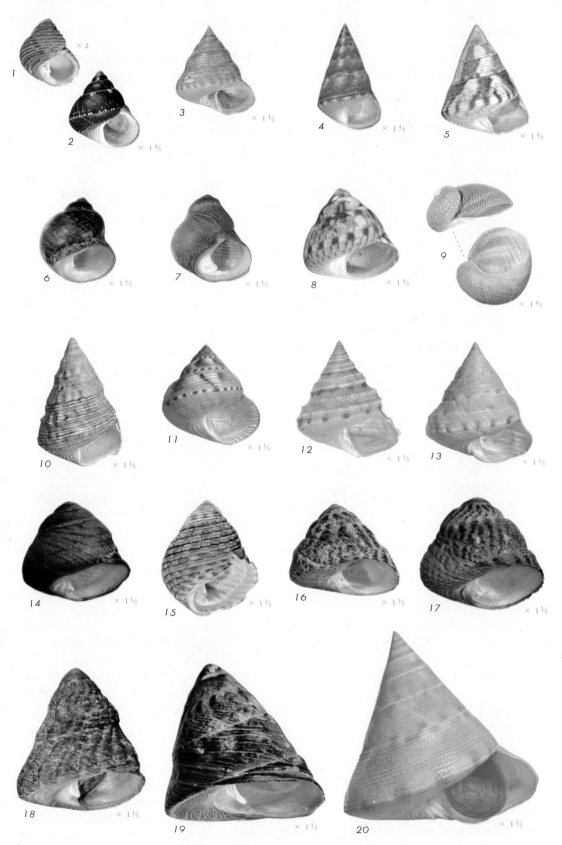

Family Trochidae (2)

1. *Euchelus lischkei* PILSBRY

A small globular shell with granulated spiral striae. Purplish brown in color. One tooth on the columella and two teeth on the basal lip are characteristic. The umbilicus and the horny operculum are present. Distribution: Honshû and southwards, in tidal zone.

Euchelus, including several species, resembles *Homalopoma* (Plate 12) of Turbinidae, but is easily distinguished from the latter by the horny operculum, while that of Turbinidae is calcareous.

2. *Cantharidus jessoensis* (SCHRENCK)

A little larger than the above species; the surface is smooth, but only somewhat lustrous. Spiral striae are only found on the basal surface. The umbilicus is closed. Colors and patterns are quite variable. Distribution: Honshû and farther north, in tidal zone.

3. *Tristichotrochus simodense* (IKEBE)

Spiral striae are granulated only on the initial 3–4 whorls. The ground color is brown, with or without purplish brown spots, and the umbilicus is open. Distribution: south of central Honshû, in subtidal zone.

4. *Cantharidus japonicus* (A. ADAMS)

This shell is tall and cone-shaped with a straight spire. The outer surface is smooth, and sometimes a spiral line encircles the whorls just below the suture. Spiral striae are always present on the basal surface. The umbilicus is open, but partly covered by a callus. Surface colors are extremly diversified, varying from scarlet to greenish brown. Distribution: all over Japan, common in subtidal zone.

5. *Cantharidus (Kanekotrochus) infuscatus* (GOULD)

This conical shell, lower and broader than the last species in general shape, has granulated spiral striae covering the entire surface. The coloration is variable, but flame-like patterns of greenish brown are usually seen against the whitish background. The umbilicus is either slit-like or closed. Distribution: southern half of Honshû, in subtidal zone.

6. *Monodonta perplexa* (PILSBRY)

A globular shell with a rapidly thickening body whorl. The spire seems somewhat constricted owing to a blunt angle beneath the suture line. The outer surface is smooth, black in color, and often marked with white dots. There is a notch on the columella with a lamina on each side of it. Distribution: south of central Honshû, in tidal zone.

7. *Monodonta neritoides* (PHILIPPI)

Being taller than *M. perplexa*, the spire of this shell is not constricted at the suture. The greenish brown surface is marked with faint spiral striae and fine reddish spots. A remarkable tooth is found in front of the columellar notch. Distribution: Honshû and southwards, near the tide line.

8. *Diloma (Pictodiloma) suavis* (PHILIPPI)

The whorls are well inflated at the periphery. The suture furrow is moderately deep. The surface is smooth and pale with reddish-purple checkered patterns above and below the suture, connected by an intervening network of the same color. A pearly layer inside the aperture is beautifully greenish. The columella looks like a huge comma in shape. Distribution: common in southern half of Japan, near the tide line.

9. *Hybochelus (Granata) lyrata* PILSBRY

This shell somewhat resembles the ear shell in shape, owing to the rapidly thickening body whorl. The outer surface is densely covered by unequal spiral striae with fine growth lines between them. Minute dark spots are scattered over the light purple-brown surface. The operculum is degenerate and very small. Distribution: south of Honshû, in subtidal zone.

[PLATE 8]   Trochidae

10. Tosatrochus attenuatus (JONAS)

One of the largest species of this genus to be found in Japan. The tall, conical shell bears a row of knobs on the periphery of each whorl. The exterior is sculptured by remarkable spiral striae crossed by growth lines. The umbilical opening is narrow. Distribution: central Honshû and farther south, below the tide line down to 5 fathoms.

11. Tristichotrochus unicus (DUNKER)

A conical shell with the rounded periphery and closed umbilicus. Spiral striations on the surface bear granules only on initial whorls. This shell has a light brown background with irregular markings of dark brown and a row of small square spots of the same color encircling the whorls, but the general color pattern varies. Distribution: central Honshû and farther south, 5–10 fathoms.

12. Tristichotrochus aculeatus (SOWERBY)

The spire is a little taller than that of *Tr. unicus*. The shoulder of whorls is carinated, and there is another remarkable spiral ridge bearing spiny tubercles between the shoulder and basal edge of the shell. Minor granulated spiral striae are found between these ridges. Distribution: south of central Honshû, 30–50 fathoms deep. A related species, *T. soyoae* (IKEBE), is somewhat smaller and has a remarkable umbilicus.

13. Tristichotrochus kiiensis (IKEBE)

This closely resembles the last species, but spiral ridges are less distinct and basal surface is less inflated. Distribution: central part of Japan, 20–50 fathoms.

14. Chlorostoma xanthostigmum (A. ADAMS)

A heavy, solid shell of medium size, with a rounded apex. It is deep black and apparently smooth on the outer surface, but faint growth threads and weak spiral lines are present. The basal surface is lighter in color, and the umbilicus is hidden under an enameled layer of bright green characteristic to the subgenus. Some individuals are colored in light greenish brown. Specimens from southern Kyûshû are very large-sized. Distribution: south of Honshû, in subtidal zone.

15. Monodonta labio (LINNÉ)

The shell is globular in shape and heavy in construction. Peculiar squarish granules are spirally arranged on the surface like stone pavements. It is usually olive in color, but sometimes russet or yellowish. There is no umbilicus. The curved columella is more or less continuous to the basal lip, but separated from the latter by a notch similar to other species of *Monodonta*. Distribution: abundant everywhere south of Hokkaidô, near the tide line.

16. Omphalius rusticum (GMELIN)

This species is separated from *Chl. xanthostigmum* by longitudinal folds on the whorls. Surface sculptures other than growth striae are absent. The basal surface is not inflated and with the open umbilicus encircled by a furrow. The columella bears one tooth. Distribution: south of Hokkaidô, abundant on rocky shores near the tide line.

17. Chlorostoma lischkei (TAPPARONE-CANEFRI)

Compared with the last species, longitudinal folds are somewhat more closely spaced. The umbilicus is covered with a greenish enameled layer, though it is open in young specimens. Distribution: commonly found near the tide line, south of Hokkaidô.

18. Omphalius pfeifferi carpenteri (DUNKER)

This is larger and thicker than *O. rusticum*. The basal surface is entirely flat and sculptured by rough spiral striae. The umbilicus is deeply perforated.

19. Omphalius pfeifferi (PHILIPPI)

This species, which was the original discovery, resembles the preceding subspecies in shape, but longitudinal folds and spiral striae on the basal surface become so weak that the entire surface is nearly smooth. These two geographical strains are respectively distributed along Japan sea coasts and Pacific coasts from Hokkaidô to southernmost Kyûshû. The Pacific race, *T. pfeifferi*, sometimes includes specimens with somewhat developed surface sculptures, which suggest that both forms are belonging to the same species. They are very abundant on rocky coasts near the tide line throughout Japan.

20. *Tristichotrochus haliarchus* (MELVILL)

A fine, top-shaped shell almost triangular on side view, with its tall flat-sided spire, 9–10 whorls, and sharp basal angle. The surface is seemingly smooth, but encircled by many fine granulated spiral striae. The base is a little inflated. The umbilicus is absent. It is light brown all over, but spotted by darker brown on the spiral striae. Irregular brown or white patterns are also present. Distribution : central Japan and southwards, at 30–50 fathoms depth.

[PLATE 9]   Trochidae, Stomatiidae

Family Trochidae (3)

1. Trochus " cumingi (A. ADAMS)"

A small, cone-shaped shell with an elongated spire, acute peripheral angle and somewhat concave base, and having no umbilicus. Each whorl bears 3–4 granulated spiral striae over the surface and a row of knobs just above the periphery. It is white all over with a rose tinge on the dorsal surface. Distribution: south of the Ryukyus, in subtidal zone.

2. Clanculus clanguloides (WOOD)

This is a small but thick shell, rounded conical in shape. Inflated whorls are encircled by 6–7 granulated spiral striae. The outer surface is light brown in ground color and more or less regularly dotted by white and brown spots. The aperture is narrow; the columella and outer lip bear 3 teeth respectively, of which those on the columella and the uppermost one on the lip are especially strong. Distribution: south of Amami Islands, in subtidal zone.

3. Clanculus margaritarius (PHILIPPI)

This resembles the last species in general appearance, but the shell is larger and whorls are less inflated. The ground color is darker and reddish brown with regularly distributed black dots, while the apex is colored pink. Distribution: central Japan and southwards, in subtidal zone.

4. Astele (Coralastele) pulcherrimus (SOWERBY)

The shell is similar to *Tristichotrochus* in shape, but smaller in size. Each whorl bears 3 remarkable striae and finer lines with red-colored granules upon them. Six or seven granulated spiral striae are also found on the basal surface. The umbilicus is open. Distribution: south of the Ryukyus, 2–5 fathoms deep.

5. Trochus (Infundibulum) chloromphalus A. ADAMS

A medium-sized, thick shell, conical in outline and with a sharp basal angle. Gran-ulated spiral striae cover the entire surface. It is light green in ground color, and the body whorl is fasciated by large brown patterns, while the umbilical part shows fresh green color. The columella is screwed inward with a tooth upon it. Distribution: Bonin Islands and Formosa, on rocky shores.

6. Trochus sandwichensis SOULEYET

Similar to the former species in outline. It also resembles *Tr. sacellum rota* in having a row of tubercles on the suture and several teeth on the columella, but can be distinguished by the spur-shaped brown fasciations on the body whorl as well as by the characteristic reddish patterns on the outside of the upper margin of aperture. Distribution: southern Honshû and southwards, from the tide line down to 2 fathoms.

7. Monilea smithi (DUNKER)

The shell is considerably depressed, with a widely open umbilicus. Its outer surface is sculptured by a number of distinct spiral ribs with granules, light greenish-yellow and marked with brown cloud patterns. The basal surface is white in color. Distribution: south of southern Kyûshû, 2–5 fathoms deep.

8. Monilea belcheri (PHILIPPI)

The general shape resembles that of the above species, but spiral striae are finer and less pronounced. The outer surface is grayish or yellowish brown in color, and marked by irregular markings of white, while the basal surface is white with or without a dark ring pattern around the umbilicus. Distribution: southern Kyûshû and southwards, near 10 fathoms depth.

9. Trochus sacellum rota DUNKER

As in *Tr. sandwichensis*, prominent tubercles develop on the periphery of whorls. The tubercles vary considerably in size and shape in different specimens. The screwed columella bears several teeth on its lower part. The coloration is also variable, ranging from rose to pale blue. Distribution: south of central Japan, near the tide line down to 2 fathoms.

10. Trochus stellatus GMELIN

Somewhat larger than the former species, and marked over by coarse granulated spiral ribs. Granules tend to be larger and more or less knob-like near the periphery. The basal surface also bears 7–8 granulated spiral ridges. In the umbilical hollow, the columella is screwed inward. The columellar and basal lips are denticulated. The shell is light green all over with disconnected square patterns of purplish brown. Distribution: southern Kyûshû and southwards, between the tide line and 5 fathoms depth.

11. Ethalia guamensis selenomphala PILSBRY

The shell is shaped like those of *Umbonium* species. The surface is smooth, shining and with irregular markings of reddish or grayish brown. The widely open umbilicus is encircled by light reddish patterns. Distribution: southern Honshû and southwards, at 20–30 fathoms depth.

12. Gaza sericata KIRA

The shell looks like the preceding species, but is thinner and taller. Whorls are carinated by rather distinct spiral striae, 3 on the body whorl and 2 on other whorls. The total surface is covered by reticulately arranged fine granules formed where spiral striae are crossed by growth lines. The basal surface is inflated, and the umbilicus is widely open in younger specimens, but covered by a thin callus just before maturation. The thin outer lip is slightly reflexed outward. General coloration is light olivine with white and brown radial patterns. The base is also marked with white dots. Distribution: central Japan and southwards, under 50 fathoms.

13. Umbonium (Suchium) moniliferum (LAMARCK)

14. Umbonium (Suchium) costatum (KIENER)

These two species have not yet been adequately distinguished from each other by shell morphology. According to the auther's experience, the distinction may be summarized as follows. *U. costatum* is larger (35 mm in diameter or more), inhabits a deeper zone, prefers open coasts, has a relatively small umbilical callus, and is less variable in color patterns, whereas *U. moniliferum* is smaller (usually less than 20 mm in diameter), found in shallower zone of bays, with larger umbilical callus, and is more variable both in color and in patterns.

15. Umbonium (Suchium) giganteum (LESSON)

This is the largest species of Japanese *Umbonium*, frequently reaching 45 mm in diameter. Its smooth outer surface is ornamented by faint spiral striae only on the periphery of body whorl. The coloration is bluish gray in ground color with a disconnected blue band below the suture. Distribution: central Japan and farther south, down to 5 fathoms.

Family Stomatiidae

The shells of this family are small or medium in size, and lack both umbilicus and operculum. They resemble the ear shell in outline, but no perforations are found. The animal bodies are too large to be covered by their shells.

16. Stomatia rubra LAMARCK

The shell looks like *Stomatella* in shape with an extremely developed body whorl. Many fine spiral lines are found on the outer surface, of which two on the shoulder are granulated and especially remarkable. Oblique radial folds are also found below the suture. The basal surface is well inflated, but sunken in the center. The aperture is beautifully covered inside by a pearly layer and the columella extends toward the basal lip. Its beautiful coloration may be yellowish, reddish or light brown, purplish red, etc. Distribution: central Honshû and southwards, in subtidal zone.

17. Stomatia phymotis HELBLING

The spire is rather tall and oblique. Two remarkable spiral ridges bearing small tubercles are on the shoulder of each whorl. Spiral striae and logitudinal folds are also

[PLATE 9]   Trochidae, Stomatiidae

present. Distribution: southern half of Japan and southwards, in subtidal zone.

18. Stomatia obscura SOWERBY

This resembles the last species in its shape and sculpture, but the apex is situated more to the posterior. It might be a local type of *St. phymotis*. Distribution: southern Honshû and northwards, in subtidal zone.

19. Stomatella varia (A. ADAMS)

This minute ear-like shell is reddish brown and smooth on the outer surface. Extremely fine threads are only visible under the magnifying glass. Distribution: central Japan and southwards, in subtidal zone.

20. Stomatella planulata (LAMARCK)

This is larger and flatter than *St. varia*. The outer surface is marked by dark greenish patterns, and is sculptured by sparse spiral furrows. Distribution: central Japan and southwards, in subtidal zone.

PLATE 9

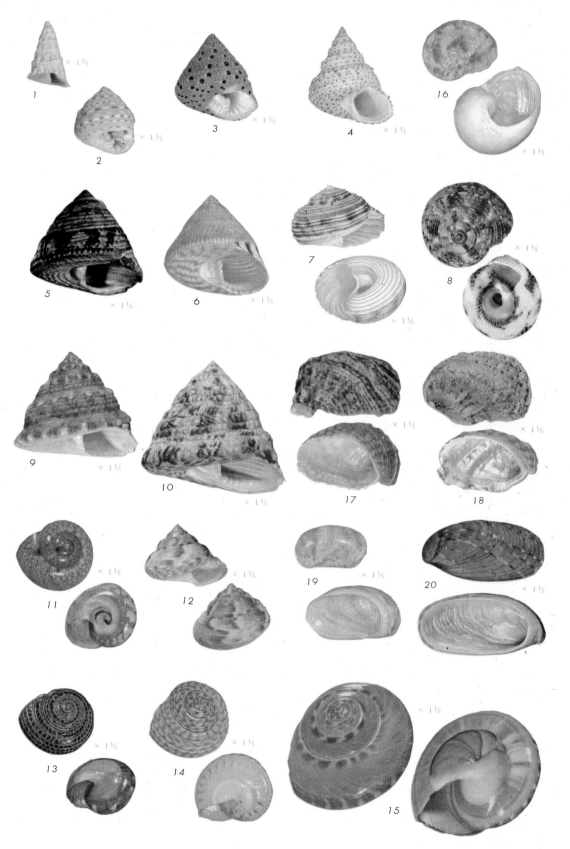

PLATE 10

a,   b,

1

× 1 2/5

2

× 1 1/5

3

× 1 2/5

4

× 4/5

5 a,   × 1

6

× 1

5 b,   × 1

7

× 3/5

Family Trochidae (4)

1. *Trochus maculatus* Linné

The shell is large, heavy, tall and top-shaped with a straight spire. The entire surface is covered by encircling ridges bearing granules, and there are also rows of beads along the suture. The columella is screwed inward with teeth upon it, and the base is marked over by fine granulated spiral striae and fine red zigzag patterns on the white background. Distribution: southern Honshû and farther south, below the tide line down to 5 fathoms.

2. *Tectus triserialis* (Lamarck)

Similar to the above species in outline. The spire is however taller and with about 12 whorls, each encircled by 4–5 fine granulated spiral striae, and somewhat constricted at the suture. The screwed columella appears like a tooth and forms a lamina at the inner end of the basal lip. The coloration is greenish brown on the dorsal surface and whitish on the base. Distribution: south of the Ryukyus, 2–5 fathoms deep.

3. *Tectus pyramis* (Born)

A large, conical shell with the wide, flat base. The outer surface is sculptured all over by greenish brown growth lines. A row of tubercles appears just above the suture and usually disappears on the last 1–2 whorls. The columellar structure is similar to that of the last species. Distribution: south of southern Honshû, at 2–5 fathoms.

4. *Tectus (Rochia) niloticus maximus* (Philippi)

The conical shell is very large, thick and heavy. A spiral row of tubercles encircles the spire just above the suture, but is weakened toward the aperture until it disappears on the body whorl. Obscure, granulated, spiral striae are only found on earlier whorls. The dorsal surface is fasciated by distinct broad bands reddis hbrown in color, while the basal surface is marked with reddish spots. Distribution: south of the Ryukyus, at 5–10 fathoms.

Family Turbinidae (1)

This family includes heavy, solid shells, large or medium in size. Tubercles or spines on the surface and the thick columella are characteristically found. The inner side of apperture is covered by a pearly layer as in Trochidae, but the operculum is heavy and calcareous.

5. *Turbo (Batillus) cornutus* Solander

It may seem rather strange that the shell is sometimes spineless (a) and sometimes very spiny (b). The presence or absence of spines depends entirely upon the environment where it lives. Violent waves of the open sea give rise to the duplicated row of long spines on the surface of this shell, while they are reduced to a single row or entirely lost in calm waters. Dr. Ino successfully demonstrated the disappearance of spines on shells transfered from open sea into artificially made still water. He also found experimentally that different colorations of the shell found in nature (reddish or greenish) are caused by differences among seaweeds upon which they live. The operculum is round, thick and spirally built, bearing granules on the convex outer surface. The inner surface of the operculum is flat and covered by a brown epiderm. This, together with *Euhaliotis* spp., represents the most common species of edible gastropoda in Japan.

6. *Turbo (Marmarostoma) argyrostomus* Linné

A heavy and solid form of turbine shell in the south sea. Very distinct spiral ribs, about 20 in number on the body whorl, encircle the whorls. Those on the shoulder are especially strong. Spaces between these ribs are finely scaled. The ground color is light yellowish brown. The umbilicus is narrowly open and the basal lip near the columella is extremely thick. The operculum resembles that of the other species, but lacks spiral sculpture on the outer surface. This shell offers material for making buttons of excellent quality. Distribution: south of southernmost Kyûshû, 5–10 fathoms deep.

It is noteworthy that different forms of

[PLATE 10]   Trochidae, Turbinidae

epiphytic *Sabia* are found living on the surface of these two turbine shells; *S. conica acuta* on *T. argyrostomus* and *S. conica* on *T. cornutus* respectively.

7. Turbo (Lunatica) marmoratus LINNÉ

This shell is very large, reaching 200 mm in diameter. Three spiral ribs, bearing blunt tubercles and especially strong at the shoulder, encircle the outer surface. The well inflated base bears a narrow umbilical opening. A well developed fasciole is found. The aperture is large, circular and closed by a circular, whitish operculum. This shell is greenish and marked with several chestnut brown bands. Young specimens are characterized by white spots which are absent in adult shells. The thick pearly layer is valued for art materials. Distribution: south of Amami Islands, 10–20 fathoms deep.

Family Turbinidae (2)

1. Astralium haematragum (MENKE)

A cone-shaped shell resembling *Trochus sacellum rota* in general appearance. Prominent longitudinal folds, running obliquely across the surface of whorls, respectively end in spiny processes that extend beyond the suture. Six or seven squamated spiral striae are sculptured on the flat base. There is no umbilicus. The columelllar end and part of the convex outer surface of operculum are sometimes reddish purple in color. Distribution : south of Honshû, in subtidal zone.

2. Pseudastralium henicus gloriosum (KIRA)

A low-conical shell, surrounded by 11–13 spines along the basal margin. The outer surface is exquisitely sculptured. A row of prominent granules encircles the whorls on the shoulder. Fine longitudinal threads and 3–4 spiral rows of fine scaly granules respectively cover the surface above and below the shoulder line. There is another row of short spines on the peripheral angle immediately below the main row of long spines. The basal surface is also marked with several spiral ribs bearing fine scales. No umbilicus. Outer lip margin is acute. The operculum is calcareous, white, flat and thick. It is pale yellow all over without any color patterns. Distribution : southern part of Honshû and Shikoku, as deep as 50–80 fathoms.

3. Galeostraea millegranosa HABE

General outline is low conical, with a sharp basal angle and deeply furrowed suture. A single row of hollow spines along the basal margin is characteristic. The dorsal surface is marked with 6–7 granulated striae. The basal surface is carinated near the spined margin, and bears fine networks of granulated striae and oblique longitudial threads. No umbilical opening. Outer lip margin is thin and sharp. The round operculum is calcareous and convex on the outer side. Distribution : southern part of Honshû and Shikoku, 50–80 fathoms deep.

4. Turbo (Marmarostoma) setosus GMELIN

The shell is globular, resembling *T. argyrostomus* in shape, sculpture and color. But it differs in somewhat smaller size and absence of umbilical opening, and in having a smooth, white operculum. It also serves as a material for making buttons, and its flesh is favored by natives of South Sea islands for food. Distribution : south of Bonin Islands and the Ryukyus.

5. Galeoastraea (Harisazaea) modesta (REEVE)

The shell is conical, solid and grooved on the suture. Tube-like spines are arranged along the periphery in 2 rows, the upper row being superior in size of spines. The total surface is densely sculptured by irregular squamated spiral striae and growth threads. Basal periphery is carinated by a row of short spines. The inner lip is expanded and coverd by a vermillion callus. No umbilical opening. It is reddish purple over the outer surface. Distribution : south of central Japan, at 10–20 fathoms depth.

6. Turbo reevii PHILIPPI

The outer surface of this turbine shell is very smooth and shining. The whorls are well inflated, reddish brown in color and encircled by several black bands. Radial or irregular white patterns are also found. The round, calcareous operculum bears faint olivaceous tone. Distribution : central Japan, at 10–20 fathoms.

7. Turbo petholatus LINNÉ

This closely resembles the former species, but the shell is more constricted at the suture, and color bands are rather greenish in color. The margin of aperture is colored in yellowish green. The outer margin of columella and basal lip are characterized by a callus fold chocolate brown in color. Distribution : south of the Ryukyus, 5–10 fathoms.

8. Turbo (Marmarostoma) chrysostomus LINNÉ

A heavy turbine shell, marked over the outside by strong spiral ridges bearing

18

[PLATE 11]   Turbinidae, Angariidae

fine scales. The tube is angled at the shoulder and basal periphery, on which tubercles some-times develop. The convex outer surface of heavy, calcareous operculum is beautifully colored in greenish brown and white. The inner side of aperture is covered by a fine golden pearly layer. Distribution: south of the Ryukyus, at 5–10 fathoms. This species is abundant in warm tropical seas, but rather rare in the Ryukyus.

9. Guildfordia triumphans (PHILIPPI)

This shell is characterized by long hollow spines, 15–18 mm in length and 7–9 in number, radiating from the periphery of the flat shell. The spines are successively dissolved again by the animal as the shell grows, barely leaving traces of older spines at the suture. The dorsal surface is marked by 7–8 granulated striae, and purplish pink in color with metallic lustre. Sometimes a band of darker color encircles the whorls just below the suture. The basal surface is white and bears a few granulated lines near the periphery as well as around the umbilical callus. The umbilical part is sunken but closed. The operculum is white, elliptic in outline, flat and disc-like. Distribution : south of central Honshû, 30–50 fathoms in depth.

10. Guildfordia yoka (JOUSSEAUME)

This is discriminated from the former species by longer spines reaching 40mm in length. Granulated spiral striae are rather irregular and disappear toward the lower half of each whorl. The surface coloration is lighter than in *G. triumphans*, and without any color patterns. The basal surface is inflated and smooth. Umbilical hollow is remarkably deep. The operculum is somewhat thinner than that of the former species. Distribution : south of central Japan, 80–100 fathoms deep.

Family Angariidae

This family includes only a small number of species. The shells are thick and heavy.

The spire is almost flat near the apex. Whorls are usually surrounded on their shoulder by a row of tubercles which are sometimes spinous or hook-like. The aper-ture is circular and closed by a round, horny operculum with a sunken nucleus.

11. Angaria atrata (REEVE)

The shell is considerably depressed and bears a row of short spines on the carinated shoulder of whorls. The basal margin is also surrounded by another row of minor spines. The entire surface is sculptured by granulated spiral striae, of which 8 rows are found between the suture and shoulder. The umbilical opening is wide and deep. Dis-tribution : south of central Honshû, at 5–10 fathoms.

12. Angaria delphinula nodosa (REEVE)

This is somewhat larger and much more solid than the preceding species. The spire is very depressed and nearly flat. There are two spiral ridges bearing irregular bosses on the shoulder and basal edge of whorls. Another ridge with minor tubercles is also found between them. Also, the surface bears granulated spiral striae which are uneven in thickness. It is white in ground color and marked with reddish purple lines on the spiral striae. The original coloration is how-ever hardly visible except near the margin of aperture due to calcareous sediments deposited on the outer surface. Distribution : south of the Ryukyus, 2–5 fathoms deep.

13. Angaria delphinula (LINNÉ)

Similar to the above form in shell size. The tubercles on the shoulder ridge are developed into irregularly curved or branched project-ions. The whorls are also encircled by two rows of short, thick spines on the periphery, and by many granulated striae over the entire surface. The basal edge is almost rounded, and the inner wall of umbilicus is densely covered by spinous processes. Distribution: south of the Ryukyus, at 2–5 fathoms depth.

PLATE 11

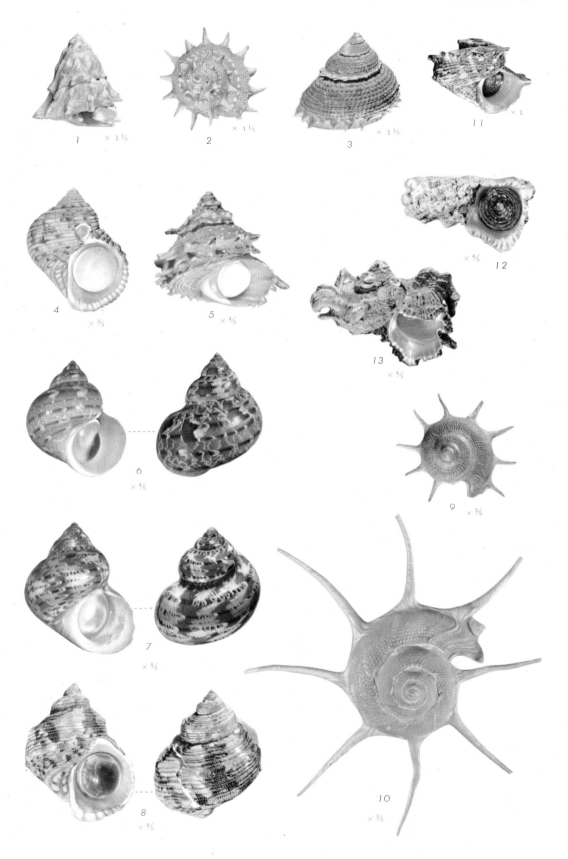

1   × 1⅕

2   × 1⅕

3   × 1⅕

11   × 1

4   × ⅗

5   × ⅘

12   × ⅘

13   × ⅘

6   × ⅘

9   × ⅗

7   × ⅘

8   × ⅘

10   × ⅗

PLATE 12

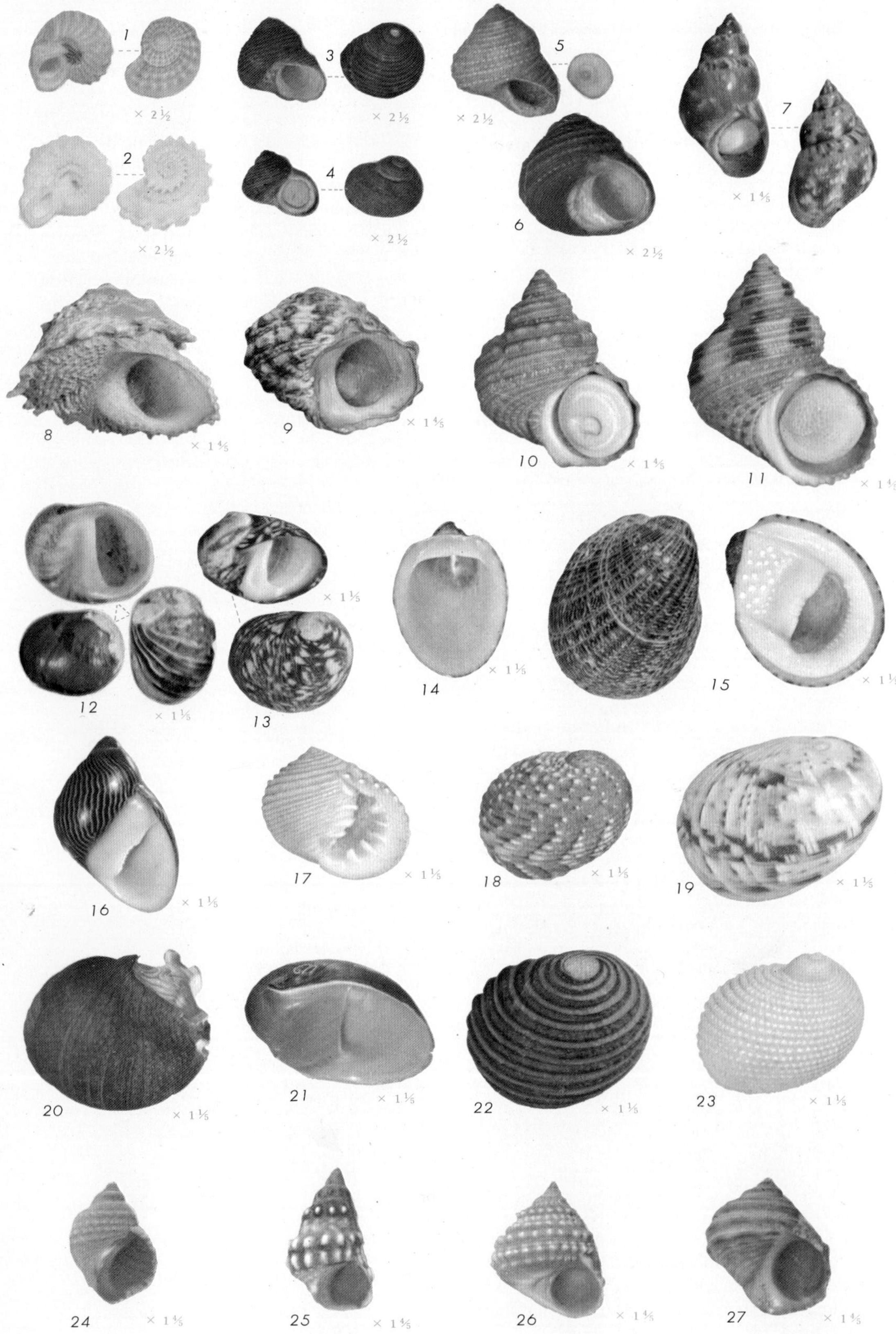
1
× 2½
3
× 2½
5
× 2½
7
× 1⅘
2
× 2½
4
× 2½
6
× 2½
8
× 1⅘
9
× 1⅘
10
× 1⅘
11
× 1⅘
12
× 1⅕
13
× 1⅕
14
× 1⅕
15
× 1⅕
16
× 1⅕
17
× 1⅕
18
× 1⅕
19
× 1⅕
20
× 1⅕
21
× 1⅕
22
× 1⅕
23
× 1⅕
24
× 1⅘
25
× 1⅘
26
× 1⅘
27
× 1⅘

Family Turbinidae (3)

1. Liotina (Liotinaria) semiclathratula (SCHRENCK)

The shell somewhat resembles those of Angariidae in shape, but is much smaller (about 5 mm in diameter). It has a flat spire, inflated base and deeply furrowed suture. The outer surface is light yellow in color and ornamented by a grid-like sculpture. The umbilicus is widely open, and the margin of aperture is thickened. The operculum is round and calcareous. Distribution: central Japan and southwards, below the tide line down to 2 fathoms.

2. Dentarene loculosa (GOULD)

This species is slightly larger than the above species, reaching 8 mm in diameter. The dorsal surface is more depressed and looks like a cogwheel owing to 2 rows of short, denticular tubercles encircling the periphery of each whorl. The entire surface is marked by fine longitudinal sculptures. The inner side of the wide umbilicus is also covered by denticles. The operculum is similar to that of the foregoing species. Distribution: south of the Ryukyus, below the tide line down to 2 fathoms.

3. Homalopoma rubrum laevicostatum PILSBRY

A minute conical shell with a rounded apex, about 6 mm in diameter. The whorls are considerably inflated and marked by many distinct spiral striae. It is moderately solid, but the margin of aperture does not become thickened. There is no umbilical opening. Distribution: southern half of Japan, in subtidal zone.

4. Neocollonia pilula (DUNKER)

This is somewhat smaller than the preceding species, and its spire is less tall. Among fine spiral striae that cover the outer surface, only the one just below the suture line is granulated. The umbilicus is small but open. The margin of aperture is not thickened. The operculum is convex on the exterior surface which bears a spiral furrow ending in a nuclear pit. Distribution: south of central Japan, in subtidal zone.

5. Homalopoma granuliferum (NOMURA et HATAI)

This shell reaches 6 mm in diameter. The surface looks like a crocodile skin due to the characteristic pattern of sculpture, consisting of granulated spiral ridges and fine longitudinal furrows which fill the space between the ridges. There is no umbilical opening. The operculum has a spiral surface structure and a hollow nucleus. Distribution: northern half of Japan north of Sagami Bay, at 30–50 fathoms.

6. Homalopoma amussitatum (GOULD)

About 8 mm in diameter. The shell is reddish-purple all over and rather sparsely encircled by granulated striae on the dorsal surface. The basal surface is somewhat inflated and finely sculptured by spiral striae. There is no umbilical opening. The operculum is quite similar to that of *H. granuliferum*. Distribution: northern half of Japan.

7. Phasianella modesta (GOULD)

An oblong globular shell, with a tall spire and well inflated whorls. The prolonged basal surface is also inflated and without an umbilicus. It is polished all over the surface and beautifully colored in reddish brown. The operculum is ovate in outline, and smoothly convex on the outer side. Distribution: south of Honshû, 5–10 fathoms deep.

8. Astralium heimburgi (DUNKER)

This conical shell bears short, flat spines on the strongly carinated periphery of whorls. The suture between the penultimate and body whorl is remarkably constricted, and the former partly hangs over the latter. The dorsal surface is marked by weak longitudinal folds and fine spiral striae, whereas the base is covered by many spiral striae bearing scaly granules. A narrow callus develops around the closed umbilicus and is colored light purple, while the operculum is purplish brown. Distribution: southern Honshû and southwards, below the tide line.

9. Lunella coronata coreensis (RÉCLUZ)

This has a low spire, large body whorl and well inflated base. The whorls are sur-

20

[PLATE 12]   Turbinidae, Neritidae, Neritopsidae, Littorinidae

rounded by granulated cords of uneven thickness. There is no umbilicus. The surface color is yellowish brown. The operculum is round, olivine in color and bears small granules on its convex outer surface. It is called *the vinegar shell* by children of Japanese seaside villages, because its operculum begins circular movement in vinegar or weak acid solution as its surface is gradually dissolved. Distribution: common throughout Japan, near the tide line.

10. Turbo (Callopomella) excellens Sowerby

11. Turbo (Marmarostoma) stenogyrus Fischer

These two spineless turbine shells closely resemble each other in shape, and it is difficult to distinguish one from the other. In *T. excellens*, the shoulder and the basal margin are more or less angled, the outer surface bears dull lustre, and 2–3 spiral ridges just below the suture are granulated, whereas *T. stenogyrus* lacks these features. The most decisive difference is found in the morphology of their opercula; viz. that of *T. excellens* is spirally sculptured and devoid of granules, while that of *T. stenogyrus* is covered by callus and fine granules. Distribution: south of central Japan. They are usually collected with the Japanese jelly-plant, but the distribution of the former species is restricted.

Family Neritidae

The shells belonging to this sea snail family are generally globular or semispherical in shape. Whorls rapidly increase in thickness and the body whorl is so large that the shape of certain species approaches that of limpets. The umbilicus is absent. A wide callus develops on the columellar side of aperture. The operculum is calcareous, semilunar in shape and bears a hook-like projection at an end of its inner surface. The septa between the whorls are secondarily absorbed by the animal, so that the inside of the shell is single-chambered or lacking spiral structure. A considerable number of species are included in this family.

12. Clithon sowerbianus (Récluz)

A small oval shell with the nearly smooth surface. The spire is mostly covered by the body whorl and often lost by erosion in matured specimens. The surface is grayish blue or brown in ground color and marked with two spiral color bands, minute triangular spots or ripple-marks. The inner lip of aperture bears small teeth, of which one is especially prominent. Two spiral folds are seen on the outer surface of operculum. Distribution: south of Kyûshû, in brackish waters.

13. Puperita (Heminerita) japonica (Dunker)

This resembles the last species in shape, but the spire is somewhat more exposed. The outer surface is devoid of any particular sculptures except growth lines, black in ground color and spotted with white. There are no teeth around the inner margin of aperture. The operculum is granulate on the exterior side. Distribution: south of Honshû, common on rocky shores near the tide line.

14. Septaria porcellana (Linné)

This is a shovel-shaped shell with an extremely expanded aperture. The apex is at the posterior end of the shell, which resembles a valve of mussel in appearance. A thin epiderm covers the outer surface and gives it a dark brown ground color on which black networks are seen. The operculum is squarish, degenerate and very small as compared with the size of aperture. Its outer surface is somewhat concave and the spinous projection on the inner surface is not curved. Distribution: south of Amami Islands, in brackish waters.

15. Thliostyra albicilla (Linné)

A medium-sized semispherical shell with a very small spire and a wide horseshoe-shaped aperture. Spiral striae and scattering patterns of black and white cover the surface. Some individuals have color bands or are reddish-brown in color. The inner and outer lip of aperture are both finely dentate. The callus on the columellar side bears granules. The operculum resembles that of *Puperita japonica*. Distribution: southern part of Japan and farther south, near the tide line.

16. Vittina turrita (Gmelin)

Oval in shape, with a somewhat tall spire.

21

The outer surface is smooth, bright and black in ground color, with many fine longitudinal stripes of brown. The inner lip bears a row of teeth. The operculum is quite similar to that of *Clithon sowerbianus*. Distribution: south of the Ryukyus, in brackish waters.

17. Ritena plicata (LINNÉ)

The shell is spherical, and the surface is covered by strong spiral ridges. The spire is small but distinct. It is beautifully colored in rose or pale yellow, and sometimes spotted with black. The inner and outer sides of aperture bear strong teeth, and the operculum is simple in its external structure. Distribution: south of the Ryukyus.

18. Ritena squamulata (RÉCLUZ)

A semispherical shell resembling *Thl. albicilla* in outline. The surface is marked by spiral ridges somewhat weaker than those of the last species. The ground color of external surface is dirty gray and many spots or cloud-like patterns are marked. The lips of aperture are finely dentate on both sides. The exterior of the operculum is granulated. Distribution: south of southern Kyûshû.

19. Amphinerita polita (LINNÉ)

This beautiful shell is larger and more solid than the former species. The surface is smooth and glossy. It is white in ground color, and bears vermillion spiral bands, dark cloud patterns, mottles and other irregular patterns. The inside of aperture is pale yellow and toothed on the inner lip. The operculum is not different from that of the preceding species. Distribution: southern Japan and southwards.

20. Clithon retropictus (VON MARTENS)

The greater part of the spire is usually lost by erosion in mature shells of this species. The uneroded surface is smooth, dark brown, and marked by growth lines as well as by tiny triangular spots. The operculum looks like that of *Cl. sowerbianus*. Distribution: south of Honshû, in brackish waters.

21. Neritina pulligera (LINNÉ)

This shell is semispherical in outline. The outer surface is smooth, dully bright, and dark brown with no color patterns. The inside of the horseshoe-shaped aperture is finely colored in reddish yellow and is weakly dentate on the inner lip. The operculum bears radial color bands of bluish green. Dirtribution: south of the Ryukyus, in brackish waters.

22. Ritena costata (GMELIN)

This globular shell is covered by a dark brown epiderm on the outer surface. Whorls are sculptured by distinct spiral ridges, about 14 in number, on which the epiderm is almost black. The aperture is narrowed by strong teeth on both the outer and inner lips. The operculum closely resembles that of *R. plicata*. Distribution: south of Amami Islands.

Family Neritopsidae

23. Neritopsis radula (LINNÉ)

The shell resembles those of Neritidae in appearance. It is white all over, and bears some 20 spiral ridges with granules. The spaces between these ridges are marked by fine growth lines. The callus on the inner lip of aperture is narrow and slightly expanded at the posterior end. The operculum is similar to those of Neritidae. Distribution: southwestern islands of Kyûshû and farther south.

Family Littorinidae

These shells are generally top-shaped, or conical. The umbilicus is absent in most species. The operculum is horny and paucispiral. The snails of this family often inhabits exposed rocky shores which dry up in low tide.

24. Nodilittorina granularis (GRAY)

This has the smallest shell among Japanese species of Littorinidae. It is spherical, and sculptured by granulated spiral striae. The outer surface is dirty gray in color, while the inside of aperture is brown. This tiny periwinkle snail is abundant throughout Japan on rocky shores above the tide level, and even frequent on dry rock surfaces where the spray of high tide barely reaches.

25. *Nodilittorina pyramidalis* (QUOY et GAIMARD)

The shell is small but a little larger than *N. granularis*. It is tall, conical, and bears several spiral rows of white granules on its black or brown outer surface. The inner side of aperture is dark brown. Distribution: south of Honshû, near the tide line.

26. *Echininus cumingii luchuanus* (PILSBRY)

A cone-shaped periwinkle, with a pointed spire. The dorsal surface is encircled by spiral ridges on which short spinous granules are regularly arranged. Fine spiral striae cover the ungranulated basal surface, and the umbilicus is perforated. Distribution: south of Amami Islands, near the tide line.

27. *Littorina brevicula* (PHILIPPI)

The body whorl is well developed. The dark brown outer surface is sparsely sculptured by spiral ridges and sometimes marked by white dots. The columellar end is somewhat prolonged toward the anterior. Distribution: throughout Japan, near the tide line. This snail occupies a somewhat lower level than *N. granularis* when they share the same habitat.

Family Turritellidae

Shells of this family are generally tower-shaped, with a tall spire and numerous whorls. The shells are thin, rough, and not lustrous. There is no umbilical opening. The operculum is horny, round, multispiral, and thin. Only a few species are found in the area adjacent to Japan.

1. Turritella terebra cerea REEVE

In this splendid shell, the number of whorls amounts to 25 or even more; although the exact number is rarely known because the topmost part of the spire is destroyed in most specimens. The cross-section of the tube is somewhat trapezoid, owing to the constriction at the suture and the obtuse angles on both ends of the basal lip. Each whorl is surrounded by spiral ribs, about 6 in number. The basal surface is striated in spirals and also somewhat concave at the uppermost part. The shell is usually light yellowish brown all over, but purplish brown individuals are also found. Distribution: Formosa and the South Seas, near 5 fathoms depth.

2. Neohaustator fortiliratus (SOWERBY)

Compared with the first species, the whorls are less inflated and fewer in number (about 14–15). The shell is purplish-brown in color and sculptured by distinct spiral ridges in the same way as in *T. terebra cerea*. Distribution: Hokkaidô and northwards, about 20 fathoms deep.

3. Kurosioia fascialis (MENKE)

This shell is much smaller than those of the preceding two species, being about 25mm tall. Whorls are considerably inflated and the spire is strongly constricted at the suture. The number of whorls is less than 20. Three strong spiral ridges are found on each whorl. The surface color is light yellowish-brown. Distribution: south of central Honshû, at 5–10 fathoms.

Family Architectonicidae

In contrast to the previous family, this family of sun dial shells is characterized by thick, flat shells with a low spire and very wide umbilicus. Some species are almost disc-like in the general shape of their shells. The protoconch, or embryonic shell, is sinistral, but hidden beneath the dextrally coiled whorls which develop later. The operculum is diversified in structure, usually horny, but may be calcareous in exceptional cases. Only a few species are native to the seas around Japan.

4. Heliacus variegatus (GMELIN)

The shell is about 12mm tall and 15mm wide, conical, and rounded at the periphery. Four spiral ridges, on which rows of black and white granules are arranged as though twisted in a rope, encircle each whorl. The spiral ridges on the basal surface, 5 in number, are somewhat more slender. The inner surface of the wide umbilicus is also spirally sculptured by 2 granulated striae. There are 3 grooves, on the inner wall of the tube, which are visible at the aperture. The inner lip is crooked and S-shaped. The operculum is multispiral and convex on both sides, each of which has a pointed nucleus. Its external surface is brown in color, while the internal surface is yellow. Distribution: south of southern Honshû, from the tide level down to 5 fathoms.

5. Philippia radiata (RÖDING)

A low cone-shaped shell, carinated at the periphery, about 11mm in height and 18mm in diameter. The external surface is smooth and glossy. The dorsal surface bears 2 spiral ribs near the peripheral margin of whorls, and is marked by a brown spiral band and radial patterns of the same color. There are also 2 granulated spiral ribs of unequal thickness on the inside surface of umbilicus. The aperture contains two grooves on its inside wall. The operculum is multispiral, round, thin, yellowish brown in color and concave on its outer side. Distribution: central Honshû and farther south, 5–10 fathoms deep.

6. Architectonica trochlearis (HINDS)

This shell is large, reaching 32mm in height and 66mm in diameter. The upper surface is sculptured by 2 spiral ribs, on

24

[PLATE 13]

the carinated periphery of whorls, and by 2 spiral furrows. The ribs are granulated and the furrows are crossed by fine radial lines on earlier whorls, but these fine sculptures tend to disappear on the body whorl. Another spiral rib encircles the basal surface near its peripheral margin. It is light brown in ground color and bears broken spiral bands of dark brown along the suture line and on the spiral ribs. Two granulated spiral ribs on the inside surface of umbilicus are also dark-colored. The horny operculum is paucispiral, rather thick and elliptic in outline. Its external surface is covered by a scaly epiderm and somewhat concave, with a nucleus protruding inward. Distribution: south of central Honshû, 20–30 fathoms deep.

7. Architectonica maxima (PHILIPPI)

Closely resembling the preceding species, this shell has a somewhat lower spire. There are 3 furrows on the dorsal surface of whorls, in contrast with the 2 in *A. trochlearis*. The spiral ribs on the inside wall of umbilicus are not dark-colored. The nucleus of operculum is slightly eccentric. Distribution: the same with the preceding species.

Family Siliquariidae

8. Siliquaria (Agathirses) cumingi MÖRCH

The shelly tube of this shell gradually increases in thickness, and is rather evenly and closely coiled in initial few whorls, but becomes loosely coiled in subsequent whorls with wide spaces between the whorls, finally ending in more or less randomly waved, worm-like state near the aperture. The tube bears a row of sparsely arranged tiny holes, which are connected with each other finally to be a slit in the last part of the tube. The surface is finely sculptured by longitudinal threads and irregular growth lines. The tube is circular in cross-section and less than 6–7mm in diameter. The operculum is round, horny, and multispiral, with a thickened margin. Distribution: south of central Japan, living in sponge colonies.

Family Vermetidae

9. Serpulorbis imbricatus (DUNKER)

This worm-shell has a thicker shelly tube than the preceding species, is 12–15mm in diameter, and adheres to rock surfaces in a shape like a coiled snake. The outer surface is pale brown in color and sculptured by rough longitudinal cords bearing knobs, and growth lines. The aperture is circular, and white to pale brown inside. This has no operculum. Distribution: south of Honshû, near the tide line.

Family Potamididae

This family includes solid and elongated horn-like shells, of which surfaces are sculptured by longitudinal and lateral threads. The aperture is oval in outline, with an anterior canal at the columellar end, and is covered by a thin, horny operculum having a nucleus near its center. These species are often found in large colonies on muddy flats of estuary or coastal shallow waters.

10. Batillaria multiformis (LISCHKE)

The size, shape and coloration of this horn-shell are extremely variable. The shell is encircled by a granulated rib below the suture, and by spiral threads on other parts of the surface. It is dark gray all over or bears a white spiral band at the suture. The callus at the ends of both inner and outer lips is thickened along the posterior canal. The outer lip margin progressively extends at its middle and anterior parts. Distribution: all over Japan.

11. Cerithidea (Cerithideopsilla) cingulata (GMELIN)

The shell is tall with more than 10 whorls, and encircled by spiral ribs with granules, which are crossed by longitudinal folds on the surface. The body whorl bears a knob-like varix on the opposite side of the outer lip of its aperture. The outer lip is remarkably thickened, and its basal part characteristically proceeds along a deep notch at the anterior end of the columella. It is usually stained with mud, but the specimens in clear waters are finely colored by white or yellow of granulated ribs and by dark brown of inter-rib spaces. Distribution: Honshû and southwards, near the tide line.

12. Cerithidea (Cerithideopsilla) djadjariensis (K. MARTIN)

The shell consists of about 13 whorls, and is more stout than the last species. Each whorl is surrounded by 3 spiral striae bearing granules, which are arranged in longitudinal rows alternating with parallel furrows. The granules disappear toward the lower part of the body whorl. The aperture is similar in shape to that of *C. cingulata*, but the outer lip is less thickened and the progression of basal lip margin as well as the columellar notch is less prominent. Distribution: Honshû and southwards, in estuaries.

13. Royella sinon (BAYLE)

The small and white shell is covered by a dirty brown epiderm. Two granulated and angulate striae, sometimes bearing brown spots, surround the whorls. The whorls are separated each other by the constriction along the suture line. The anterior canal is broad and short. No progression is seen in the basal lip end. Distribution: south of central Japan, in subtidal zone.

Family Cerithiidae

This family includes horn shells of various sizes, which are comparatively firm in their construction. They are sculptured by both longitudinal and spiral striae, and characterized by the presence of a distinct anterior canal. All of them dwell in shallow waters along the coast. Dead shells are often observed to be settled by hermit crabs.

14. Clypeomorus subbreviculus OOSTINGH

This horn shell is a short, stout species with the inflated body whorl. The surface is spirally covered by 5–6 granulated striae, alternating with a few smooth threads. It is dark brown on the outer surface, and white inside the aperture. The anterior and posterior canals are short. Distribution: south of southern Honshû, in subtidal zone.

15. Clypeomorus humilis (DUNKER)

The spire is moderately tall, with little constriction at the suture. Three granulated spiral striae and a few intervening threads encircle the whorls. There is a longitudinal rib on the opposite side of aperture on the body whorl. The canals at both ends of aperture are short. The color is dark brown or black, with occasional irregular white spots. Distribution: south of central Japan, in subtidal zone.

16. Cerithium kobelti (DUNKER)

This is an elongated shell, marked by a longitudinal ridge on the body whorl. Tubercles are formed on the surface where 2 granulated spiral striae intersect with longitudinal folds. There is also a fine granular line along the suture. The coloration is variable, but usually light to dark brown. The anterior canal is siphonal. Distribution: south of central Japan, in subtidal zone.

17. Clypeomorus bifasciatus (SOWERBY)

Longitudinal ribs are apparent on earlier whorls of this shell, but they become gradually weaker toward the body whorl. The number of granulated spiral striae on each whorl is about 3, whereas it is 6 on the body whorl. The shell is white in ground color and is decorated by rows of fine black spots. The canals at both ends of aperture are short. A varix is found on the body whorl on the opposite side of the thickened outer lip of aperture. Distribution: south of central Japan, in subtidal zone.

18. Rhinoclavis (Proclava ?) kochi (PHILIPPI)

The outline of the shell is slender, with turreted or tower-shaped spire composed of 14–15 whorls. Two white granulated striae surround each whorl on both sides of suture line. Besides, 2 brown granulted striae and intervening lines are also seen. All the granules on the striae are regularly arranged along weak longitudinal folds. The aperture is rather small, and the end of anterior canal is curved backward. Distribution: Honshû and southwards, in subtidal zone.

[PLATE 13]

19. Rhinoclavis (Ochetoclava?) sinensis (GMELIN)

This resembles the preceding species in outline, but is larger and more stout, bearing a more prominent varix. The outer surface is encircled by a spiral rib bearing tubercles just below the suture and by a few granulated lines. It bears rows of alternately white and brown spots, together with purplish brown cloud patterns. The anterior canal is deep and is curved backward. Distribution: south of central Japan, in subtidal zone.

20. Clypeomorus coralium (KIENER)

Resembling the preceding species, the shell is smaller and has a weaker varix. Each whorl bears 3 granulated spiral striae and some 6 on the body whorl, which are cut by fine longitudinal folds. It is dark brown all over and purplish brown within the aperture, of which the anterior end forms a short canal. Distribution: south of the Ryukyus, in subtidal zone.

21. Cerithium citrinus (SOWERBY)

This shell bears a distinct varix on the body whorl and a long canal at the anterior end of aperture. The outer surface is marked by many fine spiral striae and sparse longitudinal ridges. It is yellow or reddish yellow in color and the inside margin of its aperture is characteristically colored in deep yellow. The anterior canal develops into an inclined siphon, of which the foremost end is often purple-colored. The margin of outer lip is reflected. Distribution: south of central Japan, in subtidal zone.

22. Cerithium nodulosus (BRUGUIÈRE)

This shell somewhat resembles C. citrinus in outline, but is far larger, and solid and robust in construction. The outside is marked all over by spiral striae and prominent longitudinal ridges bearing large tubercles. The tubercles are especially well developed on the shoulder and base of the body whorl. Dark brown spots, bands and irregular patterns are on the white background. The columellar side of aperture is strongly folded, and there is also one remarkable fold near the posterior canal. Fine laminas are also seen on the inside of outer lip. The basal lip proceeds along the anterior canal. Distribution: south of Amami Islands, below the tide line down to 5 fathoms.

PLATE **13**

PLATE 14

1 × 1⅕

2 × 1⅕

3 × 1⅕
a, b,

11 × 1⅕

9 × 1⅕

4 × 1⅕

10 × 1⅕

5 × 1⅕

12 × 1⅕

6 × 1⅕

7 × 1⅕

8 × 1⅕

13 × 1⅕

14 × 1⅕

15 × 1⅘

16 × 1⅘

17 × ⅘

18 × 1⅘

19 × 1⅘

22 × 1⅕

23 × 1⅕

24 × 1⅕

21 × 1⅕

20 × ⅘

Family Hipponicidae

The shells belonging to this hoof shell family are saucer-shaped or conical, and attach to the surface of rocks or other shells,on which the animals secrete a subsidiary base plate. The base plate is just like a tray in shape, somewhat larger than the shell itself in area, and is connected with the shell by a contracting muscle. The range of the animal's movement is limited within the reach of this muscle. Both shell and base plate behave like a bivalve and are marked with muscle scars.

1. Antisabia foliacea QUOY et GAIMARD

This is a small, cap-shaped and somewhat depressed shell and is white in color. The apex is situated near the posterior end of the shell. Many growth lamellae are piled up on the surface like a tiled roof, and each lamella is finely sculptured by radial threads. Distribution: south of central Japan, in subtidal zone.

2. Sabia conica acuta (QUOY et GAIMARD)

This is a small hoof shell variable in its size. The shell is thick, brown in color and bears radial ribs separated by deep furrows. These furrows are irregularly crossed over by prominent oblique folds. This mollusc usually lives, attaching to the surface of shells of *Turbo argyrostomus* or *T. marmoratus*. Distribution: south of Amami Islands.

3. Sabia conica (SCHUMACHER)

This resembles the preceding species in general appearance, but is somewhat taller. The outer surface is regularly marked by radial ribs. This species usually rests upon the shells of *Turbo cornutus*, *Notohaliotis* spp., etc. in a hollow which the animal eroded in the hosts' shells. Frequently, young shells are found on adult shells of this own species. These young shells are male and become female when fully grown up. Zoologists call this type of sex reversal protandry.

4. Hipponix (Pilosabia) pilosus DESHAYS

This is a cap-shaped shell, marked over its outer surface by a decussate sculpture. Pale yellow, hairy processes cover the whole surface. Distribution: south of central Japan, in subtidal zone.

Family Capulidae

This mollusc bears a cap-shaped shell, that has an extremely expanded body whorl and a tightly coiled apex near its posterior end. The interior of the shell is smooth and marked with a muscle scar. There is no operculum. These shells cling to the surface of other shells when alive, and sometimes even drill the hosts' shells to absorb nutrients.

5. Capulus dilatatus A. ADAMS

This species is usually parasitic on *Amusium japonicum*, *Pecten albicans*, *Decatopecten striatus*, etc. The shell may be limpet-like when this is parasitic on such smooth shell-surface as that of *Amusium*, but may bear rib-like folds when this is parasitic on such ribbed shells as Pectinidae. A shortly fibrous epiderm covers the whole outer surface that bears radial brown color bands. Distribution: south of central Japan (see Plate 72).

Family Calyptraeidae (1)

The shells of this group are mostly thin, flatly conical or low dome-shaped, and have a circular to oval aperture. The apex is situated centrally or posteriorly. The surface is usually sculptured, but is smooth in some species. The shells are characterized by a cup-shaped appendage on the inner side, and lack the operculum.

6. Cheilea pileopsis (QUOY et GAIMARD)

This small cup-and-saucer shell is tall cone-shaped, and sculptured by fine radial threads and irregular folds on its dorsal surface, but lacks concentric lines. The inside cup is oval in cross-section, and cut off at the posterior end.

7. Cheilea scutula (REEVE)

The shell is low conical and circular in basal outline. It is marked on its exterior by fine radiating ribs and circular growth lines. The appendage is short and vertically hangs down with an opening on the posterior side.

8. Cheilea bulla (REEVE)

The outer surface bears a rather coarse, decussate sculpture. The appendage is large and elongated.

These three species are all white in color and usually attach to the underside of dead corals with a subsidiary base plate on the substratum. Distribution: south of Amami Islands, below the tide line down to 2 fathoms.

Family Trichotropidae

The shells of this family are usually top-shaped, having a tall spire, but some of them are also of a low-spired form. The whitish outer surface is covered by an epiderm, occasionally bearing hairy processes. They have an opening umbilicus and a horny operculum which is multispiral, with a nucleus at the center.

9. Trichotropis nobilis A. (ADAMS)

The apex of this shell is coiled at its posterior end, and the aperture opens just like the shape of a trumpet. The dorsal surface is sculptured by 2 radial cords, white in ground color and covered by a brown epiderm. Distribution: the Kuriles and farther north, sometimes found at considerable depths associated with deep-water species as the hosts.

10. Amathina tricarinata (LINNÉ)

The apex is directed backward and slightly coiled. The outer surface bears 3 carinated ribs which develop into semitubular spines at the aperture. The outside is white, but usually covered by a yellowish brown or olive epiderm. Distribution: south of central Japan, in subtidal zone, attaching to the shells of Ostridae.

11. Lippistes (Separatista) helicoides (GMELIN)

A low-spired shell with the smooth surface. This is surrounded by 3 spiral cords on its periphery, and the body whorl is characteristically isolated from the penultimate whorl. The columella is well developed, and straight. Distribution: south of central Japan, at 5–10 fathoms depth.

12. Iphinoe unicarinata (SOWERBY)

This shell is screw-shaped, and encircled by spiral cords on the carinations at the shoulder of each whorl and at the basal periphery. The smooth outer surface is pale yellow in ground color and is covered by a brown eipderm which is grossly spinose on the shoulder. Distribution: Honshû and southwards, 5–10 fathoms in depth.

13. Trichotropis bicarinata SOWERBY

Each spire is encircled by 2 strong cords on the peripheral carinations. The whole surface is covered by a brown epiderm bearing hairy spicules on the peripheral angles. The umbilicus is slit-like. Distribution: northeastern half of Honshû and northwards, at 10–30 fathoms depth.

Family Epitoniidae

Many species of this family are found in Japan. The shells are generally thin and white, and characterized by the turreted spire, ornamented by many varices either plate- or thread-like. In a few species, the whorls are only loosely coiled, and are isolated from each other. These staircase shells are one of the favorites of shell collectors because of their neat style and rarity.

14. Papyriscala latifasciata (SOWERBY)

This wentletrap shell is thin, and has a tightly coiled, tall spire. Each whorl bears 20–30 fine longitudinal threads or costae over its surface. It is white in ground color, and marked on the body whorl by 3 spiral bands brown in color, while on other whorls there are only 2 similar bands. The umbilicus is narrowly open, being covered by the columellar end. Distribution: central Japan, at 5–10 fathoms.

15. Depressiscala aurita (SOWERBY)

This closely resembles the preceding species in general appearance, but is more slender. The costae are usually fine, and irregularly interspersed by thicker ones. The color bands are wider than those of P. latifasciata. Distribution: central Japan, at 5–10 fathoms.

16. Papyriscala bifasciata KIRA et HABE (n. sp.)

The costae are plate-like, thin, and variable in number and space between them. One or two brown color bands are seen. The umbilicus is open. Distribution: central Japan and southwards, at 5–10 fathoms.

The above 3 species are the inhabitants of rather shallow waters.

17. Cirsotrema (Elegantiscala) varicosum KURODA

The spire of this shell is fairly slender and tall. The shell is thick and white in color, without open umbilicus. Flat and short spines are densely arranged on the strong varices, which are angulated at the shoulder. Many spiral threads are seen in the spaces between the varices, but they disappear on the very varices. This has no open umbilicus. The operculum is horny, round, paucispiral and black in color. Distribution: obtained by dredging from Tosa Bay and Bungo Channel, Shikoku, at 100–150 fathoms depth.

18. Glabriscala stigmatica (PILSBRY)

This shell is white in ground color, marked by oblique brown patterns which are irregular in size and tone. The umbilicus is almost covered by the callus of inner lip. Distribution: central Japan, at 5–10 fathoms.

19. Gyroscala perplexa (PEASE)

This is a small and moderately thick shell. The costae are longitudinally continuous throught the whorls. Sometimes the whorls are isolated at the suture between the costae. The base bears a single spiral rib and this has no umbilicus. Distribution: south of central Japan, at 5–10 fathoms.

20. Amaea magnifica (SOWERBY)

The shell is the largest among Japanese Epitoniidae. The spire is slender, composed of well-inflated whorls, and deeply constricted at the suture. Fine longitudinal and spiral threads cross each other and produce a coarse reticulate network. The base bears a single weak spiral rib, starting from the posterior end of aperture. The operculum is horny, yellowish ivory in color and paucispiral. It has no umbilicus. Distribution: Honshû and southwards, at 20–40 fathoms.

21. Epitonium scalare (LINNÉ)

The shape and structure of this shell is most exquisite. It is moderately large, and white in color, with a faint fleshy tone. The whorls are loosely coiled, leaving open spaces between them, and sparsely bear thin and high varix-plates which are connected with those of the next whorls at the inter-whorl spaces. The umbilicus is widely open, and the spiral can be looked into through its inside. A round aperture has a reflexed margin, and is closed by a dark purple operculum, which is horny, round and paucispiral. Distribution: Honshû and southwards, at 20–30 fathoms. This splendid species was originally recorded from China Sea.

Family Janthinidae

These thinnest shells are generally globose in shape and have a low spire. The body whorl is well inflated, and bears a large aperture that lacks the operculum. The animal has a large mucous bubble or bladder under its foot, and has no eyes. The eggs are laid in the bladder. The molluscs of this family are pelagic or freely float on the surface of ocean, occasionally drifting ashore after a gale.

22. Janthina janthina (LINNÉ)

23. Janthina balteata REEVE

24. Janthina (Violetta) globosa SWAINSON

J. globosa has much larger and more inflated body whorl than the other two species. It has a notch in the center of

outer lip margin. It is light violet in color
all over the shell. The spire of *J. janthina*
is taller than that of *J. balteata*. The
purple color of the shells in these two
species is darker on the base than on the
dorsal side, but the latter can be discriminated from the former by the white tone
around the umbilicus.

Janthina balteata
with its bladder
(after ADAMS)

Family Calyptraeidae (2)

1. Crepidula (Bostrycapulus) gravispinosa KURODA et HABE

This slipper limpet is low, looks like an ear shell in appearance and lives attached to solid objects. The apex is laterally placed at the end of the shell. The entire outer surface is marked with spiral striae bearing fine spines. On the underside of the shell, a white deck or septum covers the posterior half of aperture. The color is brownish, marked with whitish rays. Distribution: south of central Honshû.

2. Syphopatella walshi (REEVE)

The shell is flat and pure white, resembling a petal of a white camellia flower in shape and color. The smooth outer surface bears growth lines and is covered by a thin yellowish epiderm. In the interior it has a small deck connected with the main part of the shell only along its one side. The living shells are usually found, attached to the inside of other dead shells, so they often warp outwards. Distribution: south of central Honshû.

As in *Sabia conica* (Plate 13), young individuals of these two species sometimes rest upon the back of mature shells of their own species. The reversal of sex with the progress of growth stage is also known.

3. Crepidula grandis MIDDENDORFF

This slipper shell is remarkably convex on its outer surface and usually attached to the shells of other species. The outside is light-colored, and covered by a reddish brown epiderm. The septum on the interior is thick and covers the posterior half of aperture. Distribution: Hokkaidô and northwards.

Family Xenophoridae

The carrier shells of this family are low conical in shape, with irregular folds on the dorsal surface. The base is surrounded by a peripheral carination, on which leaf-like or spiny protrusions sometimes develop. This mollusc has a peculiar habit of cement-ing dead shells of other species or small pebbles on the outer surface of its own shell. The large flat aperture has a simple outer lip, and a deeply curved basal columella. The operculum is thin and horny, and bears concentric rings with a nucleous near one side. The species belonging to this family are few in number.

4. Onustus exutus (REEVE)

The thin shell is fairly flat, and carries a very little amount of fine sand cemented near its apex. A thin, plate-like appendage with sinuate or waved margin hangs down over the carinated basal periphery. Its exterior is yellowish brown in color and finely marked by oblique longitudinal folds. The base of body whorl is surrounded by a radially sculptured marginal zone, which is fringed by the broadly protruding peripheral appendage. The umbilicus is open and the operculum is oblong. Distribution: south of central Honshû, at 10–20 fathoms depth.

5. Xenophora pallidula (REEVE)

This carrier shell is more solid in its construction than the preceding species, and is devoid of the peripheral appendage. This carries a number of dead (or sometimes living) shells of other species all over its upper surface. The cemented materials may be clams (5b), snails (5c) or gravels (5d), indicating the nature of substrata on which the animals grew. When the loads are removed (5a), traces of oblique folds are seen on the shell surface. The basal surface is white or light yellowish brown in color and bears distinct growth lines and spiral threads. The slit-like umbilicus is barely open, but is often covered by a dilated callus of the inner lip of aperture. Distribution: south of northeastern Honshû, at about 20 fathoms.

6. Xenophora tenuis FULTON

This is generally similar to the last species in shape, but is smaller and less solid, bearing dental tubercles on the peripheral keel. Cemented shell fragments are also smaller and less. The remarkably concave base is white-colored, bearing very fine growth lines and spiral threads. Distri-

[PLATE 15]   Calyptraeidae, Xenophoridae

bution: south of central Honshû, 50–80 fathoms deep.

7. *Xenophora turrida* KURODA et ITO

This shell can be distinguished from the preceding species by deep radial folds on its back surface and dark brown color of the shell. Growth lines on the basal surface are strongly ridged and granulated. This shell usually carries small pebbles. Distribution: south of central Honshû, at 20–30 fathoms depth.

PLATE **15**

1

× 1⅕

2

× 1⅕

3

× 1⅕

4

× 1

5 a,

× 1⅕

5 b,

× 1⅕

5 c,

× 1⅕

5 d,

× 1

6

× ⅘

7

× ⅘

PLATE 16

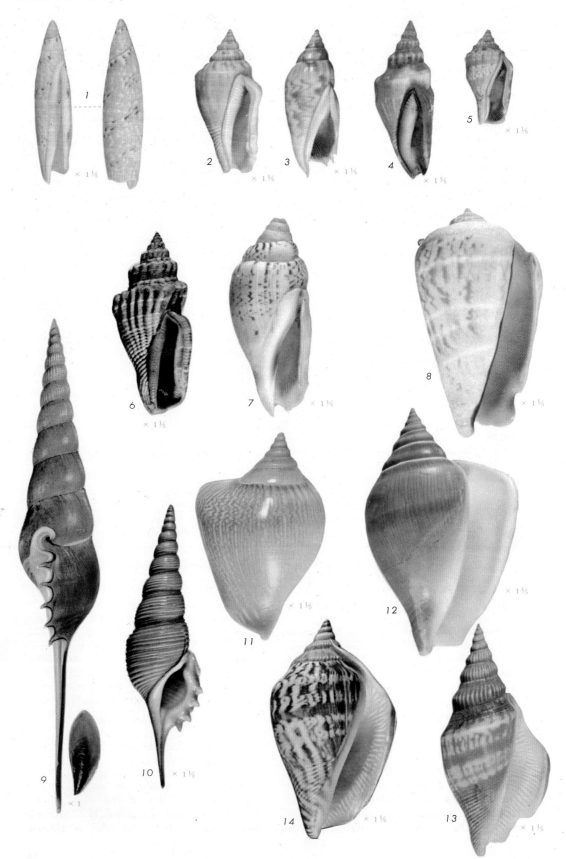

Family Strombidae (1)

The conch shells are variable in size and shape, but are generally thick. They are characterized by a narrow oblong aperture and a well-developed outer lip which sometimes greatly expand or become thick or bear spiny appendages. The outer surface is entirely smooth in some species, but is often delicately sculptured in others. The operculum is horny and oblong in shape with a nucleus at its anterior end. The shells are prized for their beautiful color and unique shape, but are not suitable for art materials because of the lack of pearly layer. Certain species offer delicious flesh for food, though they are rather scarce and of little economic importance.

1. Terebellum terebellum (LINNÉ)

This is an elongated spindle-shaped shell with glossy exterior surface. The whorls are only 3 in number. The last whorl develops very well. It is almost white in ground color and is densely marked all over the surface with light purplish brown dots. Four rows of deep purple spots encircle the body whorl. The inner lip of aperture is longer than the outer lip. Distribution: south of the southernmost islets of Kyûshû District, 5–10 fathoms deep.

A subspecies, *T. t. delicatum* KURODA et KAWAMOTO, is distributed from Honshû to Kyûshû. This is characterized by the smaller and thinner shell as well as well as by the darker color and white spots.

2. Canarium mutabilis (SWAINSON)

This shell has a typical form of this family, with a pointed spire and the extraordinarily well developed body whorl that occupies more than two-thirds of the total length of shell. Each whorl is surrounded by a row of granules on their shoulder, which, however, disappears on the last whorl. The outer surface is smooth except some radial threads on the anterior part of body whorl and on the outside of outer lip. The lips of aperture are thickened and finely sculptured in its inside by parallel grooves. The outer lip margin curves in at its anterior end, forming a so-called 'stromboid notch'. The inside of aperture is beauti-

fully colored in salmon-pink. Distribution: central Honshû and southwards, below the tide line down to 5 fathoms.

3. Canarium dentatum (LINNÉ)

The entire surface is smooth, but bears a row of longitudinal folds on the shoulder. Three spiny protrusions near the anterior end of the outer lip margin are characteristic of this species. The outer lip is shorter than the inner lip as in *Terebellum terebellum*. Only the interior of the inner lip is sculptured by fine threads and is dark brown. Distribution: south of Amami Islands, below the tide line down to 5 fathoms.

4. Canarium urceus (LINNÉ)

This is very close to *C. mutabilis* in appearance, but the aperture is remarkably narrowed toward the anterrior end and colored in black along the inner margins of both lips. Distribution: south of Amami Islands, from the tide line to 5 fathoms depth.

5. Canarium microurceum KIRA

This little conch also resembles *C. mutabilis*, but bears a more widely open aperture whose inner margin is black in color. Distribution: south of central Honshû, between the tide line and 5 fathoms depth.

6. Canarium labiatus [RÖDING]

The spire is relatively taller than those of the preceding 4 species. The exterior surface is covered by prominent longitudinal folds, which end in tubercles on the shoulder of each whorl. Outer and inner lip margins of aperture are sculptured by fine threads and furrows. The inside of aperture is orange-yellow in color. Distribution: south of Amami Islands, from the tide line to 5 fathoms depth.

7. Gibberulus gibberulus gibbosus [RÖDING]

The general appearance of the shell is somewhat like that of the next species, but this is much elongated in shape and has a taller spire. The spire is twisted.

34

[PLATE 16]   Strombidae

The surface is covered by encircling ribs which become indistinct on the body whorl. Reticulate patterns of purplish brown sparsely decorate the exterior. The inside of aperture is violet-colored and the outer lip is striated inside. Distribution : south of Amami Islands, below the tide line to 5 fathoms depth.

8.   Conomurex luhuanus (LINNÉ)

This shell resembles the cone shell in outline and in the nature of epiderm, but can be easily distinguished by the stromboid notches on both ends of the outer lip. The spire is low, but has a distinctly pointed apex. The smooth surface of large body whorl is white in color with sparse reticulate patterns of brown. There are also a few encircling bands of yellowish brown color. It is salmon pink within the aperture and a black longitudinal line is seen on the inner lip margin. The flesh of this mollusc is edible. Distribution : south of central Honshû, at 5–10 fathoms depth.

9.   Tibia fusus (LINNÉ)

This shell is of a slender spindle-shape, characterized by a very tall spire and an extremely long anterior cannal of almost half of the total length of shell. The whorls are well inflated and bordered by the deep suture. Earlier whorls are marked by longitudinal ribs and spiral threads on the surface, but the last 4 whorls are entirely smooth except a thick spiral rib near the base. The outer lip bears 5 spiny protrusions. The short posterior canal spirally extends upward along the body whorl, while the anterior canal is straightly elongated. The outer lip margin is bordered by a thread of reddish brown color. The epiderm is velvet-like. The operculum is horny and resembles a broad hook in shape. Distribution : from Formosa to the East Indies, 5–10 fathoms deep.

10.   Tibia powisi (PETIT)

This is a smaller shell of the same genus as the preceding species. It bears 6–7 thick spiral ridges on each whorl together with 1–2 fine spiral threads on the suture. Also fine longitudinal threads are seen in spaces between the ridges. The body

whorl is characteristically carinated at the shoulder on the 3rd spiral ridge below the suture. Among the 5 spines on the outer lip margin, the most posterior one is wider than the others and bears a blunt point. The posterior canal is not coiled, unlike that of *T. fusus*. The anterior canal is almost as long as the aperture and slightly curved toward the side of outer lip. The entire surface is light brown in color. Distribution : along Pacific coasts of Honshû and Shikoku, at 50–80 fathoms depth.

11.   Laevistrombus canarium (LINNÉ)

The shell is smaller than the next species, from which this can be distinguished by a well developed round shoulder on the body whorl and the tower-like spire with concave side slopes. The thick outer lip extends outward like a Japanese *kimono* sleeve that tapers toward the anterior end. The inside margin of aperture lacks any sculpture. It is white in ground color, but is covered entirely by fine ripple patterns of brown color. Distribution : Formosa and southwards, 5–10 fathoms deep.

12.   Laevistrombus canarium (LINNÉ) forma isabella (LAMARCK)

In this conch shell, the spire is straight and the body whorl has no distinguished shoulder. The surface is smooth, bearing only a granulated line on earlier whorls. The ' sleeve ' of the outer lip is wider than that of *L. canarium*, but is somewhat round-shouldered. The outer surface is from light brown to brown, and sometimes encircled by dark color bands. Distribution : south of central Honshû, at 10–30 fathoms depth.

13.   Doxander vittatus japonicus (REEVE)

This shell is spindle-shaped with a tall spire. Each whorl is sculptured by longitudinal ribs at the shoulder, which are crossed by spiral striae to form a reticulated sculpture. The extension of the outer lip tapers at both ends by curved stromboid notches, and is sculptured inside by fine furrows. The ground color is white and the outer surface is marked over by brown reticulate patterns. The operculum is horny and elongated hook-shaped, with sharp spines along one side (see textfigures on p. 38). Distribution: south of central Honshû, 10–30 fathoms deep.

14. Dolomena marginata robusta (SOWERBY)

The spire of this shell is lower and the body whorl is more inflated than those of the last species. The expanded outer lip is broad and terminates in a peculiarly prolonged posterior canal that reaches the 2nd or 3rd whorl from the aperture. The exterior is marked by brown reticulate patterns and irregular white spots arranged in spiral zones. Distribution: south of central Honshû, at 5–10 fathoms depth.

[PLATE 17]   Strombidae

Family Strombidae (2)

1. *Labiostrombus epidromis* (LINNÉ)

The shape and sculpture of whorls resemble those of *D. vittatus japonicus*, but the outer lip is thin and broadly expanded, with a somewhat thickened margin and a stromboid notch only at its anterior end. The posterior canal is short and reflexed. The interior of aperture bears neither sculpture nor coloration. The surface is without lustre, dirty white in ground color and spotted by faint brown patterns. Distribution : south of the Ryukyus, from the tide line to 5 fathoms depth.

2. *Euprotomus aurisdianae* (LINNÉ)

The dorsal side is rough and ragged. Each whorl bears thick spiral cords and longitudinal ribs with tubercles on the shoulder. Both lips bear a thick callus, covering almost all of the ventral side of the shell. The 'sleeve' of outer lip is well developed, has a blunt projection at the shoulder, and has two notches at both ends. Fine threads are indistinctly marked over the inside of posterior canal. The anterior canal is short and reflexed toward the dorsal side. The inside color of aperture is orange brown or pinkish. Distribution : south of Amami Islands, below the tide line down to 5 fathoms.

3. *Euprotomus bulla* [RÖDING]

The shell is like the last species in shape, but the surface of the dorsal side is smooth, glistening and less ragged. The surface sculpture consists of tubercles and very weak spiral striae. The projection on the shoulder of 'sleeve' is a little longer than that of *E. aurisdianae*. The surface is marked by irregular light reddish-brown patches. The interior of aperture is smooth and colored orange-rose. Distribution : south of Amami Islands, between the tide line and 5 fathoms depth.

4. *Euprotomus vomer* [RÖDING]

This shell closely resembles the preceding species in dorsal appearance. The body whorl is slightly more slender. The long projection on the shoulder of 'sleeve' tends to be semi-tubular. The inside of aperture is densely ornamented by raised and distinct threads, and is reddish-purple in color, especially between the threads. Distribution : south of Amami Islands, from tide line to 5 fathoms depth.

5. *Lentigo lentiginosus* (LINNÉ)

The shell is solid and heavy with a low spire. The body whorl is remarkably large, about 2/3 as long as the shell length. The outer surface is ragged, as in *E. aurisdianae*, owing to an encircling row of tubercles which develop into large rounded knobs on the dorsal side of body whorl, as well as to small tuberculated ribs and thick spiral cords. The ventral side is marked by greenish-brown mottles overlaid by a translucent and shiny glaze. The 'sleeve' is well expanded and thick with 2 tongue-like projections on the shoulder. The interior of aperture is smooth. Distribution : south of Amami Islands, near the tide line down to 5 fathoms depth.

6. *Tricornis sinuatus* (HUMPHREY)

This handsome shell is moderately large and solid. The dorsal side, with large pyramidal knobs, is rather monotonously ornamented by indistinct spiral threads and by light brown color bands, 14–15 in number. The ventral side, on the other hand, is strikingly beautiful with its deep purple coloration within the aperture and with its 'sleeve' of unique shape, showing palm-like expansions. The inner lip is marked by brown reticulate patterns under a translucent callus layer. The middle part of the outer lip margin is remarkably thickened and also has alternately white and brown stripes on its surface. Distribution : south of the Ryukyus, 5–10 fathoms deep.

7. *Tricornis thersites* (SWAINSON)

The outline of the shell is rather simple and resembles that of *E. aurisdianae*, but this is much larger, heavier and more solid. The knobs on the dorsal side are also very prominent. Two stromboid notches are seen on both ends of the heavy outer lip. Light brown patterns are barely visible on the ventral side of body whorl.

Distribution: Amami Inlands and farther south, at 5–10 fathoms depth.

8. *Tricornis latissimus* (LINNÉ)

This heavy shell is even larger than the preceding species. The body whorl is nearly 3/4 as long as the shell length, and the spire is almost covered by the broadly expanded outer lip or 'sleeve'. The dorsal side bears large, low and round knobs and a white band on the brown ground color, though the original coloration is more or less stained by sediments in most specimens. The posterior part of the sleeve is round in outline and thin-edged, and bears spiral folds on its dorsal side. The outer lip margin is very thick, especially around a notch at its anterior end, where it reaches 20 mm or more in thickness. The ventral side of body whorl and the outer lip margin are marked by light and dark brown patterns. The callus on the inner lip widens toward the posterior canal. The anterior canal is short and thick. Distribution: south of Amami Islands, at 5–10 fathoms depth.

9. *Lambis crocata* (LINK)

This spider shell owes its name to its odd shape with 7 long spines around its aperture. For the same reason, the Japanese calls it the scorpion shell. The whorls are encircled by 3 rows of small knobs and many spiral threads. The spines on the outer lip, including the one enveloping the posterior canal, are tubular in structure, but are usually filled up when the shell has fully grown up, whereas only the most anterior spine remains tubular as the anterior canal. The outer surface is white in color and spotted with brown, but is covered over by a dark brown epiderm. The interior of aperture is smooth and orange-red in color. Distribution: south of Amami Islands, 10–20 fathoms deep.

10. *Lambis (Millepes) scorpius* (LINNÉ)

This is similar to the last species in shape and sculpture, but the 7 spines of this shell bear each 2–3 knots, and a few short spines occur in each space between the main spines. The inside of aperture is deeply reddish purple in color, and laterally sculptured by parallel white threads. Irreg-

ular knots are also seen on the threads on the outer lip side. Distribution: southern part of Honshû and southwards, at 10–20 fathoms depth.

11. *Lambis lambis* (LINNÉ)

This spider shell resembles *L. crocata*, but is moderately large, solid, and simply colored. This also differs from *L. crocata* in thick and relatively short spines. The interior of aperture does not show any sculptures. The outer lip extends laterally, without forming a thick margin. Distribution: southern part of Honshû, at 10–20 fathoms depth. *L. truncata* (HUMPHREY) is a related species with a much larger shell.

12. *Lambis (Harpago) chiragra* (LINNÉ)

This is the secondly largest species among Japanese Strombidae next to *L. truncata*. The spines on the outer lip are 6 in number and very thick, and project radially on all sides of the shell. The margin of outer lip thickens into a remarkable rim with a deep notch. Only a spine enveloping the anterior canal remains tubular. The scarlet-colored aperture is narrowly open, owing to the terrace-like lamina that develops along the inside of the outer lip, on which fine threads are sculptured. The dorsal side of the shell is marked by numerous deep brown spots. Distribution: southern Honshû and southwards, at 10–20 fathoms depth.

As shown on the textfigure, the opercula of this family are horny and resemble an elongated hook in shape. Their size becomes larger in proportion to the size of the shell; the operculum of *L. chiragra* reaches 60 mm in length, 16 mm in width and 3 mm in thickness. They are used by the annimals as a prop in jumping or turning movement.

Opercula of Strombidae
Left: exterior,   right: interior surface
Lambis   *Doxander vittatus*
chiragra   *japonicus*

The habitat of the last 3 species had been said to be the subtidal zone, south of Amami Islands, but recently they were also found to reach as far north as the Pacific coasts of southern Honshû. Specimens from Kii Channel, Tosa Bay, etc. are, however, thinner in shell construction and lighter in coloration, as compared with southern races.

PLATE **17**

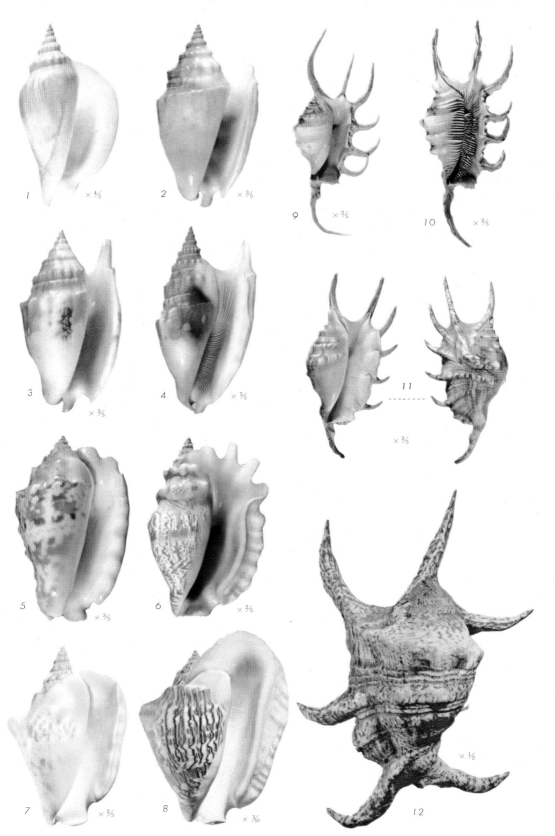

PLATE 18

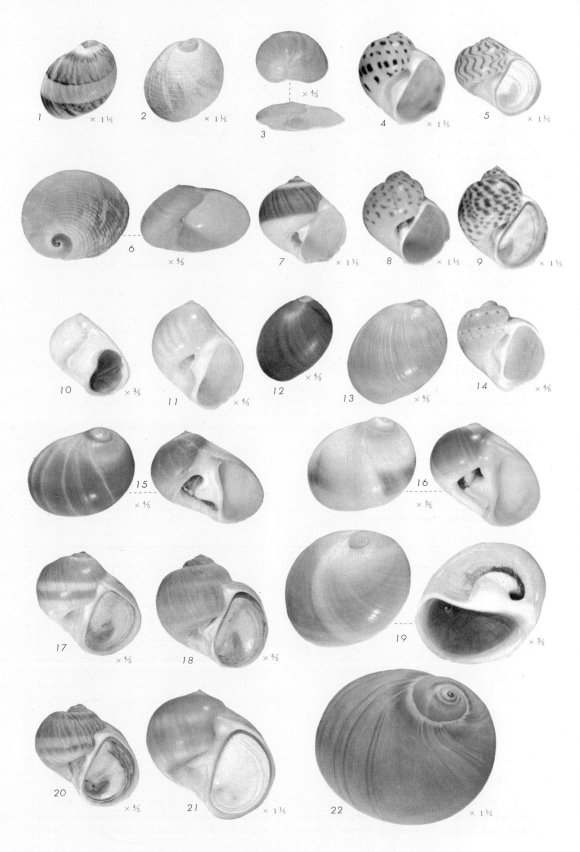

1 × 1⅕
2 × 1⅕
3 × ⅘
4 × 1⅕
5 × 1⅕
6 × ⅘
7 × 1⅕
8 × 1⅕
9 × 1⅕
10 × ⅗
11 × ⅘
12 × ⅘
13 × ⅘
14 × ⅘
15 × ⅘
16 × ⅗
17 × ⅘
18 × ⅘
19 × ⅗
20 × ⅘
21 × 1⅕
22 × 1⅕

Family Naticidae

This group of the moon shells includes many species, of which the shells are usually globular or oval in shape. There are also some of disc-like shells. The outer surface is generally smooth, but fine sculptures are seen in a few species. The whorls are few in number, and the shelly tube rapidly increases in diameter. The aperture is semi-circular, fringed by a thin outer lip. The umbilicus is open, with a block of callus or a funicular pad in it. The operculum, if it exists, is either calcareous or horny.

The molluscs of this family are known as the predator that perforates other shells to eat their flesh.

1. *Mammilla simiae* (DESHAYES)

The shell is oblong globular in shape. This has a small spire and a large body whorl, which bears irregular chestnut-brown patterns all over its surface, except on a patternless zone surrounding the middle part. The umbilicus is slit-like and mostly covered by a dark-brown callus on the inner lip. The operculum is horny, reddish-brown in color, and half-coiled in shape. Distribution: Honshû and southwards, at 5–10 fathoms depth.

2. *Eunaticina lamarckiana* (RÉCLUZ)

This moon shell is almost globular and sculptured by fine spiral furrows on the exterior of the shell. It is white all over its surface, but is covered by a yellowish brown epiderm. The umbilicus is barely open. The operculum is horny, rather thin, and yellowish brown in color, and its structure is somewhat exceptional for the family, as shown in the textfigure. Distribution: Honshû and southwards, below the tide line down to 5 fathoms.

Operculum of *Eunaticina lamarckiana*

E. papilla (GMELIN), a closely related species to this, has a slightly more elongated shell and inhabits somewhat deeper waters.

These two species differ in the structure of radula, but are hardly distinguishable from each other in their shell morphology.

3. *Sinum (Ectosinum) planulatus* (RÉCLUZ)

The baby ear shell resembles a flat-disc in shape, having a broadly expanded last whorl. The white outer surface bears no sculpture other than growth lines and is covered by a light yellowish brown epiderm. The callus on the outer lip has a thin and sharp edge.

S. (E.) undulatus (LISCHKE) looks alike in the shape of shell, but is characterized by spiral furrows on its surface. *S. japonicus* (LISCHKE) is also a related species, but the shell is somewhat inflated, bearing spiral striae, and showing a slight brown coloration on the protoconch. The body of these molluscs is very large and lacks the operculum. Distribution: central Honshû and sowthwards, commonly found in shallow waters.

4. *Naticarius onca* [RÖDING]

This is almost globular in shape, with a comparatively large funiclar pad within the opening umbilicus. The white outer surface is encircled by 5 rows of dark brown spots. The operculum is calcareous and semi-circular, with 7–8 spiral cords on its exterior surface. Distribution: south of central Honshû, at 5–10 fathoms depth.

5. *Notocochlis zebra* (LAMARCK)

The shell is similar to the preceding species in shape. The smooth outer surface is sparsely ornamented by waved radial patterns of brown color. The funicular pad is small. The calcareous operculum is semi-circular, and coverd with a smooth layer, on which 4 spiral cords are sculptured. Distribution: south of central Honshû, 10–20 fathoms deep.

6. *Sinum javanicus* (GRIFFITH et PIDGEON)

This baby ear shell resembles *S. (E.) planulatus*, but is more inflated and larger, reaching about 48 mm × 40 mm × 20 mm in size. The outer surface is marked by coarse spiral furrows, which become weaker toward

[PLATE 18]   Naticidae

the periphery and completely disappear on the base of body whorl. The umbilicus is entirely covered by the parietal callus. The margin of outer lip is thin. This is white in color, with a purplish brown spot at the apex, and is usually covered by a yellowish brown epiderm. Distribution: south of central Honshû, 5–10 fathoms in depth.

7.   Natica bibalteata SOWERBY

This is a globular shell, with the smooth but non-glossy outer surface. Each whorl is encircled by a brown band on the white background. The umbilicus is open, and the funicular pad is connected with the upper part of parietal callus. The operculum is calcareous, semi-circular and white in color. Distribution: south of Kyûshû, at 5–10 fathoms depth.

8.   Notocochlis hilaris (SOWERBY)

This resembles the last species in general shape of shell, but the spire is taller. The outer surface is light brown, smooth, and randomly spotted with brown. The funicular pad is isolated and small. The operculum is calcareous and semi-circular in shape, and is covered by a smooth layer, except on a spiral rib along the outer margin. Distribution: south of central Honshû, 10–20 fathoms deep.

9.   Notocochlis tigrina [RÖDING]

The spire of this shell is even taller than that of the preceding species. The surface coloration is white, with numerous dark brown dots, which tend to be jointed together into radial patterns. The operculum is similar to that of the preceding species. Distribution: south of central Honshû, 5–10 fathoms in depth.

10.   Polinices pyriformis (RÉCLUZ)

A pretty moon shell with the polished and pure-white surface. The general shape of this shell is oblong oval, owing to the considerably tall spire. A well developed funicular pad fills up the umbilicus, and is entirely covered by the parietal callus. The operculum is half-coiled, corneous and yellowish brown. Distribution: southern

Honshû and southwards, 5–10 fathoms deep.

11.   Polinices vavaosi (?) (REEVE)

This can be distinguished from the last species by the more inflated whorls, the brown coloration on the protoconch and the opening umbilicus. Distribution: southern half of Honshû and farther south, 5–10 fathoms deep. *P. flemingianus* (RÉCLUZ) is a yellow-colored shell, closely related to this species.

12.   Mammilla maura (LAMARCK)

The shell has a very small spire and the well inflated body whorl, and is oblong globular in shape. The exterior surface is smooth, and is covered by a polished, light chestnut-brown epiderm. The umbilicus is barely open like a slit, being covered by a brown smooth layer. Distribution: south of the Ryukyus, 5–10 fathoms in depth.

13.   Mammilla opaca (RÉCLUZ)

The shape of this shell also closely resembles that of *M. maura*, but this is larger in size and light-colored, and the body whorl is much more inflated. The white ground color of the outer surface is marked by 3 faint spiral bands of light brown, and is much faintly colored by longitudinal lines. Dark brown coloration is seen around the umbilicus, that opens like a slit, and on the parietal callus. The anterior part of columellar lip margin is somewhat angulate. The horny operculum is semi-circular in outline, and is marked by black spots around the nucleus. Distribution: southern Honshû and southwards, 5–10 fathoms deep.

14.   Naticarius alapapilionis [RÖDING]

The shell is globular in outline. The tube of the body whorl is angled and expanded at the shoulder and at the basal periphery. The lower part of columella is elongated forward. The smooth and fleshy brown surface is covered by a thick epiderm, and is encircled by 4 white bands sparsely dotted by brown. It is also colored in brown within the large aperture. The operculum of this shell may be the most intricately sculptured among the calcareous opercula of this family; that is, its surface is marked by numerous spiral ribs and is concave around the nucleus. Distribution: central Honshû, at 10–20 fathoms depth.

15. Polinices sagamiensis PILSBRY

This moon shell is thick and heavy. The shell exterior is glossy-smooth and white in color, and is marked by a wide brown band encircling the central part of each whorl. The umbilical area consists of a well developed funicular pad and a deep semi-circular furrow surrounding it. The operculum is corneous and half-coiled. Distribution: Honshû and southwards, 5–10 fathoms in depth.

16. Polinices powisianus (RÉCLUZ)

This shell very closely resembles the preceding species in shape, but differs in the following characteristics: the spire is slightly taller; the funicular pad is smaller; the furrow around the pad is shallower and wider; the umbilicus itself is more deeply perforated. The operculum is horny, half-moon shaped, and reddish brown in color. Distribution: southern Honshû and southwards, at 5–10 fathoms depth.

17. Natica vitellus (LINNÉ)

A globular shell, with the glossy-smooth and white-colored outer surface. Two wide and narrow color bands of fleshy brown color encircle the whorls on the shoulder and the lower part, respectively. The funicular pad is small and the umbilical wall is deep. The calcareous operculum has a callus layer over its surface, and its margin is bordered by 2 remarkable ribs. Distribution: south of the Ryukyus, at 5–10 fathoms.

18. Tectonatica janthostomoides KURODA et HABE

The shell is globular, and its outer surface is smooth, without glossiness. Two or three white bands surround the dirty brown surface of whorls. The inside of aperture is white. The umbilicus is small, and is almost filled up by the funicular pad. The operculum is calcareous, and covered by a callus layer, and bears 1–2 ribs along

the outside margin. Distribution: south of the southwestern part of Hokkaidô, at 10–20 fathoms depth.

T. russa (GOULD), having a smaller umbilicus entirely sealed up by the funicular pad, is distributed in northeastern Hokkaidô and northwards.

19. Polinices albumen (LINNÉ)

This species has a compressed shell, with a very flat spire and greatly expanded body whorl. It has the smooth surface, from white to dark brown in color. In colored specimens, a white band runs along the suture. The umbilical area is also white-colored, and is very wide, almost as wide as the total basal side of shell; a shallow depression surrounds the strongly developed funicular pad. The operculum is horny, semi-circular and half-coiled, and reddish or yellowish brown in color. Distribution: southern Honshû and southwards, at 5–10 fathoms. This shell is sold as food in the market of Kagoshima City, southernmost Kyûshû.

20. Natica spadicea (GMELIN)

This is a northern race of N. vittelus, similar to the latter species in shape of the shell, and structure of the umbilicus and operculum. The difference is only in the larger diameter, somewhat more expanded body whorl, and the dirty brown coloration. Distribution: central Honshû and Shikoku, at 10–20 fathoms depth.

21. Natica stellata (CHENU)

This natica shell is slightly larger than N. spadicea, but both are similar in the shape of shell, and the structure of operculum. The glossy-smooth surface is beautifully colored in amber, and marked by 4 faint white color-bands. The umbilicus and funicular pad are partly covered by the parietal callus. Distribution: south of Amami Islands, at 5–10 fathoms.

22. Neverita (Glossaulax) didyma [RÖDING]

This species is most common on beaches all over Japan. The large specimens may reach 80 mm × 90 mm in diameters.

[PLATE 18]

Naticidae

The external surface is rather smooth, bearing only growth lines, and is colored in purplish or yellowish brown on the dorsal side, while the base is white. The widely opening umbilicus contains a purple-colored

Tectonatica   Neverita
janthostomoides   didyma

Sand-cup or mixed mass of sand and eggs of certain Naticidae

funicular pad. The semi-circular operculum is horny, and half-coiled.

A group of closely related species and subspecies are also found in Japan. *N. (G.) didyma vesicalis* (PHILIPPI) is smaller and thinner, and has a smaller funicular pad. In *N. (G.) didyma bicolor* (PHILIPPI), the shell is somewhat thicker than that of the original species, and its funicular pad is rather weakly developed. *N. (G.) reiniana* (DUNKER) having a taller spire is smaller than *didyma*. *N. (G.) hosoyai* KIRA can be distinguished by the structure of its funicular area. These molluscs lay their eggs in sand, which, mixed with the sand, make up such a horseshoe-shaped solid lump as illustrated in the attached figure. Japanese seaside dwellers call it the sand-cup.

Family Eratonidae

The shells of this family are generally small. Some are oval in form, while others are cylindrical and pointed at both ends. The shell structure is more or less similar to that of cowries, and the narrow aperture is margined by teeth on both lips. The epiderm and operculum are missing. The number of species is rather few in Japan.

1. Proterato (Sulcerato) callosa (ADAMS et REEVE)

This small shell is oblong oval in shape, with a thick outer lip. The aperture is very narrow and elongated, and bears fine teeth on both lips. The color is olive to pink, like a grain of pomegranate. The shells are commonly found on sandy bottom of shallow waters. *P. (Erotoena) nana* (SOWERBY) is a resembling species, bearing fine granules and one single longitudinal groove on the dorsal surface of the shell. Distribution: south of Honshû, below the tide line to 2 fathoms depth.

2. Trivirostra oryza (LAMARCK)

This is a small, somewhat elongated globular shell, and the color is pure white all over its surface. The spire is entirely hidden beneath the last whorl, as in cowries. Many fine ribs spirally cross the dorsal surface, leaving a longitudinal groove at its center. The aperture is narrow, and dentate on both lips. Among the related species, *T. vitrea* (GASKOIN) is less elongated, and more sparsely sculptured; *T. pellucidula* ("GASKOIN" REEVE) has no groove line on its dorsal surface; and *T. exigua* (GRAY) is characterized by pink spots. The first 3 species are found in shallow waters, south of central Japan, while the last one is found in Amami Islands and farther south.

3. Pseudotrivia eos (ROBERTS)

A deep-sea species larger than *Tr. oryza*. This shell reaches 27 mm (length) × 18 mm (width) in its size. The small pointed spire is nearly covered by the large and inflated body whorl. The outer surface is pure white, and wholly covered by fine spiral ribs, starting from the central groove on the dorsal surface and reaching the margins of aperture ending in dentations on both outer and inner lips. The outer lip is remarkably thickened. Distribution: southern Shikoku, near 100 fathoms depth.

Family Ovulidae

These lovely shells are diversified in size, thickness and form. They may be globular, spindle- or beak-shaped. They either lack teeth on both lips or have only on the outer lip. Since small-sized species of this family lives attached to sea-whips or sea-fans, their coloration and size are usually rich in variety.

4. Primovula (Prosimnia) coarctata (ADAMS et REEVE)

The shell is elongated spindle-shaped, about 10 mm long, and somewhat pointed at both ends. The body whorl does not swell and is microscopically sculptured by spiral lines all over its surface. The elongated aperture is bordered by the slightly thickened outer lip. The shell size and coloration are very variable; the color may be light rose, rouge, yellow, purple, etc. Distribution: central Honshû and southwards, epiphytic on sea-fans.

5. Pseudosimnia (Diminovula) punctata (DUCLOS)

In this small and oval shell, the spire is entirely hidden beneath the well inflated last whorl, of which the exterior surface is glossy-smooth, and light rose in color. Several reddish brown spots are marked on its surface, usually arranged in two rows. Both ends of the inner and outer lips protrude to form curved canals. The outer lip is curled and thickened, with teeth. Distribution: south of central Honshû; host animals are unknown.

6. Primovula rhodia (A. ADAMS)

This is a pretty shell, fusiform in shape, and somewhat larger than the last species. The aperture is rather wide, with short and canal-like extremities. The anterior end of aperture is especially wide,

44

[PLATE 19]   Eratonidae, Ovulidae, Cypraeidae

and there the columella is twisted. A fold or lamella is seen at the posterior end of inner lip along the canal. The outer surface is smooth, and usually pink-colored, though the coloration is variable. Distribution: south of central Honshû; epiphytic on sea-fans.

7. Calpurnus (Procalpurnus) lacteus semistriatus (PEASE)

The outline of the shell resembles that of *Ovula ovum*, but is less inflated in shape and much smaller in size. The outer surface is smooth and ivory-colored, without any patterns. This looks like a true cowry in appearance, but the outer lip alone is dentate, while the inner lip is smooth. Distribution: southern Honshû and southwards, below the tide line to 5 fathoms depth.

8. Pseudosimnia (Margovula) ishibashii (KURODA)

This is slightly larger than the former species, reaching 40 mm × 20 mm in size. The outer lip is thickened at its margin and toothed on the inner side. The posterior end of inner lip is strongly twisted, and connected with the outer lip, forming a pointed beak. The outer surface is smooth, and pinkish white, without any color patterns. The ends of both anterior and posterior canals are pink in color. Distribution: southern Honshû and Shikoku, rarely found at 80–100 fathoms depth. *Ps. (M.) sinensis* (SOWERBY) is a related species somewhat smaller than *ishibashii* and lacking pink coloration at the extremities. The latter is distributed in China Sea south of Amami Islands.

9. Volva (Phenacovolva) philippinarum (SOWERBY)

This is a slender shell about 30 mm in length. The spire is entirely enfolded within the last whorl. The aperture is fairly straight, very narrow and elongated, but is slightly widened near its anterior end. Both extremities of the aperture are tubular. The outer lip margin is thick, both lips having no teeth. The exterior is smooth, and is simply colored in white, creamy white, light rose, etc. The shell size is also variable. Distribution: central Honshû and southwards, 5–10 fathoms in depth.

10. Volva (Phenacovolva) brevirostris rosea (A. ADAMS)

The shell is longer than the preceding species, owing to the much elongated canals at both ends. It is usually deep rose in color, but other colorations can be seen. Distribution: southern Honshû and southwards, at 5–10 fathoms.

11. Volva (Phenacovolva) birostris (LINNÉ)

The general shape of this shell is simillar to that of the last species, but the canals are extremely elongated and bent inward. Distribution: central Honshû, rarely collected from 10–20 fathoms depth.

12. Volva volva (LINNÉ)

Resembling the preceding species in the shell structure, this is much larger, reaching 100 mm or more in length, and has the well swollen body whorl. The outer surface is fleshy pink in color and smooth, but is faintly sculptured by spiral threads. Characters of the Japanese specimens are considerably different from those of the original species named by Linné, and may be a different species. Distribution: fairly common along Pacific coasts of Japan, at 5–10 fathoms depth.

13. Pellasimnia hirasei xanthochila (KURODA)

The shell resembles *Pr. rhodia* in shape, but is larger and thinner. The outer color is white, with faint pink tone, and the aperture is margined by yellow. Distribution: rarely found in deep waters near 100 fathoms along southern coasts of Honshû and Shikoku.

14. Calpurnus verrucosus (LINNÉ)

This is a cowry-like species characterized by a ridge laterally crossing the dorsal surface and a small round granule inlaid at each end of the surface. The aperture is narrow and contains fine teeth only on the outer lip. This is china-white all over with rose tint at both ends of the aperture. Distribution: south of the Ryukyus in shallow waters.

45

15. Ovula ovum (LINNÉ)

This is the largest species of Japanese Ovulidae. The oval shell is thick, and glossy white like a porcelain. Only the inside of aperture is colored in deep purplish brown. The outer lip bears many fine and irregular-sized folds or blunt teeth. This is often used as a material for shell-works. As the living body of this animal is black-colored and entirely covers its shell, it is difficult for collectors to find it alive. Distribution: southern Honshû and southwards, at 3–10 fathoms.

Family Cypraeidae

This cowry family includes a number of species, of which the shells are usually oval in shape and characterized by the well developed, inflated body whorl and polished surface. Since the animals entirely wrap theirs shells with extended mantles when alive, the whole exterior surface of the shells is covered by a glossy callus layer, under which the spire is almost concealed. The aperture is long and narrow like a slit, with dentations on both sides. The operculum is missing. Cowries have long been prized by people for their peculiar shape and pretty colors, and were once used for money in ancient times. Certain rare species get high price among collectors. They are also one of the most commonly used materials of shell-works.

16. Pustularia bistrinotata mediocris SCHILDER

This and the following two cowries are characterized by their plump form and two pointed processes on each end of the shell. The upper surface of this shell is covered by minute granules, bearing a longitudinal crease on its midline. It is glossy and golden brown in color, and is usually marked on its dorsal side by a pair of quadrilateral brown spots and 2 pairs of smaller spots of the same color. The lower side or base of the shell is rather flat, bearing fine crossing threads near its aperture, which are connected with the teeth on both lips. Distri-

bution: south of Amami Islands, below the tide line to 5 fathoms depth.

17. Pustularia margarita tetsuakii KURODA

This is different from the the first species in having the smooth outer surface bearing neither granules nor a crease. Fine, tiny, brown spots are scattered all over the entire grayish brown surface. Both ends of of the ventral surface show yellow tinge. Distribution: south of Kyûshû, from the tide line down to 5 fathoms.

18. Pustularia cicercula (LINNÉ)

The shell is slightly larger than those of the former two species. This bears fine granules and a central crease on the dorsal surface, as the first species, but no color patterns are seen on the light brown ground color except a small dark brown spot above the base of posterior canal. Distribution: south of central Honshû, below the tide line to 5 fathoms depth.

19. Pustularia (Ipsa) childreni samurai SCHILDER

This cowry is rather stocky in shape, and larger than the preceding three species of *Pustularia*. The exterior surface is closely sculptured by fine threads, which are interrupted only by a longitudinal furrow on the dorsal midline and connected with the teeth on both lips. There is a spiny process on the inner lip side of posterior canal and the outer lip side of anterior canal, respectively. This is light brown, without any color patterns. Distribution: rarely found in shallow waters below the tide line in the Ryukyus and farther south.

20. Staphylaea (Nucleolaria) nucleus (LINNÉ)

This shell is oval in outline. The upper surface bears many small nodules and a midline crease. The entire base is rather sparsely covered by crossing ribs terminating in the lip teeth. The dorsal and ventral sides are colored in grayish and yellowish brown respectively. Distribution: south of central Honshû, below the tide line.

[PLATE 20]   Cypraeidae

Family Cypraeidae (2)

1. Palmadusta punctata (LINNÉ)

This tiny cowry is oval in outline. This is milky white, with scattered dark brown spots on the upper surface, while the base is white, and marked by light brown transverse lines which are connected with the teeth on both lips of aperture. Distribution: south of the Ryukyus, below the tide line.

2. Purpuradusta fimbriata marmorata (SCHRÖTER)

The shell is similar to the last species in size, but is somewhat more slender. The dorsal side is light purplish brown in ground color, on which microscopic spots and discontinuous color bands are marked in dark brown. It bears also a pair of minute violet spots on each extremity. Distribution: south of southern Honshû, in subtidal zone.

3. Paulonaria beckii (GASKOIN)

An oval-shaped cowry slightly larger than the preceding species. The dorsal surface is light brown in color, and sparsely spotted with white and chestnut brown, though the white spots are often worn away. The base is marked only by chestnut brown spots. A row of the spots is especially remarkable along the outer lip margin. Distribution: southern Honshû and southwards, in subtidal zone.

4. Palmadusta clandestina moniliaris (LAMARCK)

This shell is even a little larger than the above species. The dorsal side is marked by brown and zigzag hairlines on the milky white callus, under which brown spiral bands are barely visible. The under surface is white. An eroded specimen closely resembles P. artuffeli. Distribution: central Honshû and southwards, in subtidal zone.

5. Melicerona felina pauciguttata SCHILDER

The basal outline of this cowry is elongated elliptic. The translucent callus layer on the dorsal surface bears only brown-colored cloudy patterns, but the ground color looks gray, owing to the black coloration of the subsurface layer. The base of the shell is white. It is also spotted with black on the sides. Distribution: south of central Honshû, below the tide line.

6. Erosaria labrolineata (GASKOIN)

This is oval in outline and slightly larger than the last species. The upper surface is yellowish brown, and marked by a number of round white spots of various sizes. The sides are dotted with brown, while the base is white. Distribution: central Honshû and southwards, in subtidal zone.

7. Derstolida hirundo neglecta (SOWERBY)

This is a small oval cowry, with irregular dark brown blotches on its milky white surface. Three spiral bands of black color underlying the surface callus are seen. Small dark brown spots are distributed around the sides. The base is colored white. Distribution: southern Honshû and southwards, in subtidal zone.

8. Palmadusta ziczac (LINNÉ)

The shell becomes somewhat narrower toward its anterior end. Three white bands containing zigzag patterns are marked against the light brown background of dorsal surface. Both the sides and base bear brown spots. Distribution: south of Amami Islands, in subtidal zone.

9. Palmadusta artuffeli (JOUSSEAUME)

This is very similar to the above species in size and shape. It is monotonously colored in light brown on the dorsal side and in white on the base, respectively. Three spiral bands of dark brown are seen on the upper surface. Distribution: Honshû and southwards, common in subtidal zone.

10. Palmadusta asellus (LINNÉ)

This also resembles the preceding two

PLATE 19

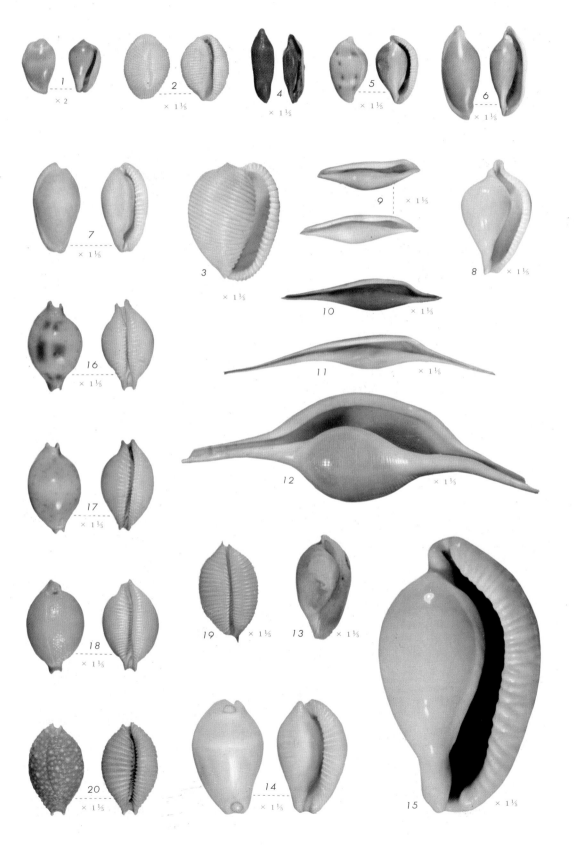

PLATE **20**

1   × 1⅘

2   × 1⅘

3   × 1⅕

4   × 1⅕

5   × 1⅕

6   × 1⅕

7   × 1⅕

8   × 1⅕

9   × 1⅕

10   × 1⅕

11   × 1⅕

12   × 1⅕

13   × 1⅕

14   × 1⅕

15   × 1⅕

16   × 1⅕

17   × 1⅕

18   × 1⅕

19   × 1⅕

20   × 1⅕

21   × 1⅕

22   × 1⅕

23   × 1⅕

24   × 1⅕

25   × 1⅕

26   × 1⅕

27   × 1⅕

28   × 1⅕

species in shape and size. This is china-white all over the surface and is crossed by 3 black bands on the upper side. The lip teeth are slightly extended onto the base. Distribution: southern Honshû and southwards, in subtidal zone.

11. Erosaria tomlini ogasawarensis SCHILDER

The central part of this shell is especially inflated. The upper side is light reddish brown in its ground color, and scattered with white spots. The sides are more lightly colored with purplish brown dots. The base is white, and folded around its margin. Distribution: south of Amami Islands, in deeper part of subtidal zone.

12. Staphylaea staphylaea (LINNÉ)

The upper side of this oval shell is covered by a milky white callus layer, through which the purplish brown sub-surface layer is visible. It is densely covered by minute nodules, bearing a longitudinal crease nearly at the center of upper side. Both extremities are tipped with orange brown. The teeth extend over the entire basal surface, which shows white color or faint brownish tinge. Distribution: south of Honshû in subtidal zone.

13. Blasicrura interrupta (GRAY)

This cowry is somewhat cylindrical in form. Five spiral rows of black spots on the subsurface layer are barely seen through the uppermost layer bearing brown cloud patterns. The base is white and with somewhat extended teeth. Distribution: south of the Ryukyus, below the tide line.

14. Erosaria helvola (LINNÉ)

This shell is well inflated, expanded on both sides especially at the central part, and slightly margined around its base. It is dark brown above and marked by many small yellowish spots. The fringe of the upper side as well as the base is colored in reddish brown. The teeth are slightly extended onto the basal surface. Distribution: Honshû and southwards, in subtidal zone.

15. Derstolida stolida (LINNÉ)

A medium-sized cowry, characterized by a large quadrilateral brown spot on its bluish white upper surface. Four brown spots are also marked on the sides and connected with the four corners of the central spot. The ends of teeth somewhat extend over the white basal surface. Distribution: south of Amami Islands, at several fathoms depth below the tide line.

16. Purpuradusta gracilis japonicus (SCHILDER)

The upper surface of the shell bears an irregular brown pattern at its center over the bluish brown ground color. It is also marked by small black spots on the marginal areas of both upper and basal sides. The base is white in color. Distribution: all over Japan, abundant in shallow waters.

17. Erosaria poraria (LINNÉ)

The shell is brown on the upper side, and marked with white and dark brown spots under a translucent surface layer. The sides and base bear violet coloration that fades out near the aperture. Distrbution: southern Honshû and southwards, in subtidal zone.

18. Cribraria cribraria orientalis SCHILDER

This shell is entirely white throughout the development of whorls, and only the last whorl is covered by a light brown layer, except along its dorsal margin and on the base. Round white spots of different sizes are clearly marked over the back side. Distribution: central Honshû, in subtidal zone.

19. Staphylaea limacina (LAMARCK)

Japanese specimens of this species are divided into two types. One type is characterized by milky white granules sparsely scattered all over the purplish brown upper surface and by the narrow aperture. In another type, the surface is smooth, with white spots, and the aperture is a little wider. Common to both types are the folds on the marginal callus and the orange coloration at both ends of the shell. Distribution: south of

[PLATE 20]   Cypraeidae

central Honshû, in subtidal zone.

20. Monetaria annulus harmandiana (ROCHEBRUNE)

The central part of this cowry shell is particularly expanded on both sides. This is milky white all over the surface and marked on the upper side by a distinct yellow ring. Distribution: central Honshû and southwards, abundant in shallow waters.

21. Erronea cylindrica (BORN)

A cylindrically shaped cowry, with a rather wide aperture. This is bluish brown in ground color of the upper side, bearing cloud patterns of brown all over the surface and an irregularly shaped blotch of dark brown at the center. Each extremity is also marked by 2 black spots. The central teeth on the inner lip are shorter than others. Distribution: Kyûshû and southwards, in subtidal zone.

22. Erronea errones (LINNÉ)

This shell resembles the last species in general shape, coloration and the structure of aperture, but lacks black spots at the extremities. The base is light flesh-colored. Distribution: south of Amami Islands, in subtidal zone.

23. Monetaria moneta rhomboides SCHILDER

The shell is flattened, and somewhat triangular in outline. The upper surface is smooth, but uneven due to a few humps on the back. The subsurface layer is deep violet in color, but is hardly visible under the yellow or light yellow surface callus. The teeth on both lip margins are very small and short. Distribution: southern Honshû and southwards, common in shallow waters.

M. monetoides IREDALE can be distinguished from the present species in having tubercles on both lips.

24. Ravitrona caputserpentis reticulum (GMELIN)

This common cowry is characterized by

a well expanded and somewhat flattened margin and the remarkably upheaved back. The marginal zone is colored in shining, deep reddish brown, while the color fades away on the base. The central area on the back is marked by many small white spots. Both lips are coarsely dentate. Distribution: south of Amami Islands, abudant in shallow waters.

A subspecies, R. c. mikado SCHILDER, has a less developed margin, almost elliptic outline and lighter coloration of the base. This is found in central Japan.

25. Erosaria erosa (LINNÉ)

This shell somewhat resembles the last species in shape, but is a little depressed, bearing a remarkably wrinkled margin around its base. It is light grayish brown in ground color on the back side and is densely covered all over the upper surface by small white spots. A large brown blot is seen below the surface callus on each side of the shell nearly at the middle position. The teeth on the outer lip are extended over the basal surface. Distribution: south of central Honshû, below the tide line.

26. Luria (Basilitrona) isabella rumphii SCHILDER

This cowry is cylindrical in shape with round ends. The light flesh-colored surface is irregularly marked in black by longitudinal scratchy lines. It also bears yellowish brown color-spots at both ends. The base is white and the aperture is minutely toothed on both lips. Distribution: south of southern Honshû, in subtidal zone.

27. Talostolida teres (GMELIN)

The shell is oblong elliptic in outline, and has a light purplish brown upper surface, on which three transverse bands of brown zigzag patterns are faintly marked. The base is white in color. The lips are rather weakly toothed. Distribution: south of Amami Islands, in subtidal zone.

28. Erosaria boivinii amoena SCHILDER

This cowry is somewhat elongated, and

elliptic in shape. The teeth are coarse and short. The scattered purple spots on the back side are covered by a light purplish brown surface layer. The base is white in color. Distribution: Honshû and southwards, in subtidal zone.

[PLATE 21]   Cypraeidae

Family Cypraeidae (3)

1. *Gratiadusta hungerfordi* (Sowerby)

A small, oval cowry whose anterior end trapers sharply. The apical point is depressed. The basal surface is not flat, but inflated on both sides of the aperture having short, small teeth. The subsurface pattern on the dorsal side consists of 3 lateral bands of dark brown, while minute brown dots are marked on the surface callus layer. On the lower, peripheral zone of the sides many black spots are seen. Both ends of the shell and the basal surface are colored in light flesh. Distribution: south of central Honshû, as deep as 30–50 fathoms.

2. *Lyncina vanelli* (Linné)

This is nearly of the same size with the preceding species, but is rounder in its outline. The base is flat, and margined by blunt keels. The subsurface pattern of purplish cloud on the dorsal side is overlaid by sparse, dark brown spots. The peripheral zone also bears similar spots under the surface callus. The margins of aperture are colored by orange between the teeth. Distribution: southern Honshû and farther south, 10–20 fathoms deep.

3. *Erosaria inocellata* (Gray)

The shell is also similar in size to the preceding two species. The back side is densely covered by small white spots on its light brown ground color under a transparent surface layer. No pattern is seen on the lateral sides. The base is white. The aperture is comparatively wide, and bordered by rough teeth. Distribution: south of Honshû, from the tide line to 5 fathoms depth.

4. *Adusta onyx* (Linné)

This is a medium-sized species, with comparatively wide aperture and coarse lip teeth. Three, broad, lateral bands of black color are visible on the back surface through the translucent surface layer, which, however, becomes milky white in fully matured shells. The base, like the lower part of side surface, is very dark brown in color. Distri-

bution: south of central Honshû, 5–10 fathoms deep.

5. *Ovatipsa chinensis* (Gmelin)

This is a little smaller than the last species. The dorsal surface is ornamented by cloud patterns of light brown, and scattered by white spots, while its base, lower area of the sides, and both ends of the shell are light purple, and are, on the sides, spotted with dark purple. The margins of both lips are spotted with orange between the coarse teeth. Distribution: southern Honshû and southwards, 5–10 fathoms deep.

6. *Arabica scurra* (Gmelin)

This species has a somewhat cylindrical, slender shell weakly pointed at both ends. The lip teeth are fine and numerous. The back surface is bluish brown in its ground color, and filled with a network of brown. The color of the sides and base are dark flesh-brown, and on the marginal area dark brown spots are seen. The teeth are also brown-colored. Distribution: south of the Ryukyus, 3–5 fathoms in depth.

7. *Mystaponda vitellus* (Linné)

This cowry is medium-sized, and oval in its outline. The back surface is scattered with small white spots of different sizes, and 3 brown bands on the subsurface layer are seen under the spots. The basal surface is white. Distribution: central Honshû and farther south, at 5–10 fathoms depth.

8. *Erronea caurica* (Linné)

The shell is rather small and elongated in shape, bearing coarse teeth along the fairly wide aperture. The dorsal part is light greenish brown in its ground color, and marked by fine brown clouds and a cloudy blotch of dark brown on the subsurface and surface layer, respectively. Several dark brown spots are also seen scattered on the lower part of lateral sides. The base and the spaces between lip teeth are lightly flesh-colored. Distribution: south of Amami Islands, from the tide line to 5 fathoms depth.

9. Arabica eglantina couturieri (VAYSSIÈRE)

Resembling *A. arabica* in its general appearance, this shell is smaller and more slender. The base is slightly marginated by a thickened callus. The ground color of the back surface is light greenish brown, on which fine, interrupted lines of dark brown are densely and longitudinally marked, leaving numerous, small, empty spots all over the surface. Dark brown spots on the marginal callus are smaller in size than those of *A. arabica*. The lip teeth along the narrow aperture are of purplish brown color. Distribution: south of the Ryukyus, from the tide line to 5 fathoms depth.

10. Ponda carneola (LINNÉ)

The size and shape of this cowry are almost similar to the preceding species, but its dorsal surface is flesh-colored with reddish tinge, and crossed by 5 lateral bands of of deeper tone. The peripheral callus seen around the base is light brown, sparsely bearing minute spots. The teeth on both lip margins are purple in color. Distribution: south of southern Honshû, below the tide line down to 2 fathoms

11. Talparia talpa (LINNÉ)

A moderately large cowry with a very dark brown base and yellowish brown back surface, through which brown lateral bands can be seen on the subsurface layer. This resembles *A. onyx* in its coloration, but can be distinguished from that species by its larger size, different number of brown bands (4 versus 3 in *A. onyx*), narrower aperture and finer teeth. Distribution: southern Honshû and farther south, 2–5 fathoms in depth.

12. Peribolus mauritiana calxequina (MELVILLE et STANDEN)

The shell is large, very heavy and margined by a broad and thick callus zone. The back is remarkably humped, while the base is slightly concave. The aperture is fairly wide, and bordered by a comparatively small number of thick teeth. This is black or very dark brown, and is marked by round,

brown spots over its dorsal surface. A longitudinal line of light color usually runs across the back surface, indicating the position where the mantles from both sides meet when the animal is alive. Distribution: south of Shikoku, at about 5 fathoms depth.

13. Arestorides argus (LINNÉ)

This is a pretty, cylindrical shell, moderately large in size. The aperture is fairly wide. The light brown surface of back side is scattered by a number of small brown rings, and more sparsely by round brown spots. The base is light fleshy brown, with 2 dark brown blotches on each of the lips. The teeth are also brown in color. Distribution: Amami Islands and farther south, 2–5 fathoms deep.

14. Leprocypraea mappa (LINNÉ)

This shell is well inflated, and nearly round in outline. It is light brown in ground color, with fine, longitudinal lines of dark brown densely covering the dorsal surface, except scattered empty spots and a branched longitudinal band situated more or less leftward from the central line. Lower part of the sides is marked by brown spots. The teeth are colored in light brown. The surface of fully matured shells is frequently stained by a pinkish hue. Distribution: south of the Ryukyus, at 2–5 fathoms depth.

15. Arabica arabica asiatica SCHILDER

The Arabian cowry is smaller than the preceding species, but fairly thick and heavy. The apex is not infrequently exposed, though only slightly. As compared with the related species, *A. eglantina*, described above, this is more prominently marginated, and has a relatively narrow aperture. The back side almost lacks empty spots, and is filled with dark brown, longitudinal lines and bars. The sides are marked on the expanded marginal callus by black spots which extend on the outermost part of the base. The flat base is light flesh-brown, except on the brown teeth. Distribution: central Honshû and farther south, 2–5 fathoms deep.

[PLATE 21]

16, 17.   Cypraea tigris LINNÉ

The shell of this well-known tiger cowry is large, heavy, oval in outline and well inflated on its back.   Whole dorsal and lateral sides are white or yellowish white in color, with scattered round spots of dark brown.   The base, including the teeth, is entirely white.   As in other cowries, the wall of body whorl in this tiger cowry consists of layers of different colors.   As shown in Fig. 16, the coloration on different layers is especially diversified in this species, which makes it one of the best suited shells for Cameo-works.   Distribution: south of southern Honshû, 5–10 fathoms deep.

18.   Chelycypraea testudinaria (LINNÉ)

A large, heavy and cylindrical cowry. This is light brown in the ground color of dorsal side, on which dark brown clouds are marked.   The sides bear large, brown blotches, while the basal surface is fleshy brown.   Distribution: south of Amami Islands, at 5–10 fathoms depth.

PLATE 21

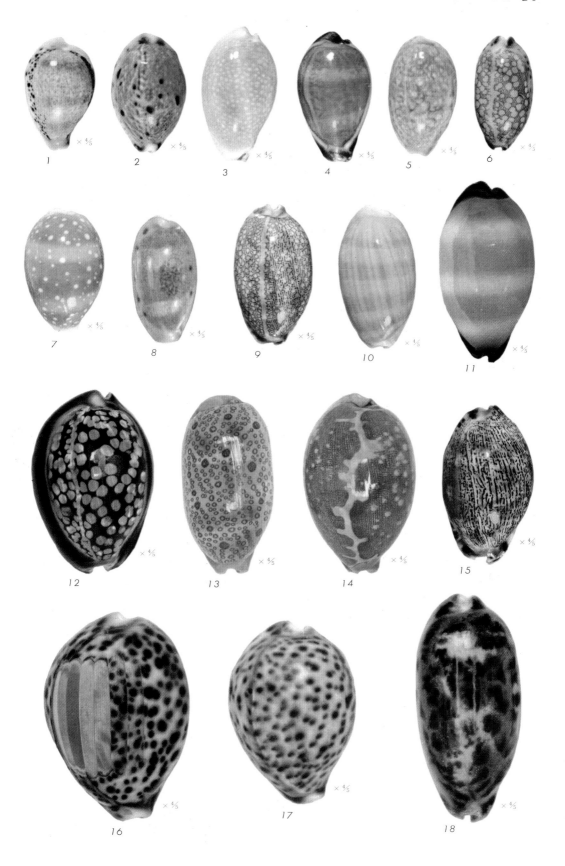

PLATE 22

1 × 3/5
2 × 3/5
9 × 3/10
10 × 3/5
17 × 3/5
3 × 3/5
4 × 3/5
11 × 3/5
12 × 3/10
13 × 2/5
5 × 1/2
6 × 3/5
14 × 2/5
15 × 2/5
7 × 3/5
16 × 3/10
18 × 3/5
8 × 1/5
19 × 2/5
20 × 2/5

Family Oocorythidae

1. *Geleoocorys leucodoma* (DALL)

The shell is similar to the following species in size, but thinner in texture. The spire is taller, the body whorl is more swollen and the anterior end tapers more steeply. The surface of whorls bears spiral rows of wart-like tubercles, which become finer anteriorly and are transformed into fine granulated ribs near the columellar end. A thin callus expands over the inner lip side of the wide aperture. The outer lip is thickened, and reflexed, and has teeth inside. The exterior surface is white and covered by a thin, yellowish brown epiderm. The operculum is horny, and oval in shape, having a slightly reflexed margin. Distribution: central Honshû and farther south, at 70–100 fathoms depth.

Family Cassididae

This is the group of helmet shells. The shells are large- or medium-sized, and usually heavy in their construction. The spire is small, while the last whorl is well developed. They often bear strong longitudinal ridges or varices at irregular intervals on the outer surface. The parietal callus is developed very well, extending over the ventral side of the shell. The outer lip is thickened and reflexed, and bear tooth-like sculptures. The siphon is not so long but reflexed backwards, and extends over the dorsal side. The operculum is small and horny, with a nucleus at the center.

2. *Morum (Onimusiro) grande* (A. ADAMS)

This medium-sized shell is thick, heavy and approximately oval in outline, though the surface is ragged. The spire is low and pointed. The surface of well developed body whorl is roughly sculptured by coarse spiral ribs (about 15 in number) and longitudinal ridges (about 14). Granules are raised on their intersection points, while a few, thin, plate-like folds run longitudinally in each space between the ridges. The callus on the inner lip is broadly expanded, ending in an isolated margin. The outer lip is thick and reflexed. Inner sides of both lips bear many tooth-like folds. The siphon is slightly curved backwards. The exterior of the shell is yellowish white, and encircled by 4 bands of light brown. The color of lips and callus are pure white. The operculum is horny and very small. Distribution: Pacific coasts of southern Honshû, as deep as 100 fathoms.

3. *Semicassis persimilis* KURODA

This is an elongated globular shell with swollen whorls. The smooth exterior surface is covered by many, shallow, spiral grooves. The parietal callus is thin but becomes somewhat thicker on the columella and covers the fasciole. A few folds occur on the anterior end of inner lip. The outer lip is reflexed to form a thick, rounded margin, and bears blunt teeth on its inner side. It is usually light brown in ground in color, and is spirally marked by rows of dark brown, square sports, of which the number is about 5. The tint is, however, very variable. The horny operculum is fan-shaped. Distribution: south of Honshû, 10–20 fathoms deep.

4. *Semicassis japonica* (REEVE)

This is a species closely related to the last one. It is generally larger than the last species, and spiral grooves are wider and more deeply sculptured on the surface. Fine longitudinal threads are also marked across the spiral sculpture more or less distinctly. The structure of aperture is also like that of *S. persimilis*; the difference is only that the anterior part of outer lip margin is bluntly carinated. Distribution: south of Honshû, 20–30 fathoms deep.

5. *Phalium bandatum* (PERRY)

This shell is more solid than the preceding species. The spire is sharply pointed and smaller, while the last whorl is relatively large. The spire bears a weak reticulate sculpture, whereas the surface of the last whorl is glossy smooth, except a row of tubercles along the shoulder line. A few, distinctly raised varices run across the whorls at irregular intervals. The white surface is covered by a sparse, light brown network of spiral and longitudinal color bands. The end of the reflexed siphon is tipped with a black spot. Distribution: south of central

[PLATE 22]   Oocorythidae, Cassididae, Cymatiidae, Bursidae

Honshû, 20–30 fathoms deep.

6. Bezoardicella strigata (GMELIN)

The shell is almost the same with the preceding species in size and shape. The shallow reticulate sculpture on the outer surface almost vanishes on the dorso-central part of body whorl. Brown longitudinal stripes beautifully cover the white background. The end of siphon is not colored in black. Distribution: south of Honshû, at 10–20 fathoms depth.

7. Cypraecassis rufa (LINNÉ)

This is a big helmet shell, heavy in construction and with a low spire. The dorsal side of the shell is covered by 4 thick spiral ribs bearing large knobs, and by 2 wide ribs encircling the most anterior part of whorls that bears longitudinal folds. The interspaces are filled with interstitial spiral ribs and fine longitudinal folds. The callus around the aperture broadly expands over the entire ventral side of the shell. The aperture is narrow and elongated, with the teeth on both sides. The reflexed outer lip margin is very thick. The siphon is strongly curved backwards, and its end is deeply notched. The ground color of dorsal side is purple, on which cloud patterns of milky white and dark brown are marked. The vental callus layer is orange-brown in color, and the depressions between parietal teeth are especially deep-colored, while the blunt teeth on the outer lip are white. The outer lip margin bears faint, lateral, brown bands, of which the number is 8. Distribution: south of the Ryukyus, 2–5 fathoms deep.

8. Cassis cornuta (LINNÉ)

This helmet shell reaches an enormous size, and is very heavy and solid. The spire is almost flat, and the well developed body whorl bears 3-4, strong, spiral ridges with tubercles. The one on the angled shoulder is by far the strongest, and the tubercles on it are large and horn-like in shape. The interspaces are marked by a fine, reticulate sculpture. The callus on both lips is well developed, and expands like a thick plate around the narrow aperture. The inner lip margin bears many folds, while blunt teeth are seen on the central part of outer lip. The anterior siphon is strongly curved toward the dorsal side. This is encircled by several, light brown bands and brown disconnected lines on the white outer surface, but they are usually seen only on the ventral side of the shell, whereas the dorsal surface is covered by calcareous sediments. The inside of aperture is orange brown in color. The operculum is horny, small, and elongated in shape. Distribution: this species lives in shallow waters, 2–5 fathoms in depth, buried in sand; south of Shikoku.

Family Cymatiidae (1)

The shells of this triton family are variable in size, but generally solid in construction. They are characterized by prominent varices on the surface, but the number of varices on a single whorl does not exceed 2, and those on adjacent whorls are rarely connected longitudinally with each other. In this character, the tritons are distinctly different from the members of the rock shell family (Muricidae), which frequently bear 3 varices on each whorl. The shells have a corneous operculum. Certain species are very beautifully colored, and some are known for their edible flesh. See also Plate 70.

9. Fusitriton oregonensis (REDFIELD)

This shell is comparatively large and spindle-shaped, and has a tall spire and a long, straight siphon. The surface of inflated whorls is marked by a sparse network of spiral and longitudinal ribs with fine granules on the knots. Fine interstitial ribs are also seen. A knob is formed on the posterior part of inner lip margin in matured specimens. The shell is white in color, but is entirely covered by a light yellowish brown, hairy epiderm. Distribution: Honshû and farther north, as deep as 70–100 fathoms.

10. Distorsio reticulata [RÖDING]

This is a medium-sized, fusiform shell, of which the whorls are characteristically distorted and irregularly piled into a tall spire. The body whorl is large, and swollen like a hump on its dorsal side. Under a hariy epiderm, the exterior surface is covered by a reticulate sculpture. The callus on the

55

inner lip broadly expands over the ventral side of body whorl. The outer lip is also broadly and flatly callused. The opening of aperture is narrowed and intricately margined by many teeth on both lips, by a notch on the columella and by a wart-like nodule at the posterior end of inner lip. The siphon is relatively short. The callus area around the aperture is flesh-colored. The operculum is horny and small, as compared with the size of aperture. Distribution: south of central Honshû, 10–20 fathoms deep.

11. Charonia saulias (REEVE)

This is a large and thick shell resembling the triton's trumpet. It is spindle-shaped owing to a tall, straight spire, the swollen body whorl and a moderately long siphon. The outer surface is somewhat rough, and bears several varices and a spiral ridge with prominent tubercles on the middle part of whorls. A few spiral ribs are also shallowly sculptured above and below the ridge. The aperture is widely open and elliptic in its outline. The inner lip bears a fold on its posterior part as well as many plaits on the anterior part, while the outer lip is slightly dentate. The exterior is encircled by brown bands, which are not so distinctly marked as in the following species. The outer lip margin is colored brown. The operculum is elliptic in shape. The flesh is eaten by the inhabitants of Japanese coasts. Distribution: south of Honshû, at 5–10 fathoms depth.

12. Charonia tritonis (LINNÉ)

The triton's trumpet is the largest of all Japanese shells, reaching 400 mm in length. The spire is very tall, occupying more than 1/3 of the total length. Besides thick, round, spiral ridges filling the surface of whorls, several varices and fine, interstitial, spiral lines are seen. A flat rib running immediately below the suture bears fine longitudinal folds. The oval aperture is bordered by the reflexed margin of inner lip bearing many plaits and by the outer lip having a wavy margin. The glossy outer surface is encircled over the yellowish white ground color by many clear-cut rows of crescent brown blotches running on the spiral ridges. The inter-plait spaces on the inner lip are

colored in chocolate brown. Since ancient times, the Japanese used this shell as a kind of horn, mainly for military and ceremonial purposes. Distribution: south of Kyûshû, 5–10 fathoms deep.

13. Monoplex echo (KURODA et HABE)

A moderately large shell like a fat spindle in shape. The varices occur irregularly, but are mostly restricted to the last whorl. The body whorl bears 5 strong spiral ribs with tubercles, of which only 2 extend over other whorls. Many folds are seen on the reflexed margin of columella, while the thick outer lip bears a row of teeth grouped in pairs. The outer surface is colored brown under a thick, hairy epiderm. The margin of aperture is dark brown, and its inner part is flesh-colored. Distribution: Honshû and farther south, 5–10 fathoms deep.

14. Septa pilearis (LINNÉ)

This resembles M. echo in the appearance of shell, but is somewhat more elongated than the former. The surface sculpture consists of intersecting spiral and longitudinal ribs as well as small granules on the intersections. The varices are prominent. The structure of aperture margin is also like that of M. echo, but the paired teeth on the outer lip are arranged in double rows. The siphon is longer and slightly curved. It bears brown spots both longitudinally and laterally, together with white bands, but the coloration is rich in variety. The inner margin of aperture is colored brown. This shell has the cover of hairy epiderm. Distribution: the same with M. echo.

15. Cymatium lotorium (LINNÉ)

The shell is thick and heavy in construction, and has a distorted spindle-shape. Very thick varices and a row of shoulder tubercles on them are characteristic. The surface is marked by shallow spiral ribs and interstitial lines, which are crossed by fine longitudinal threads to raise small granules on the intersection points. The aperture is narrowed by the extraordinary thickening of the toothed outer lip. There are many folds on the columella. The siphon is long, thick and obliquely situated,

[PLATE 22]

Oocorythidae, Cassididae, Cymatiidae, Bursidae

but not reflexed. It has a large fasciole. The surface color is light brown, and the inner side of aperture margin is spotted with black on both lips. Distribution: the same with the last species.

16. *Distorsio anus* (LINNÉ)

D. reticulata and this species resemble each other in outline and structure of the shells, but this is larger in size. The outer surface is covered by many small tubercles formed by the intersection of longitudinal and spiral ribs of heterogeneous thickness. The callused area around the aperture widens like a plate all over the ventral side of the shell, on which many nodules are scattered. The margin of aperture is remarkably narrowed by the denticles on both lips. The siphon is reflexed backwards. The white background of the exterior is marked by brown lateral stripes. The operculum is very small. Distribution: south of the Ryukyus, below the tide line down to 5 fathoms.

17. *Biplex perca* (PERRY)

The whorls are slightly compressed dorsoventrally, and a row of thin, longitudinally connected varices develop like a fin respectively on each side of whorls, consequently giving the shell a very flattened appearance. Spiral ribs extends over the fins, and are granulated on the surface of whorls due to the intersection with longitudinal threads. The aperture is almost circular, and contains a nodule near the posterior end of inner lip. The operculum is horny, round and dark brown in color. Distribution: south of central Honshû, at 30–50 fathoms depth.

Family Bursidae

The shells range from small to large size, but are all fairly thick and heavy. As in the tritons, the varices are less than 2 in their number per whorl, but are longitudinally connected from one whorl to the next to form prominent continuous ridges on both lateral sides of the shell in most species. The anterior end of aperture terminates in a tubular canal. The operculum is horny, with a nucleus mostly at the center.

18. *Bursa dunkeri* KIRA

In this medium-sized heavy shell, thick varices develop on both lateral sides of whorls, continuously from the apex to the body whorl. Since these varices are the remnants of former outer lip left behind the growth of shell, traces of posterior canal are also seen with them. Tubercles are arranged on a few strong ribs encircling the surface of whorls, and interstitial ribs are only shallowly or indistinctly marked. The margin of aperture is thickened, with many folds and paired teeth on the inner and outer lip, respectively. The aperture contains the posterior and anterior canals, which are both tubular. The outer surface is bluish brown, while the inside of aperture is orange-yellow in color. The operculum has a nucleus anteriorly to the center. Distribution: Honshû and southwards, in subtidal zone of Pacific coasts.

19. *Bursa (Gyrineum) rana* (LINNÉ)

A moderately large and thick shell, somewhat compressed dorso-ventrally. The longitudinal rows of varices on both sides are somewhat fin-like, and bear short spines. Granulated spiral ribs run over the outer surface of the shell, and the one on the shoulder sparsely bears spiny tubercles. The posterior canal opens between the body whorl and the most posterior spine on the outer lip margin. Both inner and outer lips are dentate. This is light brown in color, the inside of aperture remaining colorless. The operculum is somewhat like a fan in shape with a nucleus at the center. Distribution: south of central Honshû, at 5–10 fathoms depth.

20. *Bursa (Tutufa) bufo* [RÖDING]

This is a large and stout shell with a tall, turreted spire. Pointed knobs are arranged on the varices, including the outer lip margin, and on the angled shoulder. Granules or short spines also develop on low spiral ribs running on both sides of the shoulder line. The aperture is surrounded by a very wide callus zone, opening like a trumpet. The outer lip bears sparse teeth. Both anterior and posterior canals are fairly long and narrowly tubular. The shell exterior is indistinctly marked with white bands and spots against the light fleshy background. The callus zone around the aperture is glossy and pretty with scarlet tone. Distribution: south of central Honshû, at 10–20 fathoms depth.

[PLATE 23]

Tonnidae, Ficidae, Muricidae

Family Tonnidae

This family includes a rather small number of species having a large- or medium-sized, thin shell. Their outline is globular or like a pear, resembling a tun. The structure, sculpture and coloration are generally poor in variety. The spire is small, while the body whorl is large and well inflated, and ends in a very wide aperture. The outer surface is usually sculptured by thick spiral ribs. The protoconch is colored in most species differently from other parts of the shell. The animals lack the operculum. The tun shells are sometimes used for shell-works, and the flesh of certain species is edible, though not so delicious.

1. Tonna chinensis (DILLWYN)

The shell is medium-sized and thin. Spiral ribs are rounded, and alternate with comparatively wide inter-rib furrows, of which the ends protrude at the inside margin of outer lip. A fasciole develops along the anterior canal. The body whorl is encircled by 5–6 light brown bands each containing 2–3 rows of alternate dark brown and white spots. Distribution: central Honshû and farther south, 5–10 fathoms deep.

2. Tonna chinensis magnifica (SOWERBY)

The whorls of this subspecies are more inflated than those of the original type described above. Spiral ribs are flattened, so that the shell exterior may rather be described as a flat surface dissected by narrow spiral furrows. The color bands are slightly darker in color, and the spots are less clearly marked than those of the original form. The ends of spiral furrows only slightly protrude within the outer lip. It should be noted that a wide range of individual variation is found in this species, and that the subspecific differences stated here are concerned only with typical forms. Distribution: the same with the preceding form.

3. Tonna allium (DILLWYN)

The spire is somewhat taller than the foregoing species. Spiral ribs are rounded, fine, and separated by wide interspaces. The outer lip margin is remarkably thickened. This is white all over, or only colored in light brown on the ribs. Distribution: the same with *T. chinensis*.

4. Eudolium inflatum KURODA et HABE

The members of the genus *Eudolium* have a pyriform shell with the spire taller and larger than that of other tun shells. This shell bears fine spiral ribs and interstitial ribs on its outer surface, which are crossed by longitudinal threads. A few ribs near the shoulder are granulated. The outer lip margin extends outward, bearing teeth on the inside. It is very light brownish in color, only the ribs being lightly brown-colored. Distribution: southern Honshû and southwards, as deep as 100 fathoms.

5. Eudolium pyriforme (SOWERBY)

This has a larger number of fine spiral ribs than the preceding species. It is purplish brown in ground color, and marked by minute brown spots along the ribs. The outer lip margin, similarly shaped to that of *E. inflatum*, shows a pink tone, which, however, tends to fade away during storage. Distribution: south of central Honshû, 50–80 fathoms in depth.

6. Tonna perdix (LINNÉ)

The shell is large and somewhat elongated as a whole. The surface is covered by rounded spiral ribs and shallow inter-rib grooves. The anterior end of aperture is bordered by a fasciole. The outer lip margin is only slightly thickened. The ground color is light purplish brown, while the ribs are brown with white spots. Besides, 5 bands of light brown are faintly marked around the body whorl. The coloration thus somewhat resembles that of a quail. To this resemblance the shell owes its Japanese name 'quail shell'. Distribution: central Honshû and farther south, about 10 fathoms in depth.

7. Tonna fasciata (BRUGUIÈRE)

A globular shell of fairly large size. The width of spiral ribs and furrows are very heterogeneous. The outer lip is moderately thickened, and dentate on the inside.

The shell is pure white, bearing 4 spiral bands of brown. Distribution: the same with the last species.

8. Tonna luteostoma (KÜSTER)

This is a globular shell with a flat spire and largely swollen body whorl. The suture is deeply depressed. In specimens living in inland seas, shells of very large size are often seen, the flattened spiral ribs are about three times as wide as inter-rib spaces, and the surface is covered by the alternation of brown and white or yellowish spots somewhat merging each other. Those living in open seas, on the contrary, have smaller shells, narrower ribs, and the coloration composed of whitish background and scattered, clear-cut, brown spots. The differences between these two types are fairly distinct, but they are usually treated as the same species. Distribution: throughout Japan, ranging from shallow (5–10 fathoms) to great depths (100 fathoms).

9. Tonna tessellata (LAMARCK)

The spiral ribs are narrow and spotted with brown. The inter-rib spaces are twice as wide as the ribs at the posterior end of whorls, but gradually narrows toward the anterior part. The outer lip is a little thickened. Distribution: south of central Honshû, about 10 fathoms deep.

10. Tonna olearium (LINNÉ)

The shell is not inferior to *T. luteostoma* in its size. The surface sculpture is characterized by the presence of 1, 2 or 3 interstitial ribs between main spiral ribs. It is brown, without patterns on the outer surface, except a white zone along the suture. Distribution: south of Honshû, at 10–20 fathoms depth.

Family Ficidae

The shells of this family resemble the tun shells in the low, small spire and large, inflated body whorl, but the anterior end of body whorl is characteristically prolonged, thus showing a form resembling a fig fruit. The surface is usually covered by a fine reticulate sculpture. The family is small and represented by only a few species in Japan.

11. Ficus subintermedia (D'ORBIGNY)

This is the commonnest fig shell in Japan. It is medium-sized, and has a flat spire. A groove encircles the spire along the suture. The surface sculpture is finely reticulate. The outer lip is scarcely thickened. The pattern is various; several spiral zones containing light and dark brown spots are most frequently seen. The ground color is light brown. Distribution: south of Honshû, abundant at 5–10 fathoms depth.

12. Ficus gracilis (SOWERBY)

This is larger than the preceding species, reaching 150 mm in the length of shell. Spiral threads are thicker than longitudinal ones. The surface is light brown. Distribution: south of Shikoku, as deep as 100 fathoms.

Family Muricidae (1)

The rock shell family is one of the largest groups of marine Gastropoda. This includes a rich variety of forms. The shells are mostly spindle- or fist-shaped and bear varices ornamented by spines or tubercles. They usually possess an anterior canal in the aperture, which sometimes develops into a tubular siphon. Not only their form but also their size is diversified. The animals inhabit shallow waters, and are carnivorous. Some of them are known as being detrimental to the oyster culture in Japan. Certain species secrete a purple pigment that had been used as dye in ancient Europe. The operculum is horny. See also Plate 70.

13. Chicoreus (Triplex) rosarius (PERRY)

This pretty, medium-sized shell is fusiform, and bears regularly arranged 3 varices on each whorl, which are connected longitudinally from one whorl to the next. The varices bear prominent, tubular spines with their ends somewhat expanded. The most posterior spine on each whorl is usually forked at its end. The surface is covered by coarse spiral ribs that extend over the spines. The aperture is round, and bears

[PLATE 23]   Tonnidae, Ficidae, Muricidae

paired teeth on the outer lip margin. The inner lip margin, on the other hand, bears small granules. The anterior canal is very long and almost tubular, being covered by the columellar margin. The exterior is encircled by brown stripes on the white background, and the inside of aperture is also white. The inside of spines are dark brown, while the apical part of the tall spire is beautifully colored with rose-pink. The operculum is horny, and oval in outline, with a nucleus anteriorly biased. Distribution: south of central Honshû, at about 20 fathoms depth.

14. Chicoreus (Triplex) torrefactus (Sowerby)

Though the shell closely resembles the preceding species, this differs in the following characters. The spines on the varices are less expanded at their ends, as compared with those of *Ch. rosarius*, and the first spine is not forked. The coloration is darker, the margin of aperture is flesh-colored, and no granules are seen on the margin of inner lip. Distribution: the same with *Ch. rosarius*.

15. Chicoreus asianus (Kuroda)

The spines of this shell, are neither expanded nor forked at their ends. The most remarkabe character of this species is that a sharp fang-like process occurs between the 3rd and 4th spine on the outer lip. The surface is marked by 3 broad, spiral bands of chestnut brown, and by cloudy patterns of lighter color, but the coloration is usually hidden beneath gray-white calcareous sediments. It is also slightly pink around the margin of aperture. Distribution: south of Honshû, 10–20 fathoms deep.

16. Siratus pliciferoides (Kuroda)

The spines are more slender than those of the foregoing 3 species. The spine at the shoulder is by far the largest, and others are of medium length, alternated by very short ones. The siphon is long, and almost tubular, bearing spiny processes. The surface of whorls bears 1 or 2 tubercle-like, longitudinal folds on each space between the varices. This is white in color, and marked by a few spiral bands of light brown. Distribution: the same with the last species.

17. Chicoreus ramosus (Linné)

This is the largest species of this genus, resembling *Ch. asianus*. It can be distinguished from the other species by its larger shell, lower spire, and larger body whorl. Distribution: south of Kyûshû, at 10–20 fathoms depth.

PLATE 23

PLATE 24

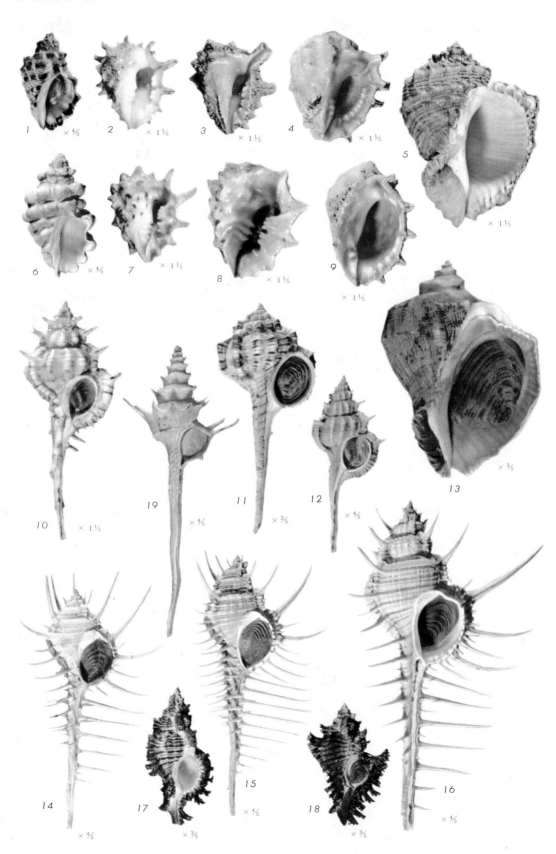

1   × 4/5
2   × 1 1/5
3   × 1 1/5
4   × 1 1/5
5   × 1 1/5
6   × 4/5
7   × 1 1/5
8   × 1 1/5
9   × 1 1/5
10   × 1 1/5
19   × 4/5
11   × 3/5
12   × 4/5
13   × 3/5
14   × 4/5
15   × 4/5
16   × 4/5
17   × 3/5
18   × 3/5

Family Muricidae (2)

1. Thais clavigera (KÜSTER)

This is a common snail, spirally bearing 4 rows of round tubercles and a fasciole on the body whorl. A few interstitial threads also encircle the whorls in every space between the rows of tubercles. No umbilicus is seen. The surface is gray brown in ground color, while the tubercles and the inner margin of outer lip are dark brown. The columella, together with a row of small knots along the inside of outer lip, bears flesh color. The horny operculum is dark brown. Distribution: abundant everywhere in Japan, near the tide line of rocky shores.

2. Drupa albolabris (BLAINVILLE)

The shell is small, globular and thick. Its outer surface is covered by prominent spines arranged on 5 spiral ridges. Fine interstitial ribs with scales are also encircling. Both lips are thickened, and the aperture bears strong teeth, by which the aperture is narrowed. This is entirely white all over the surface and within the aperture. Distribution: south of central Honshû, near the low tide level.

3. Drupa grossularia [RÖDING]

The exterior of this drupe shell is surrounded by 2 rows of tubercles along the shoulder as well as by 3 thick ridges and finer ribs on the anterior half of the last whorl. The strong ridges terminate at the outer lip in finger-like processes, of which the first one is the longest and semitubular, containing the posterior canal. The inside of the narrowed aperture and toothed lip margins are yellow in color. Distribution: south of Kyûshû, near the low tide level.

4. Drupa rubuscaesius [RÖDING]

This is somewhat larger and heavier than the foregoing drupe shells. The tubercles and spiny processes are also more stout. The aperture is less narrowed as the lip margins are less thickened and the teeth are finer. The inside of aperture is reddish purple, while the margin of lips bordering

the aperture is yellowish brown in color. Distribution: central Honshû and farther south, near the low tide level.

5. Rapana bezoar (LINNÉ)

This shell is considerably large and globular in outline. This has a small spire, large body whorl, wide aperture and well developed, thick fasciole. Many spiral ribs are crossed over the outer surface by thin, plate-like, longitudinal ridges, showing a wrinkled, reticulate sculpture. The longitudinal plates are especially well developed like fins on the shoulder, near the base and over the fasciole. The umbilicus is widely open. This is light yellowish brown all over the surface, except the inner margin of aperture which remains white. Distribution: south of Honshû, at 5–10 fathoms in depth.

6. Thais bronni (DUNKER)

Young shells of this species look like *Th. clavigera*, but in adult shells the tubercles on the surface become round and very thick. The ends of the 4 tubercle-bearing, spiral ribs respectively form sinuses on the margin of outer lip. The aperture contains no lip teeth. The inside margin of aperture is colored flesh-yellow. Distribution: throughout Japan as far north as Hokkaidô, near the low tide level.

7. Drupa ricina (LINNÉ)

This resembles *Dr. albolabris* in shape and structure of the shell, but the spines are darked-colored, and the base of spines are seen as black dots through the callus layer on the inner lip side of body whorl. The inside of outer lip bears reddish brown spots at the outer end of the teeth. Distribution: south of southern Honshû, near the low tide level.

8. Drupa morum [RÖDING]

A very heavy and thick shell larger than the preceding species. Spiny processes on the outer surface are short and stout. The aperture is remarkably narrowed by large lip teeth. This is violet-colored inside the aperture. Distribution: south of southern Kyûshû, near the low tide level.

[PLATE 24]

Muricidae, Columbariidae

9. *Drupa rubsidaeus* [RÖDING]

This is characterized by a wide aperture and the scarcely thickened lips. The interior of aperture is also violet in color. Distribution: south of the Ryukyus, near the low tide level.

10. *Murex kiiensis* KIRA

The shell consists of the main part like a stout spindle in outline and a long, straight, anterior siphon. The main part comprises about 8 whorls, of which the surface is longitudinally crossed by 3 varices, each bearing a long spine per whorl. This has also a few short spines at the base of the siphon. The spire is deeply constricted at the suture, and bears 2–3 longitudinal, tubercle-like folds in every space between the varices and fine spiral threads over the outer surface. The siphon is almost as long as the main part, and its tube is closed at the base. It is white on the exterior, only encircled by several fine bands of brown. Distribution: central Honshû, as deep as 50–100 fathoms.

11. *Murex (Haustellum) haustellum* LINNÉ

Resembling the last species, this is larger and has a lower spire. Spiny processes on the varices are very short and few in number. Three or four longitudinal folds occur between the varices. The round aperture is margined by the slightly reflexed lips. Fine brown bands are spirally marked on the light bluish brown background of the outer surface. The inside margin of aperture is pink-colored, while the inner part remains white. The operculum is elliptic in shape, and its nucleus is eccentrically biased toward the columellar side. Distribution: south of southern Kyûshû, at 20–30 fathoms depth.

12. *Murex sobrinus* (A. ADAMS)

The shell also resembles *M. kiiensis* in appearance, although this is smaller in size. The siphon is relatively shorter than those of the former two species, but specimens from some localities may have exceptionally long siphons, which are twice as long as the main part of the shell. It bears 2, dark brown, spiral bands on the light brown-colored surface. The nucleus of operculum is situated anteriorly to the center. Distribution: central Honshû and southwards, 10–20 fathoms in depth.

13. *Rapana thomasiana* CROSSE

This is a large shell similar to *R. bezoar* in shape and structure. The spire is small, and the whorls rapidly increase in thickness. The surface of whorls is sculptured by 3 spiral ridges bearing tubercles, respectively on the shoulder, middle and basal parts. Fine spiral threads are also marked all over the surface. The outer lip is scarcely thickened and bears thread-like fine folds along its inner margin. The umbilicus opens like a slit between the parietal callus and the fasciole, which longitudinally bears thin plate-like ribs overlapping each other. The outside of the shell is usually reddish brown, while the inside of aperture is colored in fleshy red. The aperture is closed by a large, dark brown operculum. The shells of this species are very variable in shape and coloration; they may be without tubercles, with or without fin-like varices, and from red to white in surface color. The flesh of this mollusc is delicious. Distribution: all over Japan south of Hokkaidô, at 10–20 fathoms depth.

14. *Murex ternispina* LAMARCK

This and the following two species are called the bone shells in Japan, because of their resemblance with the bone or skeleton of a fish. Three continuous varices, running longitudinally on the spire and extending over the long siphon, respectively bear a row of long, slender, pointed spines alternating with shorter ones. In this first species, the spines are somewhat thicker and more widely spaced than in *M. triremis*. The operculum is horny and elliptic, closely fits the aperture, and has a nucleus anteriorly situated. Distribution: southern Honshû and farther south, 20–30 fathoms in depth.

15. *Murex (Aranea) triremis* (PERRY)

The shell is a little smaller and more slender than the preceding species. Both long and short spines on the varices are larger in number. The outer surface is purplish white. The nucleus of its operculum is somewhat shifted from the center to the columellar side. Distribution: south of central Honshû, 20–30 fathoms deep.

16. Murex troscheli LISCHKE

This is larger and more stout than the preceding bone shells. The spines are less in number than that of *M. triremis*, but are thicker and longer, reaching 50 mm in their maximum length. Unlike the plain coloration of the former two species, this shell is surrounded by several brown lines on spiral ribs extending over the spines. The operculum resembles that of *M. ternispina*. Distribution: south of central Honshû, 10–20 fathoms deep.

17. Chicoreus (Triplex) microphyllus (LAMARCK)

This shell is medium-sized, thick and heavy like a mass of rock. Besides 3 continuous varices with thick processes, the exterior surface is sculptured by spiral ribs and by 2 or more tubercle-like, longitudinal folds in every space between the varices. The processes on the varices are rather short, slightly expanding at their ends, but not forked. The outer lip is finely grooved inside. The siphon is moderately long and almost tubular. This is dark brown on the varices and spiral ribs, while the ground is light brown. The margin of aperture is light yellow in color. Distribution: south of Amami Islands, from the low tide level down to 5 fathoms.

18. Chicoreus brunneus (LINK)

The general appearance is like the preceding species, but the spire is lower and the processes on the varices are especially elongated at the shoulder of each whorl. This can also be separated by the pink coloration of aperture margin and the smaller number (one) of longitudinal, tubercle-like fold intervening between the varices. Distribution: south of central Honshû, between the low tide level and 5 fathoms depth.

Family Columbariidae

19. Columbarium pagoda (LESSON)

This is a peculiarly shaped shell, with a moderately tall spire and a very long siphon. The protoconch is relatively large and papilla-shaped. The whorls are encircled by a row of flat, triangularly shaped spines, which are continuous from one to the other at their bases and radiate obliquely. Besides, 2 spiral rows of minor spines are also seen on the anterior part of body whorl and the base of siphon, respectively. The siphon is almost twice as long as the main part of the shell, and somewhat twisted. The shell is entirely light brown in its color. The operculum is horny and oval, with an anteriorly biased nucleus. Distribution: central Honshû, at 20–30 fathoms depth.

[PLATE 25]   Muricidae, Rapidae

Family Muricidae (3)

1. Ocenebra japonica endermonis (SMITH)

The shell is small, but fairly thick. Each whorl bears 5–8 longitudinal ridges crossing with fine spiral ribs. Fin-like appendages rarely develop on the longitudinal ridges. The outer lip margin is dentate, and bears an anteriorly protruding, sharp spine on its anterior part. Distribution: northeastern part of Honshû and farther north, near the low tide level.

2. Trophonopsis (Boreotrophon) xestra (DALL)

A small, thin shell having a considerably long siphon. The outer surface bears no spiral sculpture, but is ornamented by thin, fin-like varices of which the number is 12–13 per whorl. They are especially well developed and erect at the shoulder. This is white-washed over the surface, as if painted with face-powder. The oval operculum is yellowish brown in color, and its nucleus is anteriorly situated. Distribution: central and northern part of Honshû, as deep as 100–150 fathoms.

3. Takia inermis (SOWERBY)

The outline is more or less similar to the preceding species. The shell is, however, somewhat thicker, and has less number (5–8 per whorl) of varices, which are thick and do not extend like fins. It is dirty white over the thick calcareous sediment covering the outer surface. Distribution: central Honshû, at about 50 fathoms depth.

4. Trophonopsis (Boreotrophon) candelabrum (REEVE)

Though this also resembles the preceding species, the shell is rather thin in texture. The varices are like those of Tr. xestra. Spiral threads are also finely marked over the outer surface. The margin of aperture widens like a trumpet. The outer surface is light brown, with brown spiral lines. Distribution: south of central Honshû, at about 100 fathoms depth.

5. Trophonopsis (Bathymurex) echinus (DALL)

The shell is heavier than the last species, and the whorls bear spiral threads as well as longitudinal ridges (6–8 per whorl) with spiny processes. This is pure white, and semi-transparent. Distribution: the same with the last species.

6. Trophonopsis (Bathymurex) gorgon (DALL)

This is a little larger than Tr. echinus. The spire is taller, and the siphon is also longer. The spines on the varices are particularly elongated at the shoulder of whorls. The coloration and distribution are similar to Tr. echinus.

7. Ocenebra japonica (DUNKER)

This can be separated from subsp. endermonis by the lack of a spiny process on its outer lip. The degree of development of fin-like appendages on the varices varies in different individuals. The surface color is grayish white to brown, and the spiral color bands of brown are also rich in variation. This inhabits rocky shores near the low tide level, and often becomes a serious pest to the oyster culture. Distribution: north of central Honshû.

8. Ceratostoma rorifluum (ADAMS et REEVE)

The fins on the varices poorly develop in this species. They are longitudinally connected in three twisted series running over the spire. The exterior is encircled by several brown lines on the yellowish white ground. Distribution: south of Kyûshû, 5–10 fathoms deep.

9. Ocenebra (Ocinebrellus) adunca (SOWERBY)

This species is characterized by broad wings radiating from the surface of whorls to five directions. Among them, the one on the outer lip is most widely developed. The coloration of the shell varies from white to brown, with or without brown spiral bands. Distribution: central Honshû and farther south, at 10–20 fathoms depth.

10. *Pteropurpura vespertilio* KIRA

The shell is slender, and thin, with glossy surface. It has 3 straight rows of thin, wing-like processes running across the whorls. The siphon is very long. The outer surface is light brown and marked by irregular brown spots. Distribution: south of central Honshû, at 40–50 fathoms depth.

11. *Pteropurpura stimpsoni* (A. ADAMS)

This is smaller than the preceding species, and lacks lustre on the outer surface. Wings are arranged in 3 rows, but not so well developed as in *C. vespertilio*. This is plainly colored in grayish white or light brown. Distribution: south of central Honshû, 20–30 fathoms deep.

12. *Pterynotus pinnatus* WOOD

A medium-sized shell, comparatively thick, but semi-transparent in texture and slenderly fusiform in outline. The surface of spire is alternately sculptured by 3 rows of continuous varices and intervening tubercles (one in each space between the varices). A fin-like, erect plate runs on each varix from the apex to the end of siphon. The surface of whorls and fins is encircled by fine ribs. A remaining siphon formed in a former stage of shell development is attached to the last siphon, with its end isolated from the latter. The shell is yellowish white all over the surface. Distribution: central Honshû 20–30 fathoms in depth.

13. *Pterynotus (Marchia) elongatus* (SOLANDER)

The structure of this shell is essentially similar to that of the preceding species, but this is much more slender with a very tall spire. The fins on the varices are mostly restricted to the last two whorls. The surface sculpture, consisting of spiral ribs alone, is more coarsely and shallowly marked than in *Pt. pinnatus*. Tubercle-like folds on the whorls between the varices are low and indistinct. The tubular appendage of siphon

is reflexed and short. The aperture is pink-colored on its inside margin. Distribution: central Honshû, at 10–20 fathoms depth.

14. *Ceratostoma fournieri* (CROSSE)

Three longitudinal rows of varices are somewhat twisted, and bear irregularly crooked, erect wings. The outer lip margin is toothed, and bears on its anterior part a sharp spine projecting perpendicularly toward the anterior. The ground color is white, with irregular brown blotches. Distribution: central Honshû, on rocky shores below the tide line.

15. *Homalocantha anatomica* (PERRY)

The spire is low, while the last whorl is longitudinally elongated. and possesses a long and flat siphon. This bears 5 longitudinal rows with radiating spines. Those around the round aperture and along the the siphon are particularly well developed, and singularly shaped. Longer spines are tubular, and expanded at their ends into forks or triangular plates. This is usually grayish white in color, but individuals of pinkish or purplish tone are sometimes found. Distribution: central Honshû, 20–50 fathoms in depth.

16. *Ocenebra eurypteron* (ADAMS et REEVE)

This is a fairly large shell, ornamented by 5 rows of prominent, broad wings, of which the posterior part is triangularly broadened with its tip posteriorly curved. The structure is comparable to that of *O. adunca*, but this shell is larger in size, and spiral ribs on the surface are almost faded. The brown ground color is lighter, and marked irregularly by spiral bands somewhat darker brown in color. This might be a deep-sea form of *O. adunca*. Distribution: central Honshû, as deep as 30–50 fathoms.

Family Rapidae (1)

The shells belonging to this family are usually small or medium in size, and mostly white, and have a characteristically fragile

[PLATE 25]   Muricidae, Rapidae

and semi-transparent texture. Many of them are globular in shape, but their surface is sometimes ornamented by elaborate sculptures. The animals are used to live on and inside reef-forming corals in shallow, warm waters. Certain species are, however, found in deep seas.

17. Rapa rapa (LINNÉ)

This large-sized shell looks like a tuberous root of turnip in outline, with its almost flat spire, largely inflated body whorl and stout siphon. The outer surface is densely covered by spiral ribs and interstitial threads. The ribs tend to be thicker anteriorly, and bear scales near the base of the shell. The suture forms a groove, in which growth lines are marked like folds. The outer lip margin is slightly thickened and grooved inside by the ends of the spiral ribs. The parietal callus widens at the anterior end, where it is isolated from the columella covering a narrow umbilicus. The anterior canal is wide. This is white in color all over the surface. The crescent, horny operculum is yellowish brown in color, and is not large enough to close the aperture. Distribution: south of the Ryukyus, below the tide line.

18. Rapa incurva (DUNKER)

This is smaller than the preceding species. The surface sculpture is similar to that of *R. rapa*, but the growth lines in the sutural groove are only weakly marked. The anterior canal is narrow and short. This is yellowish brown in the color of outer surface. Distribution: the same with *R. rapa*.

19. Magilus antiquus MONTFORT

This peculiar shell consists of an original globular shell and a pseudo-shell tube jointed together. At first, the animal lives in the original shell, but, after it is settled in the mass of coral, it begins to extend a pseudo-shell tube through crevasses of coral, and migrates into the latter. The shell left behind is filled with calcareous deposits, and turns into a solid mass. The tube is successively prolonged and filled in the same way as the animal grows, sometimes reaching one foot in length. Since the tube is usually crooked and entangled with those of other animals within a coral mass, it is often very difficult to take it out. The picture on the left shows a mass of coral including two individuals of this species, which are removed from the coral and shown on the right. One has the large shell and tube, while in another the shell is smaller and the tube grows longer. This difference is probably caused by the different stages of the shells that initially perforated the coral to settle in. Distribution: southern Honshû and farther south.

PLATE **25**

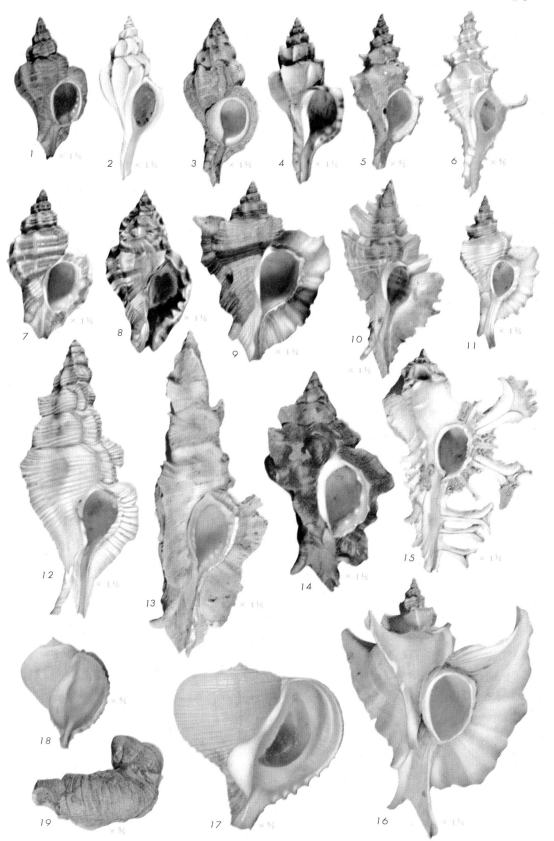

1   × 1⅕

2   × 1⅕

3   × 1⅕

4   × 1⅕

5   × ⅘

6   × ⅘

7   × 1⅕

8   × 1⅕

9   × 1⅕

10   × 1⅕

11   × 1⅕

12   × 1⅕

13   × 1⅕

14   × 1⅕

15   × 1⅕

16   × 1⅕

17   × ⅘

18   × ⅘

19   × ⅗

PLATE 26

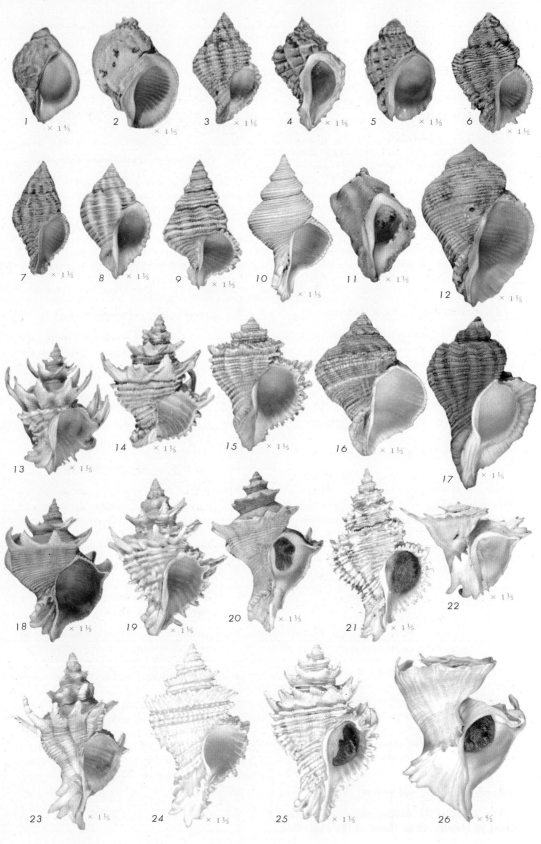

1 × 1⅘
2 × 1⅕
3 × 1⅕
4 × 1⅕
5 × 1⅕
6 × 1⅕
7 × 1⅕
8 × 1⅕
9 × 1⅕
10 × 1⅕
11 × 1⅕
12 × 1⅕
13 × 1⅕
14 × 1⅕
15 × 1⅕
16 × 1⅕
17 × 1⅕
18 × 1⅕
19 × 1⅕
20 × 1⅕
21 × 1⅕
22 × 1⅕
23 × 1⅕
24 × 1⅕
25 × 1⅕
26 × ⅘

Family Rapidae (2)

1. Coralliobia (Quoyula) monodonta (BLAINVILLE)

A small, bulbous coral shell, somewhat exceeding 10 mm in length. The spire is low, and the well developed body whorl ends in a widely open aperture. The surface densely bears fine, granulated, spiral ribs, but is usually covered by calcareous sediments. It is characterized by a plait on the columella. There is no umbilical opening. The inside of aperture is colored in light reddish purple. Distribution: south of central Honshû, near the low tide level.

2. Coralliobia violacea (KIENER)

Resembling the preceding species in shape, this is larger and heavier. Under the cover of calcareous stains, scaly, spiral ribs cover the outer surface. The inside of outer lip is finely striated. It is beautifully colored with purple inside the aperture. Distribution: the same with the preceding species.

3. Coralliobia akibumii KIRA (n. sp.)

This is a deep-sea species having a small, white shell. It is spindle-shaped, with a small but sharp spire and the pointed anterior end. The surface is rough owing to fine, spiral ribs with scales, and bears rounded longitudinal ridges about 10 in the number per whorl. The umbilicus is barely open between the fasciole and the elongated anterior canal. Distribution: Pacific sides of central Honshû and Shikoku, at about 100 fathoms depth.

4. Emozamia lamellata HABE

The outline is like the preceding shell, but this differs from the former in having coarser spiral ribs and fin-like, erect varices on its surface. This is yellowish white on the outside, and white within the aperture. Distribution: Pacific sides of central Honshû and Shikoku, 50–80 fathoms deep.

5. Coralliobia sugimotonis (KURODA)

The aperture is wider, and the anterior canal is shorter than those of the preceding

species. The surface sculpture is coarsely reticulate, accompanied by small tubercles on the intersections of spiral and longitudinal ribs. This animal lives among colonies of a sea-anemone. Distribution: Tosa Bay of Shikoku, below the tide line.

6. Coralliophila bulbiformis CONRAD

The shell is somewhat larger than the preceding species, and has a moderately tall spire. Five or six thick ridges run across each whorl, crossed by fine scaly ribs. The outer lip is finely striated inside. The inside of aperture is purple-colored. Distribution: south of central Honshû, from the tide line to 5 fathoms depth.

7. Coralliophila costularis (LAMARCK)

This resembles C. akibumii in shape, but is more slender. Longitudinal ridges on the surface are more in number (about 12 per whorl), and spiral ribs are finer than those of C. akibumii. This is also light purple inside the aperture. Distribution: central Honshû and farther south, 5–10 fathoms deep.

8. Coralliobia stearnsi (PILSBRY)

This differs from the related species, C. sugimotonis, in the tapering anterior end and lack of tubercles on the knots of reticulate sculpture. The umbilicus is distinctly open. Distribution: south of central Honshû, below the tide line down to 5 fathoms.

9. Latiaxis (Pseudomurex) crebrilamellosus (SOWERBY)

The spire is fairly tall, and constricted at the suture. The surface of whorls are obtusely carinated a little above the suture. This has 8–9 longitudinal ridges on each whorl, which are in turn crossed by moderately coarse ribs bearing scales. The body whorl anterior to the peripheral carination tapers sharply toward a short anterior canal bordered by a fasciole. The shell is entirely white. Distribution: south of central Honshû, at 20–30 fathoms depth.

[PLATE 26]   Rapidae

10. Latiaxis (Pseudomurex) eugeniae (BERNARDI)

This and the last species closely resemble in the outline of shells, but this is easily distinguished from the last one by the absence of longitudinal ridges on the surface and by the longer anterior canal. The exterior is covered by delicate, scaly, spiral ribs. The umbilicus is covered by the parietal callus, slightly opening like a slit. Distribution: south of central Honshû, at 50–80 fathoms depth.

11. Transtrafer asiatica KURODA

The spire is low, while the body whorl is laterally expanded at its central part, and tapers anteriorly. The surface sparsely bears longitudinal folds, and is densely sculptured by fine spiral ribs with scales. The inside of outer lip is toothed. Distribution: central Honshû and farther south, 5–10 fathoms deep.

12. Coralliophila pyriformis KIRA

The shell is large and thick. The last whorl is large, tapering anteriorly. Fine, scaly ribs encircle the surface of whorls. The aperture margin lacks teeth. It is reddish purple inside the aperture. According to the experience of collectors, the animal clings so strongly to the surface of coral when alive, that a piece of body is often left behind as one forcibly tears it off from the substratum. Distribution: the same with the above species.

13. Latiaxis pagodus (A. ADAMS)

The whorls are encircled on the angled shoulder by a row of flat, spiny processes, like those of *Columbarium pagoda* illustrated in Plate 24. The spines are flat, and triangular in shape, with sharply pointed tops curving inward. Besides, the body whorl bears 2 spiral rows of medium-sized spines and several rows of short spines on its middle and anterior part, respectively. The fasciole also bears long, curved, spiny processes. The callus on the inner lip is reflexed, under which the umbilicus opens like a slit. The shell is wholly white in color. Distribution: south of central Honshû, 20–30 fathoms deep.

14. Latiaxis kinoshitai FULTON

Like the preceding species, the tall spire is ornamented by an encircling row of prominent, spiny processes, which are also flat and triangularly shaped. The outer surface is sculptured by scaly, spiral ribs on both sides of the row. The cross-section of shelly tube is somewhat quadrilateral. Distribution: central Honshû, at 20–30 fathoms depth.

15. Latiaxis (Tolema) winckworthi FULTON

As compared with the preceding two species, the spire is lower, and the columellar end is more elongated in this shell. The spiny processes, forming a spiral row on the angled shoulder of whorls, are narrow and short. Where low, longitudinal ridges (15–16 in their number per whorl) cross with spiral ribs, short spiny processes rise from the surface. Distribution: southern Honshû and farther south, at 30–50 fathoms depth.

16. Coralliophila erosa [RÖDING]

The shell is approximately rhombic in lateral view, being pointed on both ends. The shelly tube is bluntly angled on the periphery. It is covered by fine, scaly, spiral ribs over the surface, but lacks spiny processes. Although longitudinal ridges are also seen, the degree of their development is different according to individuals. The umbilicus is shallowly open. Distribution: south of central Honshû, from the tide line to 5 fathoms depth.

17. Coralliophila (Genkaimurex) varicosa KURODA

The shell, consisting of a small spire and large body whorl, densely bears scaly, spiral ribs over its surface, and some 10 ridges run longitudinally across each whorl. The outer lip is widely margined by a fin-like appendage. The anterior canal is fairly elongated, and compressed on its ventral side. The umbilicus is closed. The surface coloration varies from white to light or dark brown in different specimens. Distribution: northern Kyûshû, at 30–50 fathoms depth.

69

18. Latiaxis deburgiae purpuratus CHENU

The spire is small but sharply pointed, while the body whorl is large and well inflated, showing a quadrilateral cross-section. A row of flat, triangular spines with their tops curved inward encircle the angled shoulder. Scaly, spiral striations covering the outer surface are fine and dense. The umbilicus is open, and the fasciole bears a row of spiny processes. The shell is semi-transparent in its texture and milky white, often with purplish or pinkish hue. Distribution: south of central Honshû, 20–30 fathoms in depth.

19. Latiaxis tosanus HIRASE

This resembles L. pagodus or L. kinoshitai in appearance, but the anterior canal is longer, and the spines on the shoulder of whorls are somewhat narrower. Spiral ribs anterior to the shoulder are coarse, and bear small, radiating spines where they are crossed by longitudinal ridges. Distribution: Pacific coasts of Shikoku, 30–50 fathoms deep.

20. Latiaxis kawamurai KIRA

This has a tall, turreted spire, and a long siphon. The shoulder of whorls is carinated and bears a row of triangular, tooth-like spines, while the suture is deeply depressed. Other parts of the outer surface are covered by very fine, scaly, spiral striations. The opening umbilicus is shallow. The processes on the fasciole are blunt, and nodule-like. The anterior siphon is somewhat compressed. Distribution: Tosa Bay of Shikoku, as deep as 80–100 fathoms.

21. Latiaxis kiranus KURODA

The shell has a considerably tall spire. The processes arranged in a row along the shoulder of whorls are narrow and spine-like. Smaller spines also radiate from the crossing points of longitudinal ridges and coarse spiral ribs. The fasciole bears small, blunt spines. The umbilicus is open. Distribution: Tosa Bay of Shikoku, at 80–100 fathoms depth.

22. Latiaxis pilsbryi HIRASE

The spire is almost flat, and the whorls are sharply carinated at the shoulder, from which flat, triangular spines radiate horizontally. The shell is thus like a cogwheel as seen from above. The last two whorls are loosely coiled and separate at the suture, so that the aperture is also separated by a short distance from the spire. The outer surface is densely sculptured by very fine, spiral threads. The wide umbilicus is surrounded by a carinated fasciole, bearing a row of minor flat spines. The anterior canal is flattened and semitubular. Distribution: south of central Honshû, at 80–100 fathoms depth.

23. Latiaxis armatus (SOWERBY)

The shell resembles L. pagodus in its appearance, but the spiral ribs are finer and bear no spines. Spiny processes are seen in a row only on the shoulder of whorls. The umbilicus is open, and the anterior canal is flatly compressed. Distribution: south of central Honshû, 20–30 fathoms deep.

24. Latiaxis (Tolema) lischkeanus (DUNKER)

A splendid, milky white shell, with semi-transparent texture and elaborate surface sculptures. Long spines radiating from the shoulder of whorls are flat, like an equilateral triangle and extend obliquely with slight inward curvature. On both sides of this row of long spines, the outer surface is covered by many spiral ribs with smaller spines, of which the length diminishes with increasing distance from the shoulder. The spines, however, again become a little longer near the anterior end of body whorl and on the fasciole. The umbilicus is open. The anterior canal is flat. Distribution: south of central Honshû, 30–50 fathoms deep.

25. Latiaxis (Tolema) japonicus (DUNKER)

This is as pretty and elaborate as the preceding shell. The most important difference from L. lischkeanus is that two rows of large, triangular spines encircle the shoulder of whorls, instead of a single row in the former species. This bears obtuse longitudinal ridges on the surface of its body

[PLATE 26]   Rapidae

whorl, and the spiral ribs are somewhat coarser than those of *L. lischkeanus*. The scaly processes on the ribs are neither erect nor spine-like. The shell lacks transparency and is entirely white. Distribution : central Honshû and farther south, at 50–80 fathoms depth.

26.   *Latiaxis mawae* (GRIFFITH et PIDGEON)

This represents the largest form among the group of deep-sea coral shells of Japan, and is characterized by its singular structure similar to that of *L. pilsbryi*. The posterior part of the whorls is almost flat, and margined at the sharply carinated shoulder. The margin bears 10 or more flat spines per each whorl, which are bent or reflexed inward. The last two whorls, together with the aperture, are isolated from the next whorls. A well developed, and compressed fasciole surrounds the wide, funnel-shaped umbilicus, bears a row of spiny processes, and contains within it an elongated anterior canal of aperture. Spiral striations covering the outer surface of this shell are very fine and indistinctly marked. Distribution: the same with the preceding species.

Family Buccinidae (1)

This is the family of whelk shells including a great number of species ranging from the tropics to the polar region. The shells are variable in size, and the species with large shells are mostly found in cold waters. They are usually thick, and spindle-shaped, and have a wide aperture containing an anterior canal. The operculum is corneous. Some of them supply us with edible flesh which is often most delicious.

1. Pusiostoma mendicaria (LINNÉ)

This small shell is very thick and solid. This has a small, conical spire and large body whorl that terminates in a narrow aperture bordered by the thickened outer lip. The shell bears coarse spiral ribs as well as longitudinal folds, of which the posterior ends form indistinct tubercles on the shoulder of whorls. The inside of outer lip is bluntly toothed. The exterior is white in ground color, and clearly marked by black spiral bands (4 rows on the body whorl and 2 on other whorls). The aperture is stained with purple along its inner margin. A yellow epiderm covers the entire surface. Distribution: south of Amami Islands, below the tide line.

2. Pollia proteus (REEVE)

A small, fusiform shell with a tall spire. It is sculptured on the outer surface, by sparse longitudinal ridges and coarse spiral ribs. The outer lip bears blunt teeth. The anterior end of the shell is truncated. Two broad brown bands are spirally marked against the white background. Distribution: south of southern Honshû, below the tide line.

3. Engina pulchra (REEVE)

Spiral ribs are somewhat thicker, and longitudinal ridges are more in number (about 10 per whorl) than in the preceding species. This also bears blunt teeth on the outer lip margin. The shell is entirely orange-yellow over the outer surface, and pink inside the aperture. Distribution: south of Amami Islands, below the tide line.

4. Ecmanis ignea (GMELIN)

This is slenderly fusiform in shape. The surface of the last 3 whorls, that occupy the greater part of total shell length, is entirely smooth, while the apical part of spire bears fine longitudinal folds. The aperture is oblong, the outer lip is thickened, and one tooth-like plait occurs on each side of the posterior canal. Vague, irregular, brown blotches are marked on the light grayish brown background of the outer surface. Distribution: the same with the preceding species.

5. Pisania (Japeuthria) ferrea (REEVE)

The outline of the shell resembles that of *E. ignea*, but this is stouter and heavier in construction. A spiral rib runs along the suture of the tall spire, and ends at the aperture in a short, slit-like, posterior canal. Fine spiral lines and growth striae are also seen over the outer surface. The inside of outer lip bears thread-like striations. The shell is purplish brown all over the surface. Distribution: south of Honshû, below the tide line.

6. Kanamarua adonis (DALL)

This spindle-shaped shell is slender, and the texture is thin. Very fine reticulate sculpture is faintly marked on the outer surface. The columellar end is truncated. The outer lip margin is thin and acute. The operculum is elliptic, and its nucleus is anteriorly situated. It is light brown all over the exterior without any patterns. Distribution: south of central Honshû, as deep as 50–80 fathoms.

7. Colus (Aulacofusus) esychus (DALL)

The spire is relatively longer, and the shell is thicker than in the last species. The outer surface is almost smooth, only with growth lines. The anterior canal is slightly longer than that of *K. adonis*, and somewhat curved. Distribution: northeastern Honshû and farther north, at 100 fathoms depth.

8. Pollia undosus (LINNÉ)

This is similar to *P. mendicaria* in out-

[PLATE 27]   Buccinidae

line, and is also thick and heavy. Two teeth occur on the anterior part of columella, and the outer lip also bears several teeth. The exterior surface, white in ground color, is encircled by fine ribs of black, of which the number is about 12 on the last whorl. Distribution: south of southern Honshû, near the low tide level.

9. Cantharus cecillei (PHILIPPI)

The shell is fairly thick, and longitudinally bears some 10 thick ridges on the outer surface. Fine spiral threads encircle the whorls, crossing the ridges. The anterior canal is short and thick, and the outer lip is finely striated inside. It is wholly dark brown, and covered by a yellowish brown, hairy epiderm. Distribution: central Honshû and farther south, 5–10 fathoms deep.

10. Phos senticosum (LINNÉ)

This has a tall spire somewhat turreted. The surface is sculptured by 8–12 longitudinal ridges on each whorl, and by coarse spiral ribs bearing small spines where they cross the ridges. The interspaces between the ribs are filled with fine, longitudinal lines. The inside of aperture is striated, and the fasciole is strongly elevated. The anterior canal is short. This is light brown over the surface and marked by a spiral band of darker color on the middle part of the last whorl. Distribution: south of central Honshû, 10–20 fathoms deep.

11. Hindsia magnifica lischkei (MAKIYAMA)

The spire is tall, conical and a little constricted at the suture. The siphon is slightly curved and somewhat longer than that of the preceding species. The fasciole is little developed. Each whorl bears 8–12 longitudinal ribs. Small granules are formed where they are crossed by coarse spiral ribs. The inner lip bears a plait near its posterior end. Distribution: south of central Honshû, at 30–50 fathoms depth.

12. Hindsia kirai (HABE)

The outline of the shell is quite similar to that of H. magnifica lischkei, but the whorls are much inflated and bear more granules on longitudinal ridges. Spiral ribs are also more in number. Distribution: the same with the preceding species.

13. Siphonalia spadicea (REEVE)

An elongated, fusiform shell, with a tall spire. The shoulder of whorls is somewhat angled, and tubercles are often seen on it in some specimens. Fine spiral threads are marked over the outer surface. The anterior canal is thick and only slightly curved. Brown blotches are scattered on the lighter brown ground. Distribution: south of Honshû, 20–30 fathoms deep. The shells from northeastern Honshû are remarkably smaller than those from Shikoku.

14. Siphonalia trochulus (REEVE)

This has a small, low spire and roundly inflated whorls. Fine, white, spiral lines are densely sculptured over the light flesh-brown surface, and only few individuals have tubercles on the shoulder of whorls. The callus on the inner lip is thickly developed, and the outer lip margin bears thread-like striations. The anterior canal is strongly curved as in most species of this genus. Distribution: south of central Honshû, 20–30 fathoms deep.

15. Siphonalia mikado (MELVILL)

The spire is taller, and the whorls are more distinctly angulate at the shoulder than that of S. trochulus. This shell bears tubercles on the shoulder, and somewhat deeply sculptured, spiral ribs. A callused nodule occurs near the anterior end of outer lip. The inside margin of outer lip is striated. The large fasciole is also angled. The light brown surface is faintly marked by brown blotches. Distribution: the same with S. trochulus.

16. Siphonalia signum (REEVE)

This is one of the largest of the Japanese species belonging to this genus. The spire is rather small, while the aperture is wide. Tubercles on the shoulder are well-developed. Other structures are essentially the same with those of other species of Siphonalia described above. The surface coloration is very rich in variety, ranging from plain white or yellow to light or chocolate brown, with spiral stripes and blotches of darker tone. Distribution: the same with the preceding species.

17. Siphonalia pfeifferi SOWERBY

Resembling *S. trochulus* in shape, this shell is larger and ornamented by fine brown dots on the spiral ribs. Distribution: the same with the last three species.

18. Siphonalia cassidariaeformis (REEVE)

This species is extremly diversified in the shape and coloration of shells. Most of the specimens seen in Japan possessing prominent shoulder tubercles and deeply sculptured spiral ribs should be included in this species.

19. Siphonalia filosa A. ADAMS

Though this is closely related to *S. spadicea* and some other species in structure, this shell can be distinguished by the somewhat broader outline, dorsally reflexed siphon, etc. Distribution: south of central Honshû, 20–30 fathoms deep.

20. Ancistrolepis trochoideus (DALL)

The shelly tube is thick, well inflated, round in its cross-section, and sculptured on the outer surface by 5 spiral ridges and some interstitial ribs. The outer lip margin is wavy. The short anterior canal is curved toward the columellar side. The white surface is covered by a thin, light yellowish epiderm. The operculum is round, thick and dark brown. Distribution: northeastern Honshû and farther north, at 20–50 fathoms depth.

21. Buccinum zelotes DALL

The spire is tall and constricted at the suture between well inflated whorls. The surface of whorls is encircled by 5 prominent ridges, between which very fine threads are reticulately marked. The outer lip is thick, and the anterior canal is short. The exterior is light brown, with a thin epiderm. Distribution: northeastern Honshû along Japan Sea coasts, about 100 fathoms in depth.

22. Buccinum nipponense DALL

The shelly tube more rapidly increases in thickness than in the preceding species. This is also broader in outline. The spiral ridges are more in number, amounting to 7 on the body whorl. The white surface is covered by a thin, light yellow epiderm. The operculum is thin and yellowish in color, with a centrally situated nucleus. Distribution: the same with the preceding species.

23. Buccinum tsubai KURODA

This is a moderately large and thin shell, with well inflated whorls and a round, wide aperture. The surface is shallowly marked by very fine, reticulate threads. The outer lip is not thickened. The anterior canal is wide and short. This is white in color of the shell, but covered by a light brown epiderm. The operculum is round elliptic in outline, and thin. Distribution: Japan Sea side of northeastern Honshû, as deep as 150–300 fathoms.

24. Siphonalia fusoides (REEVE)

The whorls are round, without tubercles on the shoulder as in *S. trochulus* and *S. pfeifferi*. Fine spiral threads densely cover the outer surface. This is usually yellowish white all over the surface, but sometimes light brown spots are seen. Distribution: south of Honshû, 20–30 fathoms in depth.

25. Siphonalia modificata (REEVE)

This shell resembles *S. filosa* and is much wider in outline. This is encircled by numerous fine threads. The anterior canal is only slightly reflexed backward. This is light yellowish brown all over the surface and orange-yellow along the inside margin of aperture. Distribution: csntral Honshû and southwards, 20–30 fathoms deep.

26. Volutharpa perryi (JAY)

The shell is very thin. The body whorl is very large and well inflated. The wide aperture is bordered by the thin outer lip. The anterior canal is wide, but short. The outer surface is shallowly marked by a fine reticulate sculpture, bears light brown blotches on the white ground, and is covered

[PLATE 27]   Buccinidae

by a yellowish brown, hairy epiderm. The operculum degrades into a tiny concave plate only a few millimeters in diameter, and even entirely disappears in some individuals. Distribution: northeastern Honshû and farther south, at 20–30 fathoms depth.

27.   Babylonia formosae (SOWERBY)

The large body whorl is about 2/3 as long as the total shell length. The spire is moderately steep, but small. The suture is depressed. The outer surface is smooth, except a fasciole surrounding the base. The outer lip is not thickened, and the umbilicus is narrowly open. The shell bears brown flame-patterns on the white surface. Distribution: Formosa and farther south, 5–10 fathoms deep.

28.   Babylonia pallida KIRA

This shell is almost the same with *B. formosae* in its shape. The umbilicus is, however, somewhat narrower. It lacks flame-patterns, and is light flesh-brown in surface color with white blotches along the shoulder of whorls. Distribution: the Ryukyus.

29.   Babylonia japonica (REEVE)

This is larger than the preceding species, though the shape and structure are essentially the same. Under a thick, dark brown epiderm, a white surface is marked by spirally arranged spots and flames of brown. This mollusc is abundant in shallow waters along Japanese coasts, and its flesh is often eaten by people. The shell, cut transversely and filled with wax or lead, serves as a top that has long been favored by Japanese children. Distribution: south of Honshû, 5–10 fathoms in depth.

30.   Kelletia lischkei KURODA

This is a spindle-shaped, thick shell of fairly large size. A row of tubercles encircle the whorls along the shoulder. The exterior surface is almost smooth, except very shallowly sculptured, spiral threads. The siphon is a little elongated, and slightly curved. This has no umbilicus. The shell is entirely white. Distribution: south of central Honshû, at 10–20 fathoms depth.

PLATE **27**

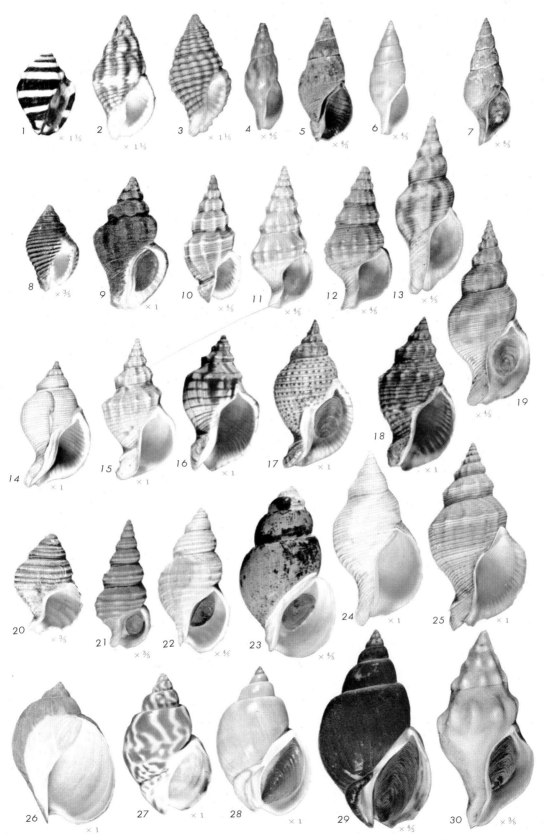

1   × 1⅕

2   × 1⅕

3   × 1⅕

4   × ⅘

5   × ⅘

6   × ⅘

7   × ⅘

8   × ⅗

9   × 1

10   × ⅘

11   × ⅘

12   × ⅘

13   × ⅘

14   × 1

15   × 1

16   × 1

17   × 1

18   × 1

19   × ⅘

20   × ⅗

21   × ⅗

22   × ⅘

23   × ⅘

24   × 1

25   × 1

26   × 1

27   × 1

28   × 1

29   × ⅘

30   × ⅗

PLATE 28

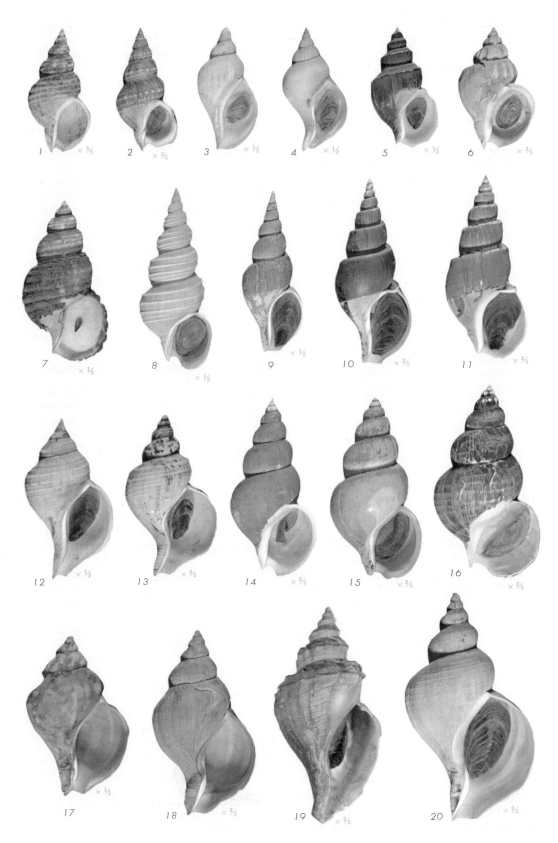

Family Buccinidae (2)

1. Buccinum leucostoma (LISCHKE)

This is one of the typical whelks having a tall and approximately conical spire. The roundly inflated whorls bear 3–4 prominent spiral ridges near the shoulder, while the basal part of body whorl is also encircled by finer ribs. The ribs are crossed by growth lines, which are partly faint and partly distinct on the outer surface. The posterior half of outer lip is slightly reflexed. The anterior canal is wide and short, and the umbilicus is not seen. It is white in color. Distribution: south of central Honshû, 30–50 fathoms in depth.

2. Buccinum glaciale LINNÉ

The spire is taller than that of the preceding species. Strong spiral ribs, surrounding the periphery of whorls, numbers 3 on the last whorl, and 2 on others. The ribs bear small tubercles, where they are crossed by growth lines. The spaces between and outside the ribs densely bear fine spiral threads. The outer lip margin is somewhat reflexed, and a columellar plait is seen. The outer surface is light brown in its color. Distribution: north of Hokkaidô, as deep as 100–150 fathoms.

3. Volutopsius middendorffi DALL

The body whorl is large in its proportion to the spire. The apical part with a large protoconch looks like a papilla in shape. The shell is smooth over its exterior surface, being marked only by growth lines. The aperture is elliptic, and the columellar end is truncated. The outer lip is neither thickened nor reflexed. Distribution: north of northeastern Honshû, at 100–150 fathoms depth.

4. Neptunea fukueae KIRA

This is a pretty whelk, with the somewhat transparent shell texture and light flesh-colored, smooth surface. This has a small and pointed spire, and a large, inflated body whorl. Only the earlier whorls bear faint spiral threads. The outer lip is not reflexed, and the anterior canal is moderately long and curved. The operculum is elliptic, with a nucleus situated anteriorly. The shell lacks the umbilicus. Distribution: Tosa Bay of Shikoku, at about 100 fathoms depth.

5. Ancistrolepis (Clinopegma) unicus (PILSBRY)

The spire is turreted, and its surface is encircled by two prominent ribs, one on the angled shoulder of whorls like a keel, and another between the former rib and the suture. The interspace between the two ribs is somewhat depressed. The base of body whorl also bears 6–7 spiral striae, and weak growth lines cover the entire surface. The outer lip margin is not reflexed. The anterior canal is wide and short. This is white in color, but is coated with a brown epiderm. Distribution: northeastern Honshû and farther north, 50–100 fathoms deep.

6. Buccinum schantaricum (MIDDENDORFF)

The shelly tube is roundly inflated, and bears wave-like folds along the periphery. The outer surface is only faintly sculptured by spiral striae, and looks almost smooth. The outer lip margin is reflexed in its posterior half. The anterior canal is broad and short, and the umbilicus is not seen. The epiderm covering the light flesh-colored surface is readily denuded. The aperture is orange-yellow inside, and closed by an oval operculum. Distribution: north of Hokkaidô, at 10–20 fathoms depth.

7. Ancistrolepis fujitai KURODA

This thin shell has a tall spire and well inflated whorls. The suture is deeply sunken. The surface is covered by thick spiral ribs, of which the number is about 12 on the body whorl, and 5 on other whorls. The aperture is large and round, containing a broad and short canal. The margin of outer lip become neither thickened nor reflexed. The degenerate operculum is very small. It is white all over the surface, under the cover of a yellowish brown epiderm. Distribution: north of northeastern Honshû, as deep as 50–100 fathoms.

8. Buccinum isaotakii KIRA

The spire of this neat shell is very tall,

[PLATE 28]   Buccinidae

and deeply constricted at the suture. The shell is comparatively thin in texture, and bears over its surface prominent spiral cords, which number 5–7 on the body whorl. Fine spiral ribs are also seen on the basal part of the shell. The interspaces between the cords are densely marked by very fine reticulate sculptures. The posterior half of outer lip is reflexed. A short canal is notched at the anterior end of aperture. This is pure white outside, and is often orange-yellow inside the aperture. The operculum is very thin, and oval in its outline, having a nucleus nearly at the center. Distribution: the same with the preceding species.

9. Beringius (Japelion) adelphicus (DALL)

This is a slender and spindle-shaped whelk that has a tall, pointed spire. A deep and narrow groove encircles the spire along the suture, from the apex till the posterior end of outer lip. The surface faintly bears spiral and growth striae. The aperture is elliptic, and closed by a brown operculum, with a nucleus at its posterior end. The outer lip is not reflexed. The exterior of the shell is white in color, but is usually covered by a light yellowish brown epiderm. Distribution: Pacific coasts of Honshû and Shikoku, 50–100 fathoms deep.

10. Beringius (Japelion) pericochlion (SCHRENCK)

The shell resembles the last species in its structure, but this is broader in outline, and the epiderm is dark brown. The spiral furrow along the suture is wider than that of the last species, being bordered by a steep ridge. Distribution: north of northeastern Honshû, at 50–100 fathoms in depth.

11. Beringius (Japelion) hirasei (PILSBRY)

This is very close to the preceding species in its appearance, but the whorls are slightly less inflated, and piled stepwise into a tall spire. The border of the spiral furrow is even more acutely ridged than that of the preceding species. The anterior canal is especially wide. Distribution: the same with the preceding species.

12. Neptunea kurosio OYAMA

As compared with the species of *Buccinum*, *Ancistrolepis* or *Beringius*, the shells of this genus have a smaller spire and much larger body whorl. On the outer surface of this shell, spiral ribs of different thickness cross with fine longitudinal threads, forming a rather feeble reticulate sculpture. The outer lip is slightly reflexed, and the anterior canal is moderately elongated. The white or pinky surface bears a dirty brown epiderm. Distribution: south of Hokkaidô, 40–100 fathoms deep.

13. Neptunea intersculpta (SOWERBY)

The outline of this shell is similar to that of *N. kurosio*, but this has a light brown surface color, and a broader siphon. The outer surface is reticulately sculptured by longitudinal growth lines and spiral ribs, of which a few on the shoulder are the most prominent. As in other species of this family, this shell is often orange-yellow inside the aperture. The flesh is delicious. Distribution: south of Hokkaidô, at 50–100 fathoms depth.

14. Buccinum bayani (JOUSSEAUME)

This shell is thin, and has the well inflated whorls. The surface is apparently smooth, bearing very fine threads both longitudinally and spirally. The aperture is elliptic, containing a broad and short canal at its anterior end, and margined by the reflexed outer lip. A brown epiderm covers its exterior surface. It is also known for its delicious flesh. Distribution: Japan Sea coasts of northeastern Honshû, as deep as 300 fathoms.

15. Buccinum striatissimum SOWERBY

This shell is almost the same with the preceding species in outline, but this is somewhat thicker, and white in color, and bears a dirty gray epiderm over the outer surface. The flesh is edible. Distribution: Japan Sea coasts, along the central and western parts of Honshû, 50–200 fathoms deep.

16. Buccinum tenuissimum IW. TAKI

Resembling the preceding two species in shape, this is larger and thin in texture. The exterior is coated by a greenish brown epiderm. The flesh is admired as the most delicious of all Japanese molluscs. This species lives in the bathyal zone of Toyama Bay, 300–400 fathoms deep, where it is caught by a kind of bamboo basket, containing some baits and sunken deep to the very bottom with a long rope.

17. Neptunea (Barbitonia) arthritica (BERNARDI)

The shelly tube of this shell is expanded at the shoulder part, on which a row of tubercles encircle the whorls. The tubercles, however, differ individually in the degree of their development, and the individuals without such tubercles are sometimes observed. The outer surface bears faint spiral threads and growth lines. The outer lip is not reflexed, and the anterior canal is comparatively short and wide. This is entirely purplish brown. Distribution: north of Hokkaidô, 50–100 fathoms deep.

18. Neptunea middendorffi MACGINITIE

This shell is very thick and heavy. The exterior surface is almost smooth, only with feeble spiral threads and growth lines. The margin of outer lip does not become thickened. This is fleshy brown in color. Distribution: the same with the preceding species.

19. Neptunea lyrata (GMELIN)

The shell is fairly thick, and has a spire somewhat taller than that of *N. middendorffi*. Erect, fin-like, longitudinal folds develop on the outer surface. Spiral ribs are indistinct. Distribution: the same with the preceding two species.

20. Neptunea intersculpta constricta (DALL)

This shell is thinner in texture than the above species, and the spire is constricted at the suture between the well inflated whorls. The surface is densely sculptured by fine spiral threads. The color of the shell is light fleshy. This and the above species both possess edible flesh. Distribution: north of central Honshû, 30–100 fathoms in depth.

[PLATE 29]   Pyrenidae, Nassariidae

Family Pyrenidae

The shells of this family are small and thick, and mostly of a spindle-shape. The spire is short, and the lips of narrow aperture are denticulate. The outer surface is usually coated with an epiderm. The operculum is corneous, and very minute. A considerable number of species is included in this group.

1. Mitrella bicinata (GOULD)

This shell is extremely various in its size and surface coloration. Only three kinds of different coloration are illustrated here. The tiny shell is spindle-shaped, and covered by a soft epiderm. The exterior is almost smooth, except some spiral lines on the basal part of the shell. The anterior part of outer lip is slightly expanded outward. Both lip margins bear fine, tooth-like folds. Distribution: all over Japan south of Hokkaidô, near the tide line.

2. Pyrene (Sundamitrella) impolita (SOWERBY)

The shell is also spindle-shaped, tapering on both ends. The smooth surface is only slightly sculptured by longitudinal folds near the apex, and also by spiral threads on the basal part of body whorl. Both lips are minutely toothed. This is brown all over the outer surface. Distribution: south of Honshû, below the tide line.

3. Anachis misera (SOWERBY)

A short and fusiform shell, longitudinally bearing fold-like ridges on each whorl. Only a few threads encircle the basal part. The inner lip margin alone is toothed. The outer surface is brown, and the longitudinal folds bear white and brown bars on their posterior and anterior halves, respectively. Distribution: the same with the above species.

4. Mitrella bella (REEVE)

The shell is slenderly fusiform, with a tall spire. The margin of aperture is minutely dentate on both lips, and the anterior canal is short. The outer surface is fasciated by brown on the white background. Distribution: the same with the preceding two species.

5. Pyrene testudinaria tylerae (GRIFFITH et PIDGEON)

This is like a fat-spindle in shape, and is smooth all over its exterior. The lips bear tooth-like processes. The white ground color of outer surface is covered by a network of brown, which sometimes looks like the grain of wood. Distribution: south of Honshû, in subtidal zone.

6. Euplica turturina (LAMARCK)

The outline is almost globular. The spire is small, but pointed. The inner lip margin bears 2 rows of minute teeth on its posterior part, while the outer lip is simply toothed. The smooth, light brown surface is marked by a spiral zone of white spots. This is beautifully reddish purple inside the aperture. Distribution: south of central Honshû, below the tide line.

7. Euplica versicolor (SOWERBY)

The shell is a little larger than the preceding species, with the taller spire and tapering anterior end. The whorls are most widely inflated at the shoulder. The surface is quite smooth, and white in ground color, bearing irregular patterns of brown. Both lips bear teeth on their inside margins. Distribution: the same with the preceding species.

8. Pyrene flava (BRUGUIÈRE)

Though the shell closely resembles *P. testudinaria tylerae*, this differs from the latter species in the following characters. The body whorl tapers more sharply toward the anterior end; large, white blotches are seen on the surface; the epiderm is somewhat thinner; the operculum bears brown spots; and, the inside of aperture is colored in light purple. Distribution: south of Honshû, below the tide line.

9. Mitrella tenuis (GASKOIN)

This is also close to *P. testudinaria tylerae* in its appearance, but the spire is

79

taller, and the lip margins are devoid of teeth. Irregular brown blotches are marked on the white ground color. Distribution: south of Hokkaidô, below the tide line.

10. Pyrene punctata (Bruguière)

This is one of the largest shells in this group. The spire is very small, as compared with the well developed body whorl. The shell reaches its maximum width at the shoulder of body whorl, tapering anteriorly. The surface of spire is marked by white spots as those seen in *P. flava*, whereas the body whorl is covered by a brown network. The inside of aperture is reddish purple, and contains fine teeth. Distribution: southern Honshû and south wards, in subtidal zone.

Family Nassariidae

These basket shells are of small or medium size, mostly thick, and oval or conical in outline. The spire is pointed, and moderately tall. A wide callus extends from the inner lip margin over the columella. The aperture is elliptic, and its margin is deeply notched at the end of the short anterior canal. The operculum is horny. The rear end of the foot of these animals is characteristically forked. This family comprises a fairly large number of species.

11. Reticunassa dermestina (Gould)

A common basket shell of small size, with a tall spire. Each whorl bears numerous longitudinal ridges, crossed by fine spiral threads. The shell is light yellow without any color patterns. Distribution: south of Honshû, below the tide line.

R. fratercula (Dunker) is a related species having a somewhat smaller shell, with black, spiral bands.

12. Reticunassa acutidentata (Smith)

This is a little larger than the preceding species. The whorls are well inflated, and the number of longitudinal ridges are less than those of *R. dermestina*. This is surrounded by light brown bands on the yellowish surface. Distribution: the same with *R. dermestina*.

13. Reticunassa japonica (A. Adams)

The shell is rather thin, and has a fairly tall spire. The outer surface, with its feeble lustre, is like a silk cloth, being densely covered by minute granules formed by the intersection of spiral threads with longitudinal ridges. The number of the longitudinal ridges is about 20 per whorl. The inner lip bears a plait near its posterir end, and the outer lip margin is striated inside. A brown band encircles the whorls on its light brown surface. Distribution: central Honshû and farther south, below the tide line.

14. Reticunassa hiradoensis (Pilsbry)

This is larger than the last species, and consists of more inflated whorls. The surface sculpture is coarser. The longitudinal ridges number about 15 on each whorl. The structure of aperture is similar to that of the last species, but the exterior surface is not glossy at all. Distribution: south of Honshû, in subtidal zone.

15. Varicinassa varicifera (A. Adams)

Among the basket shells, this species is exceptional in having prominent varices on its outer surface, which alternately occur on the opposite sides of the shell, ending in the thickened outer lip. The spire is tall and slender. The surface sculpture is not reticulate, as the weak spiral threads are interrupted by longitudinal ridges. The gound color is white, and usually marked by 3 broad, spiral bands of brown. Distribution: south of central Honshû, below the tide line.

16. Zeuxis caelatus (A. Adams)

As compared with the preceding species, the spire of this shell is lower, and the body whorl is much inflated. Fine longitudinal ridges are crossed by spiral threads on the outer surface, and their intersection points bear weak and fine granules. A thick rib encircles the whorls just below the suture. The inner lip bears a plait near its posterior end, and the outer lip margin is striated inside. This is also marked by brown, spiral bands on the exterior surface. Distribution: south of Honshû, 5–10 fathoms deep.

[PLATE 29]   Pyrenidae, Nassariidae

17. Niotha livescens (PHILIPPI)

The body whorl is even more inflated than that of the preceding species. The granules on the surface are coarse and well developed, especially on the dorsal side of body whorl. The parietal callus is broad and thick. The outer lip bears strong striations on its inside. Distribution: south of Honshû, from the tide line to 5 fathoms depth.

18. Hinia festiva (POWYS)

The longitudinal ridges and surface granules are larger and coarser than those of the preceding species. The outer lip is also thicker, but the parietal callus is rather poorly developed. Distribution: the same with the preceding species.

19. Niotha clathrata (LAMARCK)

The outline of this shell is very fat, owing to the remarkable expansion of the last whorl. Among the well developed granules arranged on longitudinal ridges, those on the shoulder part of whorls are especially large and prominent. The callus on the columella expands widely. Distribution: south of Honshû, 5–10 fathoms deep.

20. Zeuxis zonalis (A. ADAMS)

The exterior surface is smooth, except some sculptures on the apical and basal parts of the shell. A spiral row of granules is also seen immediately below the suture. The white surface is encircled by 3 color bands of dark brown. Distribution: south of Kyûshû, below the tide line.

21. Zeuxis kiiensis KIRA

The surface of this shell is almost smooth on the last two whorls, except some threads encircling the basal part, but earlier whorls are finely sculptured both spirally and longitudinally on their exterior. Besides the striations on its inner side, the outer lip bears a few, small and radiating spines near the posterior end of its margin. The shell is either plainly colored in light purplish brown or marked by 2 spiral zones of light brown. Distribution: Pacific side of central Honshû, at 10–20 fathoms depth.

22. Alectrion sufflatus (GOULD)

Resembling the preceding species, this is somewhat broader in its outline. The surface sculpture is restricted to the apical and basal parts of the shell. The outer lip is thickened like a varix, but the structure of aperture is not different from that of the preceding species. Brown spots are arranged in a row along the suture, and the rest of outer surface is irregularly spotted with brown. The outer lip margin laterally bears fine brown lines on its outside. Distribution: central Honshû and farther south, 5–10 fathoms deep.

23. Nassarius coronatus (BRUGUIÈRE)

The surface is mostly smooth and glossy. In addition to fine sculptures near the apex and the base, this bears a row of tubercles on each whorl, which becomes paticularly prominent on the shoulder of the last whorl. The margin of aperture has the structure similar to those of the foregoing two species, but the parietal callus is very thick. This is chestnut-brown or gray-brown on the outer surface, and is encircled by a dark brown band on the middle part of whorls. Distribution: south of Amami Islands, from the tide line down to 5 fathoms.

24. Zeuxis velatus (GOULD)

This looks like Z. zonalis in its appearance, but the shell is faintly marked by spiral threads even on the surface of the last two whorls. The row of granules along the suture only very weakly develops. This is entirely dark brown or yellowish brown, and bears a spiral row of light colored spots immediately below the suture line. Distribution: Amami Islands and southwards, near the tide line.

25. Zeuxis dorsatus [RÖDING]

The shell is thick and heavy in construction. The surface of body whorl is smooth on its posterior and middle parts, whereas the rest of the shell exterior is sculptured as in other species of this genus. A groove runs along the suture on its anterior side. The aperture resembles that of N. coronatus in its structure, but the parietal callus only poorly develops. It is purplish brown all

PLATE 29

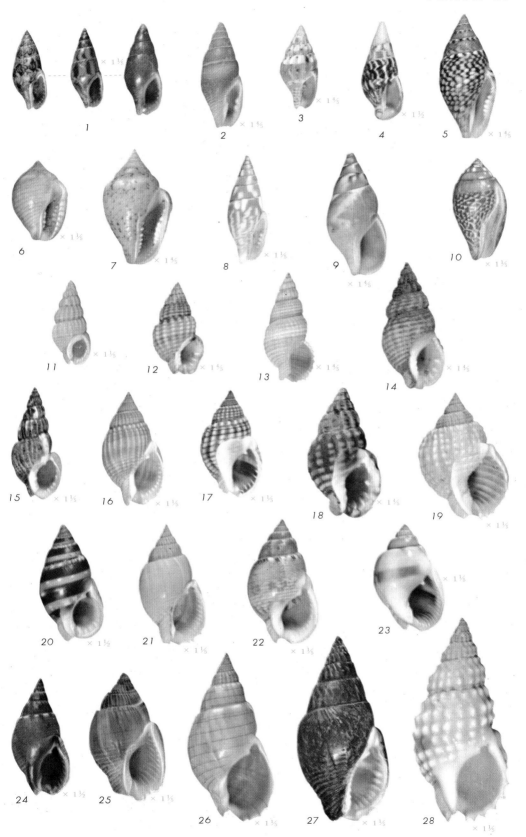

PLATE 30

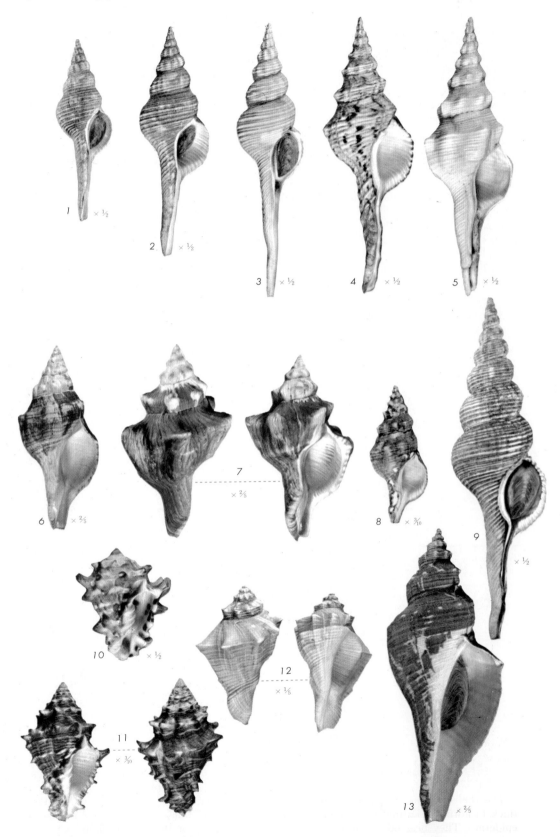

1 × ½

2 × ½

3 × ½

4 × ½

5 × ½

6 × ⅖

7

× ⅖

8 × 3/10

9

× ½

10 × ½

11

× 3/10

12

× ⅕

13 × ⅖

over the surface. Distribution: south of the Rykyus, in subtidal zone.

26. Alectrion glans (LINNÉ)

This shell is moderately large, but is thinner than the preceding species. Only earlier whorls bear sculptures, the last two whorls remaining smooth and lustrous on their surface. A plait occurs at the end of inner lip, while the outer lip lacks inside striations. The purplish brown surface is encircled by 8 fine lines of golden brown, respectively reaching the small spines on the margin of outer lip. Distribution: central Honshû and farther south, at 5–10 fathoms depth.

27. Zeuxis olivaceus (BRUGUIÈRE)

A large and thick shell, dark chestnut brown all over the surface. The shell structure generally resembles that of *Z. dorsatus.* The spire is, however, somewhat taller, and the posterior canal is fairly well developed. Distribution: south of the Ryukyus, between the tide line and 5 fathoms depth.

28. Alectrion papillosus (LINNÉ)

This is the largest of all the Japanese basket shells. The spire is tall, and the outer surface is covered by large, round tubercles, regularly arranged in decussate rows. The outer lip is not striated inside, and bears radiating spines on the anterior half of its margin. The shell is glossy china-white all over the surface, sometimes with large and isolated blotches of light brown, and the apical part bears a pinkish hue. Distribution: south of Amami Islands, 2–10 fathoms in depth.

[PLATE 30]

Family Fasciolariidae (1)

The shells of this spindle shell family are thick, fusiform in outline, and coated with an epiderm. They bear no varices on the outer surface. A long siphon develops at the anterior end of aperture, which often contains columellar plaits. The operculum is horny and considerably thick. Some of the species are caught for their edible flesh.

[PLATE 30]   Fasciolariidae, Vasidae, Busyconidae

1. Fusinus ferrugineus (KURODA et HABE)

This shell is hardly distinguishable from the next species in its shape and structure. But the size is distinctly smaller, being 90 mm (height) ×35 mm (maximum diameter) in normal size. Its habitat is completely separated from that of *F. perplexus*, never living together. The shell is sometimes wrapped by living sponges, when alive.

2. Fusinus perplexus (A. ADAMS)

The shell is 130 mm×45 mm in normal size. The outline is slenderly fusiform, with its tall spire and a very long siphon, almost 1/3 as long as the total length of shell. Coarse spiral ribs of uneven thickness cover the surface of whorls and siphon, occasionally bearing tubercles at the middle part of the shell. Longitudinal folds seen on earlier whorls disappear on the surface of later whorls. This is entirely covered by a yellowish brown, velvet-like epiderm on the white outer surface, usually marked by brown bands or spots. The nucleus of the elliptic operculum is situated anteriorly. The flesh of this mollusc is cinnabar-colored and edible. Distribution: south of Honshû, at 10–20 fathoms depth.

3. Fusinus longicaudus (LAMARCK)

This has a rather long siphon, reaching one-half of the whole shell in its length. The spire is taller and more slender than that of the preceding species. Spiral ribs on the exterior surface are more or less of even thickness. The apex is tipped with feeble pink. Distribution: south of central Honshû, at 10–20 fathoms depth.

4. Fusinus nicobaricus (LAMARCK)

The shell is somewhat like the preceding species in shape, but is more sturdy and thick. The long siphon is slightly curved. The shoulder of whorls is angled, bearing tubercles. Spiral ribs are thick. The parietal callus is reflexed, and the inner side of outer lip bears distinct striations, which terminate in short spines along the outer lip margin. The outer surface is longitudinally marked by brown, zigzag patterns against the white background. The epiderm lacks hairs. Distribution: southern Honshû and southwards, at 10–20 fathoms depth.

5. Fusinus undatus similis (BAIRD)

The exterior surface is plainly china-white in color, and polished with feeble lustre, and bears a row of tubercles on the slightly angled shoulder of whorls. The siphon is not so long, and tapers gradually toward its anterior end. Distribution: rarely found in southern Honshû and farther south, 10–20 fathoms deep.

6. Pleuroploca trapezium audouini (JONAS)

The shell is stout and thick. The siphon is shorter than those of the foregoing species of *Fusinus*. The slightly angled shoulder of whorls is tuberculated. But for some threads surrounding the basal part of body whorl, the surface is smooth. This is light flesh-brown in ground color, and encircled by many fine brown lines. The epiderm is brown and thin. The margin of aperture is deep brown, bearing striations on the inside of outer lip. Distribution: south of central Honshû, at 10–20 fathoms depth.

7. Pleuroploca trapezium (LINNÉ)

This differs from the preceding subspecies in the more inflated body whorl and the very strong tubercles on the shoulder of whorls. Other features are the same in both forms, which respectively represent the northern and southern races of the same species. Distribution: south of Shikoku, at 10–20 fathoms depth.

8. Fusinus nigrirostratus (SMITH)

The whorls are tuberculated on their shoulder, and covered by fine, spiral ribs. The inside margin of outer lip bears striations. This is dark brown on the outer surface, but is white inside the aperture. Distribution: south of Honshû, 10–20 fathoms depth.

9. Fusinus forceps (PERRY)

This is the largest form of the spindle shells in Japan, reaching 160 mm or more in length. Both the spire and siphon are much elongated. Only earlier whorls are longitudinally ridged on the surface. Spiral ribs covering the entire surface tend to form thick ridges in groups of 2-3 rows. The anterior end of the parietal callus is isolated from the columella. The outer lip margin becomes wavy, owing to the spiral furrows sculptured on its inside. Distribution: southern Honshû and southwards, at 10-30 fathoms depth.

Family Vasidae

This is a small group, represented by only two species in Japan. These shells are very thick and heavy, bearing sturdy, spiny processes along the spiral ribs on their surface. A few plaits are seen on the columella. The operculum is horny and hook-shaped.

10.   Vasum turbinellus (LINNÉ)

The spire is low, and the large body whorl sharply tapers anteriorly. The body whorl is surrounded by 3 rows of thick, horn-like spines, of which the uppermost one extends on earlier whorls. Two spiral rows of low tubercles are also seen respectively on each side of the most anterior row of spines. The elongated aperture contains 4 plaits, nearly horizontally carved on the columella. Black, encircling bands between spiral ribs on the surface are usually obscured by calcareous sediments. Distribution: south of Amami Islands, below the tide line.

11.   Vasum ceramicus (LINNÉ)

This species has a larger shell, with a taller spire. Thick spiral ribs bearing shparly pointed spines alternate with a few finer ribs. The columella bears 3 strong plaits, sometimes with additional, interven-

ing folds. The surface is marked by dark brown blotches. Distribution: south of the Ryukyus, 5-10 fathoms in depth.

Family Busyconidae

These shells are moderately or very large in size, and covered by a soft epiderm. The aperture is large, containing a wide and long anterior canal. The outer lip margin is simple, and not thickened. The number of species is few.

12.   Pugilina (Hemifusus) tuba (GMELIN)

This is a very large shell. The spire is low, while the body whorl is large and elongated anteriorly, enveloping a wide anterior canal. The whorls are carinated at the shoulder, on which sharply pointed tubercles sparsely develop. The outer surface is covered by fine spiral ribs, under the soft, velvet-like epiderm. The outer lip margin is thin and acute. This is plainly light flesh on the exterior, and orange-yellow inside the aperture, while the epiderm is yellowish brown. This species seems to be an open-sea form of the next species seen in calm waters. Sometimes, intermediate or transitional forms between the two are observed. Distribution: central Honshû and southwards, at 10-20 fathoms depth.

13.   Pugilina (Hemifusus) ternatana (GMELIN)

This form can be distinguished from the above species by the taller spire and the weaker development of tubercles on the shoulder of whorls. The tubercles even disappear in some specimens. The flesh of these two species are edible. Distribution: south of Honshû, at 15-30 fathoms depth.

[PLATE 31] Fasciolariidae

Family Fasciolariidae (2)

1. Fusinus (Simplicifusus) hyphalus (M. SMITH)

A small, slender, spindle shell, inhabiting deep seas. Longitudinal ridges are apparent on the surface of earlier whorls, but they weaken gradually toward the aperture until they disappear on the last whorl. The surface is crossed by dense spiral ribs and growth lines, showing irregular, decussate sculptures. The aperture is simple in its structure, and the long siphon is slightly curved. The shell is entirely light yellow. Distribution: south of central Honshû, as deep as 100–150 fathoms.

2. Fusinus (Simplicifusus) simplex (SMITH)

This is discriminated from the above species in the following characters. The longitudinal ridges on the outer surface are distinctly marked even on the last whorl, and bear small granules where they are crossed by fine spiral ribs. Distribution: the same with the above species.

3. Granulifusus kiranus SHUTO

The siphon is comparatively shorter and wider than that of the preceding two species. The granules on longitudinal ridges are coarse. The operculum is yellowish, and much smaller than the opening of aperture. This shell is light pinkish brown all over. Distribution: the same with the preceding two species.

4. Granulifusus nipponicus (SMITH)

This species is separated from Gr. kiranus by the smaller size of the shell, rounded shoulder, somewhat slender siphon, and larger number of surface granules. Longitudinal ridges bear brown tone. The operculum is small, and brown in color. Distribution: south of central Honshû, at 30–50 fathoms depth.

5. Fusinus gemmuliferus KIRA

This is a medium-sized spindle shell, sculptured all over its surface by many fine longitudinal ridges. One in every several spiral threads is thicker than others. The surface sculpture thus produced is coarsely reticulate. The spire is fairly well constricted at the suture. This is wholly yellowish white. Distribution: Pacific sides of Honshû and Shikoku, at 30–40 fathoms depth.

6. Fusinus crassiplicatus KIRA

The spire is very tall and slender. Longitudinal ridges are strongly and thickly sculptured on every whorl, while fine spiral ribs are deeply carved. The very long siphon is thick at the base, tapering anteriorly. The parietal callus is reflexed, and its anterior end is isolated from the columella. Distribution: Pacific coasts of southern Honshû, 40–50 fathoms depth.

7. Fusinus colus (LINNÉ)

This shell is characterized by the slenderness of the spire and siphon, and by the comparatively thick longitudinal ridges. Though an immature specimen of F. longicaudus is often misidentified with this species, this has the broader shell and siphon, and thicker ridges. Distribution: south of Amami Islands, 10–20 fathoms deep.

8. Peristernia nassatula (LAMARCK)

This thick shell is spindle-shaped, tapering on both ends. Thick and round ridges, longitudinally crossing each whorl, are about 10 in number, and intersect with fine threads which densely cover the outer surface. The anterior canal is short. Two or three plaits on the columella are deeply situated within the aperture. This is dirty white outside, with an encircling band of light brown, and reddish purple inside the aperture. The exterior is, however, usually stained by calcareous sediments. Distribution: Amami Islands and farther south, below the tide line.

9. Peristernia sulcata luchuana PILSBRY

Resembling the preceding species, this has a taller spire, and the longitudinal ridges are less in number. The inside of aperture is orange-yellow, and the anterior end of the shell is dark purple. The columellar plaits, 2–3 in number, are so deeply situated within the aperture that they are almost invisible from the outside. Distribution: the same with the preceding species.

10. Cantharus wagneri (ANTON)

This is a species of Buccinidae, inserted here by mistake (see Plate 27). Distribution: south of Amami Islands, below the tide line.

11. Dolicholatirus acus (REEVE)

This is a small and very slender shell, resembling the species of *Fusinus* in its outline. The very tall spire comprises as many as 12 whorls. The outer surface bears longitudinal ridges (about 8 in the number per whorl) and fine spiral threads. The tapering anterior canal is three times as long as the the aperture. The columella bears a fold in the deep interior of aperture, which can not be seen without destroying the shell. The color of outer surface is plainly yellowish brown. Distribution: south of southern Honshû, 50–100 fathoms in depth.

12. Benimakia rhodostoma (DUNKER)

The shell is narrow spindle-shaped, with a fairly long canal on its anterior end. Each whorl is sculptured by 6–7 longitudinal ridges, and by deeply carved spiral ribs. The columellar plait is hidden behind the inner lip margin. This is orange-yellow on its exterior, while the inside of aperture is colored red. Distribution: southwestern islands of Kyûshû and farther south, in subtidal zone.

13. Latirus (Latirulus) turritus (GMELIN)

In comparison with the tall spire, the aperture and anterior canal are short. Indistinct and low longitudinal ridges sparsely run across the surface of whorls. Each spiral ribs bear black lines, distinctly marked against the yellowish brown ground color. Besides 4 plaits on the columella, the inner lip bears another fold on its posterior end. The inside of aperture is orange-yellow. Distribution: south of Amami Islands, between the tide line and 5 fathoms depth.

14. Latirus (Latirulus) nagasakiensis SMITH

This looks like the preceding species in its outline, but is entirely dark brown on the outside. Longitudinal ridges are more prominent, and spiral ribs are denser. There is a slit between the anterior canal and fasciole. The aperture is fleshy brown inside. Distribution: central Honshû and southwards, at 10–20 fathoms depth.

15. Latirus craticulatus (LINNÉ)

This shell resembles *L. nagasakiensis*. Spiral ribs on the surface are, however, less in number, and the coloration is lighter. The columellar plaits are easily visible from the outside. Distribution: southwestern islands of Kyûshû, below the tide line down to 5 fathoms.

16. Latirus recurvirostrum (SCHUBERT et WAGNER)

A thick, spindle-shaped shell, with a long siphon and a well developed fasciole. The whorls longitudinally bear prominent, tubercle-like ridges, 8 in the number per whorl. Where the ridges and coarse spiral ribs intersect, dark brown spots are marked on the fleshy brown outer surface. The siphon is broad and almost tubular. The umbilicus is open at the end of the fasciole, encircled by the expanding wall. The columellar plaits are hidden. Distribution: southern Honshû along the Pacific, 10–20 fathoms deep.

17. Latirus polygonus (GMELIN)

As compared with that of the preceding species, the anterior canal of this shell is thicker, shorter and not tubular. The umbilicus opens like a slit. The columellar plaits are situated in the interior of the aperture, but are easily visible. The brown coloration is darker than in *L. recurvirostrum*. The horny operculum is very thick. Distribution: south of Amami Islands, 5–10 fathoms deep.

18. Latirus belcheri (REEVE)

The anterior canal is even shorter than that of the preceding species. The columellar plaits can be seen from the outside. Dark

[PLATE 31]   Fasciolariidae

brown blotches cover the outer surface in mosaic. The apex is tipped with pink. Distribution : the Ryukyus and farther south, 5–10 fathoms deep.

19.   *Latirolagena smaragdula* (LINNÉ)

This shell is very thick, heavy, and of very fat spindle-shape. The exterior surface lacks longitudinal ridges, and is ornamented by fine, black-colored spiral ribs all over the gray background. The anterior canal is very short, and the plaits are apparent on the columella. Like all species of *Latirus*, the inside of outer lip of this shell is finely striated. Distribution : south of the Ryukyus, below the tide line down to 5 fathoms.

PLATE 31

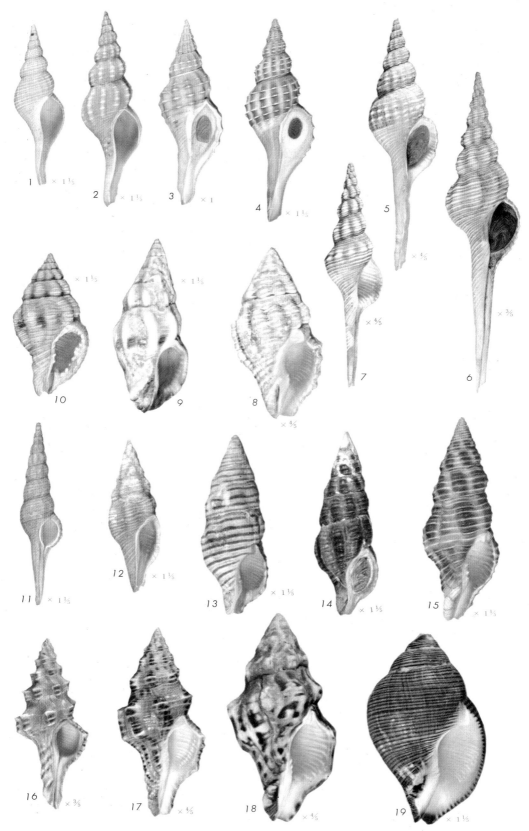

1   × 1⅕
2   × 1⅕
3   × 1
4   × 1⅕
5   × ⅘
6   × ⅗
7   × ⅘
8   × ⅘
9   × 1⅕
10   × 1⅕
11   × 1⅕
12   × 1⅕
13   × 1⅕
14   × 1⅕
15   × 1⅕
16   × ⅗
17   × ⅘
18   × ⅘
19   × 1⅕

PLATE 32

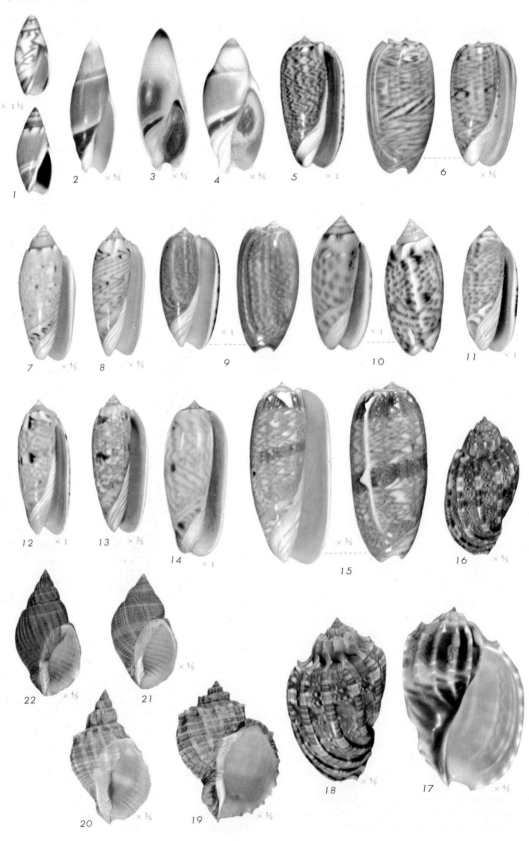

1   × 1 ⅕

2   × ⅘

3   × ⅘

4   × ⅘

5   × 1

6   × ⅘

7   × ⅘

8   × ⅘

9   × 1

10   × 1

11   × 1

12   × 1

13   × ⅗

14   × 1

15   × ⅗

16   × ⅘

22   × ⅘

21   × ⅘

20   × ⅗

19   × ⅗

18   × ⅘

17   × ⅘

Family Olividae (1)

This family includes spindle- or cylinder-shaped shells of various sizes. The spire is low or flat, while the body whorl is very large, usually occupying a greater part of the total shell length. The outer surface lacks the epiderm and is wholly covered by a beautifully shining callus. The anterior part of body whorl is surrounded by a fasciole or an elevated spiral zone. The aperture is longitudinally elongated and narrow, and terminates in a deep oblique notch at its anterior end. The operculum is horny in some species, but is absent in others. The animal lives in bottom sand of shallow waters, where the shell is almost covered by its large soft body. A number of species are found in warm seas. The lovely shells are favored by collectors, and are used for ornamentation. See also Plate 71.

1. Olivella japonica PILSBRY

This is a small spindle-shaped shell, composed of about 7 whorls and is about 20 mm in length. The spire is pointed and short. The body whorl is about 3/4 as long as the total shell length. A narrow groove encircles the spire on the suture line. The outer lip of aperture is simple, and not thickened. The color of the smooth glossy surface is variable; some are marked by brown zigzag lines against the white background (illustrated above), whereas others are purple-colored with alternately white and purplish brown spots on the suture and fasciole (below). Distribution: central Honshû and farther south, below the tide line.

2. Turrancilla suavis (YOKOYAMA)

This is larger than the preceding species (about 50 mm in length). The pointed spire is almost hidden beneath a light purplish brown callus, except the earliest 2–3 whorls. The tube of these exposed initial whorls is entirely filled up by calcareous deposits. The last whorl is 2/3 as long as the shell length. The exterior surface is light brown in color, with a broad band of purplish brown just behind the fasciole. The operculum is linear and sward-like, and is greenish brown in color. This shell is different from the following two species in having the exposed and eroded apex, and in lacking a spiral furrow on the posterior part of fasciole. Distribution: Pacific coasts of central Honshû and southwards, at 80–100 fathoms depth.

3. Baryspira hinomotoensis (YOKOYAMA)

The shell is slightly smaller than the preceding species. The tall spire is wholly covered by a glossy callus, and the apex is pointed like a nipple. The length of aperture is less than one half of the shell length. The exterior surface is colored in brown, except the white callus on the ventral side of spire. There are two dark-colored bands encircling the base and the shoulder, while the coloration inbetween is lighter. The operculum is elongated elliptic in shape, has a nucleus near its front end, and almost fills up the opening of aperture. Distribution: Pacific coasts of central Honshû, 30–50 fathoms in depth.

4. Baryspira albocallosa (LISCHKE)

Resembling the above species in shape and coloration, this shell is much larger. Its spire is less tall, and the aperture extends more than one-half of the shell length. This can be distinguished from the above species by the blunt apex, and well inflated body whorl. The operculum is elliptic, somewhat expanded in its anterior part, and much smaller than the aperture. Distribution: central Honshû and farther south, at 30–50 fathoms depth.

5. Oliva mustelina LAMARCK

This has a cylindrical shape characteristic to the shells of this olive shell genus. The spire is very flat, with a pointed apex and the last whorl is 9/10 as long as the total length of the shell (about 40 mm). A narrow groove runs along the suture ending in the posterior canal of aperture. The glossy surface is longitudinally ornamented by a number of dark brown wavy lines on its light brown ground color, while the inside of aperture is violet-colored. A white callus on the inner lip bears many columellar folds. All species of Oliva described here lack the operculum. Distribution: south of central Honshû, in subtidal zone.

[PLATE 32]   Olividae, Harpidae, Cancellaridae

6. Oliva concavospira SOWERBY

This and the last species are alike in the shape of their shells, but this is larger in diameter, and has a characteristically sunken or concave spire. The sutural groove is mostly filled up by the surface callus, except in its last part. The color is lighter than that of *O. mustelina*, and the zigzag patterns are more sparse. The inside of aperture remains white. Distribution: south of Amami Islands, below the tide line.

7. Oliva (Neocylindrus) annulata intricata DAUTZENBERG

The spire is small, but is taller than those of the preceding two species. The body whorl somewhat tapers anteriorly. The sutural groove is distinct. This is light purplish brown in ground color, and is marked all over the surface by minute cloud patterns. The last whorl also bears brown dots just anteriorly to the suture and irregular short lines of dark brown on the fasciole. The inside color of aperture is orange. Distribution: south of the Ryukyus, in subtidal zone.

8. Oliva hirasei KIRA

This resembles the preceding species in general shape, except that the spire is lower. The body whorl bears brown zigzag patterns all over the light orange-brown background. Only the area just below the suture is devoid of the patterns. The inside of aperture is pure white. Distribution: southern Kyûshû and southwards, below the tide line.

9. Oliva elegans LAMARCK

This shell resembles *O. mustelina* in appearance. The gray surface is densely marked by longitudinal, grayish brown, wavy lines. It is also white inside the aperture. Distribution: south of Tanegashima of southern Kyûshû, in subtidal zone.

10. Oliva (Neocylindrus) annulata amethystina [RÖDING]

This is almost the same in shape with the subsp. *intricata* described above. The surface pattern consists of purplish brown dots more or less regularly arranged. Gray-white individuals bearing no patterns are often found. The inside of aperture is light orange in color. Distribution: Pacific coasts of Shikoku and farther south, in subtidal zone.

11. Oliva episcopalis LAMARCK

This is similar to the last species in appearance, but the body whorl is more inflated, and thick. The exterior surface is light brown in ground color, and is wholly covered by small brown dots, which often joint together into longitudinal lines. As in the last species, the dots tend to be darker in color along three spiral rows on the shoulder, central and basal part of body whorl. The inside of aperture is finely colored in violet. Distribution: southwestern part of Kyûshû and southwards, in subtidal zone.

12. Oliva ornata MARRAT

The shell is more slenderly shaped than the former species. The sutural groove is buried by the surface callus on earlier whorls. The fasciole is also covered and smoothed by the callus. There are light gray-brown reticulate patterns all over the light brown ground color, on which three spiral rows of darker brown spots are also seen. The inside of aperture bears light violet color. Distribution: south of Tanegashima, below the tide line.

13. Oliva miniacea [RÖDING]

This olive shell reaches about 70 mm in length. The spire is small, but acute. The sutural line is distinctly and deeply furrowed. The body whorl narrows toward its anterior end. The anterior canal is deeply notched and the lower part of parietal callus extends over the fasciole. Brown reticulate patterns cover the whole surface of light brown. It has also 3 rows of dark brown blots. The inside of aperture is orange-colored. Distribution: Pacific side of Shikoku and farther south, in subtidal zone.

14. Oliva miniacea porphystica MARRAT

This shell is a little smaller than the preceding form, being about 60 mm in length. The shape of the shell is similar to that of *O. miniacea*, but the fasciole is relatively wider. The patterns are deep purple in color. The inside of aperture is colored orange. Distribution: south of the Ryukyus, in subtidal zone.

15. Oliva sericea [RÖDING]

This splendid species is often more than 80 mm in the shell length. The color and shape resembles those of *O. miniacea*, but the body whorl tends to develop largely. Specimens lacking the orange color within the aperture are frequently found. Distribution: south of the Ryukyus, in subtidal zone.

Family Harpidae

These harp shells are large- or medium-sized, and are well known for their beauty. They have a small spire, large inflated body whorl and wide aperture. The whorls bear strong longitudinal ridges or varices over the exterior surface, which respectively terminate in a short spine at their posterior end. These varices are the traces of the thickened outer lip at different stages of their growth, so that the interval between them is variable, according to the changing rate of growth. A remarkable callus covers the columellar part, and extends over the ventral side of the last whorl. They lack the columellar folds, siphon and operculum. Only a few species are found in the Japanese Archipelago.

16. Harpa amouretta [RÖDING]

This medium-sized harp shell is nearly elliptic in its side view. It is about 45 mm in length. The spire is relatively tall, and the body whorl is not so well inflated as in the next species. The surface is dully shining. The space between longitudinal ridges are filled up by composite patterns of purplish brown and white. Spiral color bands of purplish brown and fine chocolate lines run intermittently over the ridges. The parietal callus extends over the spire. Distribution: Pacific side of Shikoku and southwards, in subtidal zone.

17. Harpa conoidalis LAMARCK

The shell is about twice as large as the preceding species in length. The body whorl is much expanded than in *H. amouretta*. The general structure and the pattern of coloration are, however, similar in both species. The protoconch is reddish purple in color. This has no spiral color lines on the surface of ridges. The callus of inner lip extends over the last three whorls. The ventral side of the last whorl bears two large blotches of dark brown color. Distribution: south of the Pacific coasts of Shikoku, at 2–5 fathoms depth.

18. Harpa nobilis [RÖDING]

This is somewhat smaller than *H. conoidalis*, and has a less inflated body whorl. It differs from the preceding species in the pink coloration of protoconch, in the presence of many small spines on the outer lip margin, and in having three blotches of purplish brown on the ventral side of the shell. Fine brown lines crossing the ridges, and pink color bands on the inter-rib spaces are also characteristic of this species. Distribution: south of the Ryukyus, in subtidal zone.

Family Cancellariidae

This family includes a relatively small number of Japanese species, having whelk-like shells of medium or small size. The shells bear strong folds on the columella, and lack the operculum. The animals are mostly devoid of the radula in their mouth.

19. Solatia nodulifera (SOWERBY)

This is one of the largest shells of this family, and reachs 60 mm in length and 45 mm in dameter. Each whorl bears a keel on its shoulder, while the suture is steeply sunken. The slope of spire is thus step-like. The outer surface is coarsely sculptured by a lattice-work of many spiral lines and thick longitudinal ribs, which end in tubercles on the shoulder line. The anterior end of the shell bears a fasciole. Three distinct folds are seen on the columella, and the inner margin of outer lip is marked by fine thread-like folds. Distribution: north-eastern Honshû and southwards, at 5–10 fathoms depth.

[PLATE 32]   Olividae, Harpidae, Cancellaridae

20.   *Sydaphera spengleriana* (DESHAYS)

This shell is nearly as large as the last species, and reaches 75 mm × 45 mm in size in northern parts of Honshû, but becomes smaller in southern localities, just as is the case with the last species. Its shape and surface structure are essentially similar to those of *Solatia nodulifera*, but the spire is taller and more slender, and the last whorl is less inflated. The color is light brown. Distribution: northeastern Honshû and farther south, at 5–10 fathoms depth.

21.   *Merica reeveana* (CROSSE)

A medium-sized shell, with roundly inflated whorls. Fine spiral and longitudinal threads cross over its surface. There are many fine thread-like sculptures on the inside of outer lip, and the columella bears 3 folds. The whorls are encircled by 3 broad, chestnut-colored bands on the light brown ground color. Distribution: central Honshû and farther south, 10–20 fathoms deep.

22.   *Merica laticosta* (LÖBBECKE)

The spire is even taller, and the whorls are less inflated than in *M. reeveana*. The surface sculpture is coarser. The color bands are indistinct, but are wider than those of the preceding species. Distribution: central Honshû and farther south, 10–20 fathoms deep.

Family Volutidae

The members of this family have fusiform or spindle-shaped shells of various sizes, which are characterized by the presence of remarkable folds on their columella. Most of the species have no operculum. The animal body is relatively large, but the flesh is rarely eaten. This is a considerably large group, and a greater part of the species inhabits deep seas.

1. Lyria cassidula (REEVE)

This is a rather small-sized shell with stubby and spindle-shaped outline. It is about 32 mm in length and 17 mm in diameter. The spire is small, and the body whorl is well developed. The exterior surface is sparsely and longitudinally folded, but the folds disappear near the end of body whorl. The outer lip is thickened. The anterior canal is short, and slightly curved. This has many columellar folds that become weaker toward the posterior end of inner lip. The shell surface is flesh-brown in ground color, and surrounded by a wide spiral band of purplish or dark brown and by two white lines. It is also covered by a dark brown epiderm. The inner fringe of aperture is orange-colored. Distribution: south of central Honshû, at 10–20 fathoms in depth.

2. Fulgoraria (Saotomea) delicata (FULTON)

A medium-sized fusiform shell, with a comparatively large protoconch. The shell is thin, and sparsely bears longitudinal folds on the posterior half of whorls. Indistinct spiral threads are barely visible through a magnifying glass. Only one or two folds are present on the columella. It is light flesh-brown all over the surface, without any color patterns. This has a horny and elliptic operculum, about 1/3 as long as the length of aperture. Distribution: south of central Honshû, 100–150 fathoms in depth.

3. Benthovoluta hilgendorfi (VON MARTENS)

The shell is a little larger, and somewhat more slender than Fulgoraria delicata. Both the spire and posterior canal are longer. Longitudinal folds on the shell exterior are only seen on earlier whorls, down to the middle part of the penultimate whorl. This also bears fine spiral grooves all over the surface, which are transformed into spiral threads around the siphon. Two or three columellar folds are hidden behind the inner lip margin. Distribution: south of Chôshi, Kantô District, 100–150 fathoms deep.

4. Teramachia tibiaeformis KURODA

This shell is similar to the preceding species in size, but has a taller spire, and the anterior canal is shorter. The surface is rather densely sculptured by longitudinal folds, except on the body whorl. No spiral sculptures are seen. The columellar folds are hardly visible from the outside. The operculum is horny and elliptic, with a nucleus situated anteriorly. Distribution: southern Honshû and southwards, rarely found at 100–150 fathoms depth.

5. Fulgoraria prevostiana (CROSSE)

The shell is large, reaching 110–120 mm in length. The spire is tall, and bears a large protoconch on its apex. The well developed last whorl is longer than one half of the total shell length. It bears sparse longitudinal folds on the upper part of whorls. No spiral threads are seen. The outer lip is somewhat thickened, but not reflexed. Columellar folds are distinct, and 2–3 in number. The flesh-brown surface is marked by chestnut-brown longitudinal patterns arranged in a few spiral zones. The shells of this genus lack opercula, except the species of the subgenus Saotomea. Distribution: Pacific coasts of Kantô District, at 30–50 fathoms depth.

6. Fulgoraria (Psephaea) concinna (BRODERIP)

This is nearly of the same size with the last species. Longitudinal folds on the surface respectively bear a tubercle-like process along the shoulder of whorls. Columellar folds are 3–4 in number. The outer surface is faintly glossy, and light flesh-brown in ground color, on which chestnut-brown stripes are longitudinally marked in 3 broad spiral zones. Distri-

[PLATE 33]   Volutidae

bution : central Honshû, 80–100 fathoms in depth.

7. Fulgoraria (Musasia) cancellata KURODA et HABE

This shell is slightly thinner than the preceding species, and is more densely sculptured by longitudinal folds. The whorls are scarcely angled at the shoulder. Fine and distinct spiral threads cover the entire surface of the shell. Usually 2–3 (rarely 4) folds occur on the columella. It is simply colored in flesh-brown all over the surface. Distribution : central Honshû and farther south, at 50–100 fathoms depth.

8. Fulgoraria hamillei (CROSSE)

The whorls are obtusely angled at the shoulder. The protoconch is especially large. Longitudinal folds on the surface almost disappear on the body whorl, and spiral threads also become less distinct on later whorls. Columellar folds are large in number (6–10). Chestnut-brown zigzag stripes beautifully ornament the flesh-brown ground color. Distribution : south of central Honshû, at 50–100 fathoms depth.

9. Fulgoraria (Psephaea) mentiens (FULTON)

This shell reachs 170 mm in length, but is rather slender, not exceeding 55 mm in diameter. The shoulder of whorls is round. Longitudinal folds on the shell surface are rather weakly sculptured. Spiral threads tend to be more distinct on earlier whorls. Four or five folds are seen on the

columella. Three interrupted spiral bands of brown color are marked on the flesh-brown exterior surface. Distribution : central Honshû and farther south, 70–120 fathoms deep.

10. Fulgoraria (Psephaea) daviesi (FULTON)

Closely resembling *F. mentiens*, this differs in bearing more sparsely arranged spiral threads and many fine spiral stripes of dark flesh-brown color covering the whole outer surface. Three wide bands of dark brown also encircle the whorls. The number of columellar folds is 3–4. Distribution : the same with the preceding species.

11. Fulgoraria (Psephaea) kaneko HIRASE

The whorls of the shell have the obtusely angled shoulder, and are well inflated. The epiderm is comparatively thick. Columellar folds are 4–6. It bears no color bands on the flesh-brown ground. Distribution : from central Honshû to northwestern Kyûshû along the Japan Sea coasts, at 50–100 fathoms depth.

12. Fulgoraria prevostiana magna KURODA et HABE

This subspecies does not differ from the original race, *F. prevostiana*, in shape, surface sculpture and coloration, but is much larger, exceeding 300 mm in length. The protoconch is white in color, and is the smallest, in its propotion to the shell size, among the species of this genus. Distribution : Kantô District and northwards to Hokkaidô, at 50–100 fathoms depth.

PLATE **33**

1

× 4/5

2

× 4/5

3

× 4/5

4

× 4/5

5   × 3/5   6   × 3/5

7

× 3/5

8

× 3/5

9   × 3/5   10

× 3/5

11

× 3/5

12   × 3/5

PLATE 34

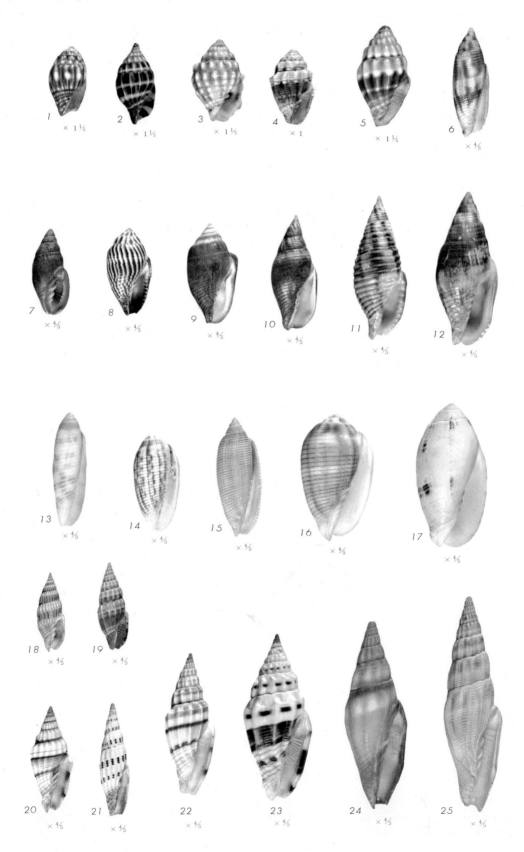

1
× 1⅕

2
× 1⅕

3
× 1⅕

4
× 1

5
× 1⅕

6
× ⅘

7
× ⅘

8
× ⅘

9
× ⅘

10
× ⅘

11
× ⅘

12
× ⅘

13
× ⅘

14
× ⅘

15
× ⅘

16
× ⅘

17
× ⅘

18
× ⅘

19
× ⅘

20
× ⅘

21
× ⅘

22
× ⅘

23
× ⅘

24
× ⅘

25
× ⅘

[PLATE 34]

Family Mitridae (1)

This family of miter shells comprises a great number of species, distributed all over the warm seas in the world. The shells widely differ in size, ranging from minute size to large form, but most of them are spindle-shaped, with a pointed apex, resembling the head of a Japanese writing brush in outline. The family is subdivided into *Pusia*-group, *Strigatella*-group, *Mitra*-group, *Pterygia*-group, *Vexillum*-group, etc. This includes exquisitely sculptured and beautifully colored shells favored by collectors.

1. Pusia pardalis consanguinea (REEVE)

In this small shell, the low spire terminates in a blunt apex, and the anterior part of the last whorl tapers to form a fat spindle-shape. It may appear like an immature shell, but the tapering end indicates the maturity. The whorls are sculptured by many longitudinal ridges all over the surface, and by fine spiral threads between the ribs. Spiral threads on the anterior part of body whorl are especially strong bearing granules. The anterior canal is short. The columella bears 4 plaits. This has a spiral row of white spots on the middle part of body whorl, and another row of smaller white spots encircles the whorls on the shoulder. Distribution: southern Honshû and farther south, below the tide line.

2. Pusia adamsi (DOHRN)

This is also a stubby and spindle-shaped shell, with a straight and pointed spire. Longitudinal ridges are distinct and narrow. The spiral sculpture is essentially the same with that of the preceding species. The exterior is black in ground color, and the ridges are white. In addition, 4 white bands surround the body whorl. Four columellar folds are also white-colored. Distribution: the same with the preceding species.

3. Pusia cancellarioides (ANTON)

The shell is wider than the preceding two species, and is covered over the exterior surface by small nodules arranged on longitudinal ribs. The nodules are connected by spiral threads. The columella bears 4 plaits, of which the posterior one is the largest. The ground color is light yellowish brown, which becomes even lighter on the nodules. Distribution: southern Kyûshû and southwards, in subtidal zone.

4. Pusia patriarchalis (GMELIN)

This shell is about the same in size with the preceding 3 species at the northern limit of its distribution (Kii Peninsula), but it grows much larger (about 12 mm in length) in regions south of Amami Islands. The whorls are angled at the shoulder, and sparsely bear thick longitudinal ridges that become lower toward the anterior end of the shell. The nature of spiral threads is as described in *P. pardalis consanguinea*. A wide dark purple band encircles the central part of body whorl over its white background. The margin of aperture is colored in scarlet, and bears 4 columellar folds. Distribution: southern Honshû and southwards, in subtidal zone.

5. Pusia porphyretica (REEVE)

Unlike the preceding species, the whorls are not angled at the shoulder. The outer surface is bluish white on its posterior half, while the rest is dark gray and bear fine white bands. This has 4 plaits on its columella. Distribution: south of central Honshû, in subtidal zone.

6. Dibaphus edentulus (SWAINSON)

A narrowly spindle-shaped shell, having a small spire and a large body whorl. Fine spiral threads cover the entire surface, reaching the inner margins of aperture. Very fine longitudinal lines are also noticed between the spiral threads. The most remarkable characteristic of this species is the absence of columellar folds. The ground color is light brown, and overlaid by 2 spiral zones of discontinuous dark brown blotches. Distribution: south of Amami Islands, in subtidal zone.

7. Zierliana waldemari solidula (REEVE)

The shell is fusiform, and is rusty brown on the outer surface bearing metallic lustre. The exterior is almost smooth, except a spiral thread below the suture line and in-

[PLATE 34]   Mitridae

distinct longitudinal folds on the spire. The outer lip is remarkably thickened, bearing fine dentations on its inner margin. It has 4 columellar folds, and the anterior canal is deeply notched. Distribution: southern Honshû and farther south, in subtidal zone.

8. Strigatella retusa (LAMARCK)

A stubby shell with a low spire. The anterior part of the last whorl is sculptured by spiral threads, but otherwise the surface is smooth and glossy. Four plaits and fine teeth are seen on the inner and outer lip margin respectively. This is longitudinally striped by clear white lines on the black background. Distribution: Amami Islands and father south, in subtidal zone.

9. Strigatella decurtata (REEVE)

This resembles St. retusa in general shape of the shell, but is a little thicker. The outer surface is dark brown in color, not shining, and smooth, except some spiral threads on the basal part. A discontinued white band and a white line encircle the whorls on the shoulder. Besides, another spiral row of white spots is seen on the basal part of body whorl. The outer lip is thickened, bearing a notch near its posterior end, but lacking teeth on its margin. The columellar plaits are 4 in number. Distribution: the same with the last species.

10. Strigatella amphorella (LAMARCK)

Resembling the preceding species in general appearance, this shell has a taller and elongated spire. The aperture is wider, and the outer lip is less thickened. It is dark brown in color, with a white band on the shoulder of whorls. Distribution: south of the Ryukyus, in subtidal zone.

11. Chrysame ferruginea (LAMARCK)

The outline is elongated spindle-shaped. The spire is tall, and larger than the body whorl. The outer surface is covered by coarse spiral ribs, without any longltudinal sculpture. The thickened outer lip bears a row of small nodules on its slightly reflexed margin. Five plaits are seen on the inner lip. This is colored in amber over its surface,

and marked by irregular blotches of brown. The inside margins of aperture are orange-yellow in color. Distribution: the same with the preceding species.

12. Chrysame chrysostoma (SWAINSON)

This has an outline similar to that of the above species. The spire is covered by a reticulate sculpture, formed by the intersection of weak spiral threads and growth lines. The surface of the last whorl is, however, mostly smooth, only bearing several spiral ridges on its basal part. The aperture is somewhat expanded anteriorly. The outer lip is thickened, and somewhat reflexed. The number of columellar plaits is 4. It bears beautiful, golden brown coloration over its exterior surface. Distribution: south of Amami Islands, in subtidal zone.

13. Pterygia elongata (HIRASE)

The shells of this genus generally resemble the cone shells in shape, but can easily be distinguished from the latter group by their columellar folds. This species has a slenderly fusiform shell, with an extremely elongated last whorl and a small spire. The surface sculpture is finely reticulate on its spire, but the body whorl bears only spiral furrows. The narrow aperture is margined by the thin outer lip and the straight inner lip, bearing 7–8 plaits. The ground color is white, marked by 5–6 brown spiral bands as well as by several longitudinal rows of brown spots. This species had originally been described, based on the fossil specimens from Kikaigashima, a small islet adjacent to Kyûshû, but was later found living along Bôsô Peninsula of Kantô District, at 5–10 fathoms depth.

14. Pterygia undulosa (REEVE)

This is rounder in outline than the last species. The surface sculpture resembles that of the last species. Brown longitudinal stripes are marked on the body whorl against its white ground color. The columellar plaits are 7–9. Distribution: south of central Honshû, 5–10 fathoms in depth.

15. *Pterygia sinensis* (Reeve)

General shape of the shell is intermediate between the former two species of *Pterygia*. The spire is considerably tall. The outer surface is ornamented by fine networks of spiral and longitudinal threads, and by small granules on the intersection points of the network. The posterior part of parietal callus is well developed, bordering a short posterior canal. The outer lip margin bears a fine tooth-like sculpture, while 9 plaits are seen on the inner lip. The surface is light brown in color. Distribution: southern Honshû and farther south, at about 50 fathoms depth.

16. *Pterygia dactylus* (Linné)

The shell is even more swollen in outline than *Pt. undulosa*. The body whorl is expanded, and the spire is low. Fine spiral furrows surrounding the whorls look light brown in color, owing to the epiderm remaining uneroded in the furrows. The ground color is white, and light brown patterns are marked on it both longitudinally and spirally. This has 6–7 plaits on its inner lip. Distribution: south of Amami Islands, in subtidal zone.

17. *Pterygia (Acuticylindra) nucea* (Gmelin)

This shell is thick, spindle-shaped and faintly shining over the exterior, having a taller spire than that of *Pt. dactylus*. The entire surface looks nearly smooth, but is covered by very indistinct spiral furrows. The columella bears 5–6 folds, and minute wart-like processes are sparsely arranged along the outer lip margin. It is marked by a small number of black spots over its white ground color. Distribution: south of the Ryukyus, below the tide line down to 5 fathoms.

18. *Arenimitra exasperatum* (Gmelin)

A small and narrow shell with a tall and pointed spire. This bears, over its outer surface, many longitudinal ribs and fine granules where the ribs are crossed by spiral threads. A few longitudinal lines are also seen in each space between the ribs. Four folds occur on the columella. Two dark brown bands encircle the whorls over the white background. Distribution: southern Honshû and southwards, in subtidal zone down to 5 fathoms depth.

19. *Costellaria semifasciatum* (Lamarck)

The shape resembles that of the last species. The spire is turreted stepwise, owing to an angulation at the shoulder of whorls. This shell is sculptured only by longitudinal ridges. The columellar folds are 4 in number. The upper and lower halves of the whorls are differently colored in white and reddish brown respectively. A spiral black line, disconnected by longitudinal ridges, runs through the white part of whorls. Distribution: the same with the last species.

20. *Vexillum rugosum* (Gmelin)

The shell is considerably larger than the preceding species, and the body whorl is more widely expanded especially at its shoulder. The surface is sculptured by a number of longitudinal ribs and spiral threads. Small granules are often formed on the longitudinal ribs. The columella bears 4 plaits. This is white all over its surface, with a bluish tone along the shoulder. Besides, the whorls are encircled by 3 brown color bands, of which the uppermost one is finer and lighter in color than others. Distribution: the Ryukyus and farther south, from the tide line to 5 fathoms depth.

21. *Vexillum (Pulchritima) sanguisuga* (Linné)

This shell is much elongated in shape, and is finely covered by longitudinal ribs, distinct spiral threads and small granules formed by their intersection. The columellar folds are 4 in number. The outer surface is beautifully colored on the longitudinal ribs by two rouge spiral zone, and by the light yellow ground color. Both ends of the shell shows a purplish tone. Distribution: the same with the last species.

22. *Vexillum balteolatum* (Reeve)

This is larger than *V. rugosum*, and less densely sculptured by sharp longitudinal ridges remarkably angled at the shoulder of

[PLATE 34]   Mitridae

whorls. Spiral threads are indistinct, except on the anterior part of the last whorl. The inner lip bears 4 plaits. This has a fine spiral band of brown color encircling the whorls a little below the shoulder, and the color of the shell surface is light brown and white respectively above and below this line. Two spiral brown bands run over the central part of body whorl, and the space between them is also colored in light brown. Distribution: south of Amami Islands, below the tide line.

23. *Vexillum plicarium* (LINNÉ)

The shell is larger and heavier in construction than the preceding species. Longitudinal ridges are somewhat less in number, but very strong. This has no spiral sculptures, except several thick threads on the basal part of body whorl. The number of columellar plaits are 4–5. An interrupted black band surrounds the whorls on the interspaces between longitudinal ridges. The body whorl are also spirally marked by a thick zone and a discontinued band both black in color. Distribution: south of the Ryukyus, from the tide line down to 5 fathoms.

24. *Vexillum vulpeculum* (LINNÉ)

This is more slender than *V. plicarium* in shape. Longitudinal folds are low and indistinct. The inner lip bears 4 folds. The color is chestnut brown all over its surface, with a white broad band encircling the round shoulder. Distribution: the same with *V. plicarium*.

25. *Vexillum ornatum coccineum* (REEVE)

This has an even more elongated and larger shell than the preceding species. The exterior is longitudinally folded, bearing distinct spiral threads all over the surface. The posterior part of aperture ends in a canal. Four plaits are seen on the columella. The ground color is light yellowish brown, and a vague white zone surrounds the whorls on the shoulder. Distribution: the same with the preceding two species.

Family Mitridae (2)

1. *Tiara filaris* (LINNÉ)

This species has a slender and fusiform shell typical to the genus. The number of strong spiral ribs on the shell surface is about 12 on the last whorl and 3 on other whorls. Spaces between the ribs are marked by very fine reticulate sculptures. The columella bears 4 plaits. Fine brown lines are clearly marked along the spiral ribs on the light flesh-brown surface. Distribution: southern Honshû and farther south, at 5–10 fathoms depth.

2. *Mitropifex hirasei* KIRA (n. sp.)

The body whorl is comparatively shorter than that of the preceding species. The surface sculpture consists of dense networks of longitudinal and spiral threads. The aperture is also short, and 4–5 plaits are seen on the columella. It bears black scattered patterns on the light-brown background. Both anterior and posterior ends of the shell are colored by a pink tone. Distribution: west coasts of Kyûshû and farther south, 10–20 fathoms in depth.

3. *Tiara yagurai* (KIRA)

Resembling *T. filaris*, this shell is more slender in shape. The reticulate sculpture between spiral ribs is somewhat coarser than that of the former species. The spiral ribs are not brown-colored. Distribution: Pacific coasts of southern Honshû and Shikoku, 30–50 fathoms deep.

4. *Scabricola granatina* (LAMARCK)

This is wider in shape, and has a lower spire than the last species. The outer surface bears rather coarse reticulate sculptures. Interrupted brown lines run along some spiral ribs, separated from each other by a few colorless ribs. The inner lip is marked by 4 folds. Distribution: south of the Ryukyus, at 5–10 fathoms depth.

5. *Nebularia inquinata* (REEVE)

This shell is quite spindle-shaped. The whorls are moderately inflated, and a little constricted at the suture. The outer surface is rather sparsely and shallowy sculptured by spiral furrows. Longitudinal threads are very fine and indistinct. Many color bands of dark brown run both spirally and longitudinally over the white ground color. The number of columellar folds is 4. Distribution: south of central Honshû, at 10–30 fathoms depth.

6. *Scabricola clathrus* (GMELIN)

The outline is similar to that of *N. inquinata*. The surface is covered by a mosaic sculpture formed by the intersection of spiral and longitudinal furrows. The ground color is pinky white, and is irregularly overlaid by dark brown blotches. The columellar plaits resemble those of the last species. Distribution: south of central Honshû along Pacific coasts, at 10–30 fathoms depth.

7. *Tiara isabella* (SWAINSON)

A considerably large shell, covered all over its exterior by many, thick spiral ribs. Inter-rib spaces are filled up by longitudinal threads. The number of columellar plaits is 4–5. The outer surface is pale white in ground color, bearing light brown longitudinal patterns, and is covered by a thin epiderm. Distribution: Pacific coasts of central Honshû, 10–20 fathoms deep.

8. *Tiara morchii* (A. ADAMS)

This shell resembles the preceding species in shape and surface sculpture, but is considerably smaller in size. It is white all over its surface without any color patterns. Distribution: Pacific coasts of Shikoku and Kyûshû, 10–20 fathoms deep.

9. *Vicimitra chinensis* (GRAY)

This is also similar in shape to the above species. The whorls are, however, somewhat more inflated, and the sculpture is very shallowly marked. The pale white surface is thus almost flat, showing faint lustre. Distribution: China Sea along the west coasts of Kyûshû, at 10–30 fathoms depth.

[PLATE 35]   Mitridae

10. Nebularia monachialis [RÖDING]

The shell is heavy, and has a well developed and swollen body whorl. Both spiral and longitudinal ribs are only lightly sculptured. The outer lip margin bears a row of fine wart-like knots, while the inner lip has 4 columellar folds. The outer surface is somewhat glossy, and pale white in color, and is marked all over by spirally arranged brown spots of heterogeneous sizes. Distribution: south of the Ryukyus, 10–20 fathoms in depth.

11. Chrysame ambigua (SWAINSON)

This is like the preceding species in shape and sculpture, but the last whorl is less swollen. The columellar plaits are 4–5 in number. It is yellowish brown all over its surface, with a white spiral band on the shoulder of whorls. Distribution: south of the Ryukyus, 5–10 fathoms in depth.

12. Chrysame coffea (SCHUBERT et WAGNER)

This shell is closely related to *Chr. ambigua*, but is smaller and chestnut-brown in its surface color. Distribution: the same with the last species.

13. Nebularia puncticulata (LAMARCK)

The shell is thick and short, having a relatively low spire. This and the following two species are characterized by a row of pointed tooth-like folds running along the suture at the posterior end of whorls. The surface is covered by thick spiral ribs, and fine longitudinal lines are also sculptured in grooves between the ribs. The outer lip bears small knots on its margin. Five plaits are seen on the columella. Two wide yellow bands encircle, respectively, the posterior and anterior parts of whorls over the light brown background. Distribution: the Ryukyus and farther south, below the tide line to 5 fathoms depth.

14. Mitra stricta (LINK)

This is much larger than the last species, but the general shape is quite similar, except that the spire is more distinctly stepped. The surface sculpture is only slightly carved, and inter-rib furrows bear punctures. The exterior is yellowish white in ground color, bearing all over its surface spirally arranged blotches of fleshy brown. Distribution: the Ryukyus and farther south, at 5–10 fathoms depth.

15. Mitra papalis (LINNÉ)

This is still larger than *M. stricta*, and ornamented over the entire surface by spiral rows of fine, dark red spots. Distribution: the same with the last species.

16. Mitra mitra (LINNÉ)

This is the largest shell among Japanese species of the miter family. The surface is almost smooth, only bearing faint growth lines. It lacks tooth-like folds along the suture, but the structure of aperture quite resembles that of the preceding three species. The outer surface is white in ground color, often covered by a light brown epiderm, and marked by bright red spots arranged in spiral rows. Distribution: the same with the preceding two species.

PLATE **35**

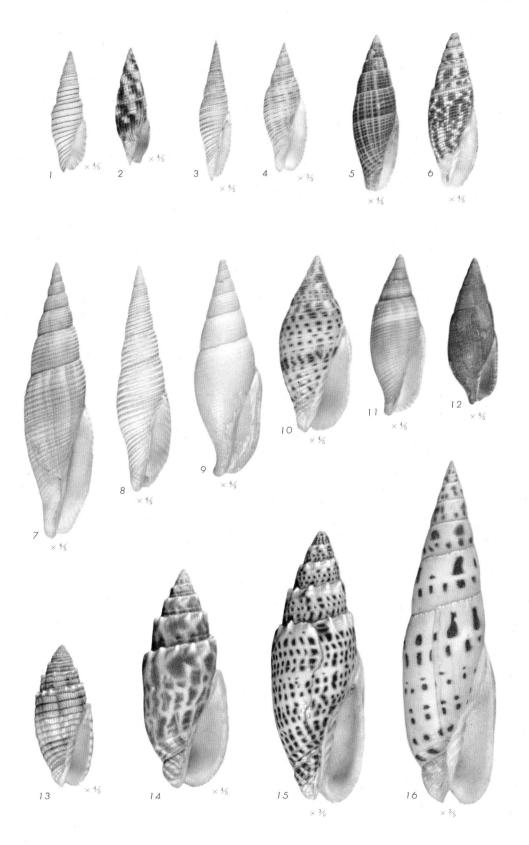

1   × ⁴⁄₅
2   × ⁴⁄₅
3   × ⁴⁄₅
4   × ³⁄₅
5   × ⁴⁄₅
6   × ⁴⁄₅
7   × ⁴⁄₅
8   × ⁴⁄₅
9   × ⁴⁄₅
10 × ⁴⁄₅
11 × ⁴⁄₅
12 × ⁴⁄₅
13 × ⁴⁄₅
14 × ⁴⁄₅
15 × ³⁄₅
16 × ³⁄₅

PLATE 36

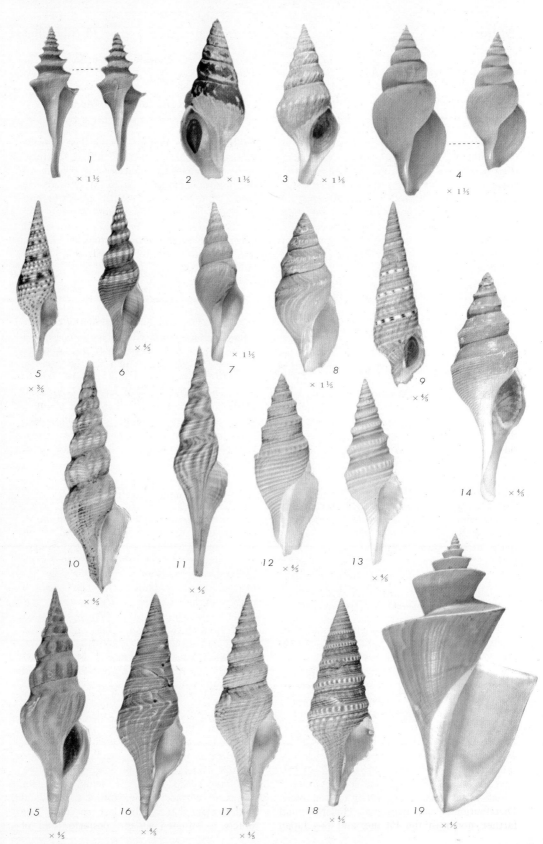

1 × 1⅕

2 × 1⅕

3 × 1⅕

4
× 1⅕

5
× ⅗

6 × ⅘

7 × 1⅕

8 × 1⅕

9 × ⅘

10
× ⅘

11
× ⅘

12 × ⅘

13
× ⅘

14 × ⅘

15
× ⅘

16
× ⅘

17
× ⅘

18
× ⅘

19
× ⅘

Family Turridae

This is one of the largest families among marine molluscs, containing a great number of species. The turret shells are variable in size, and especially rich in minute forms, but only medium- and large-sized species are illustrated here. They are usually spindle-shaped, often with a tall, and turret-like spire, and characterized by the presence of a slit or notch on the outer lip. Most of the shells are dextrally coiled, but there are also some sinistral species. The operculum is either horny or absent. Since the animals are anatomically related to the cone shells (Conidae), these two families are both included in the same superfamily Conicea.

1. Ancistrosyrinx pulcherrissimus KIRA

The shell is rather small and thin. The number of whorls is about 10. They bear a sharp keel at their shoulder, on which short spiny processes are arranged like teeth of a cog-wheel. The spire thus resembles a pagoda in outline. The outer surface between the keel and suture is fringed by a few spiral threads, and the outer lip margin of this part is obliquely notched along the suture. The anterior part of the surface before the keel bears fine spiral threads bearing granules. The aperture is narrow, and terminates in a long siphon at its anterior end. The light pinky brown color of the outer surface is ready to fade away during storage. Distribution: Pacific coasts of southern Honshû and farther south, at 80–100 fathoms depth.

2. Antiplanes contraria (YOKOYAMA)

This is one of a few sinistral species of Japanese marine Gastropoda. The whorls are well inflated, and deeply constricted at the suture. The outer surface is marked by growth lines and very faint spiral threads. The aperture with a short and broad siphon is spoon-shaped. A notch is seen at the posterior end of outer lip. The operculum is elliptic in shape and horny, with an anteriorly situated nucleus. The color of the shell is light flesh-brown, and this is covered by a dark brown, thick epiderm, which is, however, very easily eroded away. Distribution: northeastern Honshû and farther north in the Pacific, and the Japan

Sea coasts of Honshû, 30-50 fathoms in depth.

3. Makiyamaia coreanica (ADAMS et REEVE)

This shell is similar to the last species in size, but is dextral and thin in texture. A row of tubercles encircles the whorls on the angled shoulder. No spiral threads are seen. A notch occurs at the posterior end of outer lip, and the siphon is wide and moderately long. The white surface is covered by a gray-brown epiderm. Distribution: south of central Honshû, 50–80 fathoms deep.

4. Daphnella nobilis KIRA

This shell is thin, and composed of roundly inflated whorls bordered by deeply constricted suture lines. The entire outer surface bears faint spiral threads, which are crossed by growth lines, forming a fine reticulate sculpture. The posterior end of outer lip is notched, while the anterior end of aperture forms a short and broad siphon. The pinky gray color of exterior surface readily fades away. Distribution: south of central Honshû, at 50–80 fathoms depth.

5. Lophitoma crispa (LAMARCK)

A medium-sized shell, with a tall spire comprising about 15 whorls. A strong spiral ridge surrounds the shoulder of whorls, ending in a notch on the outer lip. Both anterior and posterior parts to this ridge are also encircled by finer spiral ribs crossing with longitudinal lines. The anterior end of the last whorl is remarkably elongated with the narrow siphon. The operculum is horny and elliptic. Dark brown spots and blotches are scattered over the gray-colored surface. Distribution: central Honshû and southwards, at 20–30 fathoms depth.

6. Turricula kamakurana (PILSBRY)

The tall spire is constricted at the suture. The whorls are inflated, bearing a blunt angle at the shoulder. Many longitudinal folds and fine spiral ribs are sculptured over its outer surface. The siphon is long and wider than that of the last species. The notch is situated at the posterior end of

[PLATE 36]   Turridae

aperture. It is marked by a white band on the shoulder, while the rest of outer surface is brown-colored. Distribution: central Honshû, 5–10 fathoms deep.

7. Turricula lurida (ADAMS et REEVE)

The general shape of the shell resembles that of *T. kamakurana*, but this is somewhat smaller and thinner in texture. Weak folds are arranged along the shoulder of whorls, and spiral threads are very weakly marked. The margin of outer lip is sharp and thin, with a notch at its posterior end. The operculum is horny, elliptic and yellowish brown in color, bearing concentric lines around an anteriorly situated nucleus. On the white ground color it bears a shade of yellowish pink in living shells, which, however, tends to be lost soon after death. Distribution: Pacific coasts of southern Honshû and Shikoku, 30–50 fathoms deep.

8. Riuguhdrillia engonia (WATSON)

This shell is wider in shape, but thinner in texture than the last species. The whorls bear a blunt keel at the shoulder, and are only microscopically sculptured on the surface. Fine growth lines and spiral threads are more or less evident near the anterior end of body whorl. A notch is seen on the outer lip at the end of the shoulder keel. The siphon is broad and short, and the anterior end of body whorl is truncated. A thin, gray epiderm covers the white surface. The inner side of aperture is usually white, but sometimes shows an orange coloration. Distribution: northeastern Honshû and northwards, 50–80 fathoms in depth.

9. Turris (Xenuroturris) cingulifera (LAMARCK)

This medium-sized turret shell has a tall and tower-shaped spire, and a relatively short body whorl with a short, broad siphon. The outer surface is covered by many spiral ribs of different thickness, of which the one along the shoulder is especially strong reaching a slit on the outer lip margin. The anterior end of the shell also bears a fasciole. The margin of outer lip is thin, except along the slit. The operculum is horny, oval and reddish brown.

The ground color is white, and marked by brown spots along spiral ribs; those on the shoulder ridge are most conspicuous. Distribution: south of Amami Islands, in subtidal zone down to 5 fathoms.

10. Brachystoma flavidula (LAMARCK)

The shell is moderately large, and has a relatively short siphon and a tall spire strongly constricted at the suture. Inflated whorls are sculptured on the outer surface by longitudinal folds, fine spiral threads and growth lines. A notch is seen at the posterior end of outer lip. It bears a light reddish brown band encircling the shoulder as well as another spiral band of white on the central part of whorls. Distribution: south of central Honshû, at 20–30 fathoms depth.

11. Fusosurcula mirabilis (SOWERBY)

A slender shell tapering on both ends. The posterior part of whorls adjacent to the suture is somewhat constricted, whereas the whorls are well inflated at the middle part. Coarse spiral ribs surround the whorls. The notch on the outer lip is posteriorly situated. The siphon is very long. The operculum is corneous, elliptic and yellowish brown in color. Distribution: central Honshû and farther south, at 30–50 fathoms depth.

12. Micantapex lühdorfi (LISCHKE)

The whorls are encircled on the shoulder by a keel bearing granules, which terminates in a slit-like notch on the outer lip. Another granulated rib runs spirally below the suture line. Besides, the exterior surface bears coarse, shallowly sculptured spiral ribs and oblique growth lines. The outer lip margin is acute, and thin. The siphon is considerably broad, and short. The operculum is small, resembling that of *F. mirabilis*. The surface color is light brown. Distribution: south of central Honshû, at 20–30 fathoms depth.

13. Gemmula cosmoi (SYKES)

As compared with the preceding species, the spire of this shell is more strongly constricted at the suture, while the siphon is longer and narrower. A remarkable keel on the shoulder of whorls bears granules. A spiral rib surrounding the whorls immediately above the suture is especially thick and distinct, owing to its yellowish brown coloration. The surface between the keel and suture is finely marked by spiral threads and growth lines, whereas spiral ribs anterior to the keel are coarser. Two notches are seen on the outer lip at the end of the keel and at the base of siphon, respectively, the latter notch being shallower than the former. The ground color of the shell is pure white. It is noteworthy that another different type is often found that has a smaller shell, brownish ground color and somewhat deeper anterior notch. It is not yet certain whether or not the two types represent both sexes. Distribution: the same with the preceding species.

14. *Aforia circinata diomedea* BARTSCH

This is a considerably large shell thin in texture. The shoulder of whorls bears a sharp carination, and the suture is abruptly and deeply sunken. Fine spiral threads are marked only on the surface between the keel and the base of siphon. The siphon is remarkably elongated, and extends beyond the anterior end of the columella. The operculum is corneous and round, with an eccentrically situated nucleus. The color of the shell is horny brown. Distribution: northeastern Honshû and farther north, 30–50 fathoms in depth.

15. *Turricula kaderleyi* (LISCHKE)

The shell is moderately large. The whorls are inflated, but somewhat narrowly constricted below the suture. This bears deep longitudinal folds and faint spiral threads over the exterior. The outer lip margin is thin and acute, and a notch is seen on its posterior end. The siphon is moderately long and broad. The outer surface is white in ground color, with broad and brown spiral bands, but the tint exhibits wide individual differences. Distribution: south of central Honshû, as deep as 80–100 fathoms.

16. *Turris polytropa* (HELBLING)

This is a large and thick shell, having a relatively straight spire. The whorls are only slightly constricted at their posterior part behind the shoulder, on which fine spiral threads are sculptured. The anterior half of whorls below the shoulder is, on the other hand, surrounded by alternately coarse and fine ribs. The siphon is moderately long, and a notch is seen on the posterior part of outer lip. The shell is chestnut-brown all over its surface and spirally bears fine white lines. Distribution: central Honshû and farther south, 20–30 fathoms deep.

17. *Lophitoma unedo* (KIENER)

The shell is considerably large, bearing a blunt keel on the shoulder and a strong spiral rib just below the suture. The exterior surface is rough, owing to coarse spiral ribs and growth lines. This has a deep notch on the posterior part of outer lip. The siphon is fairly wide and long. The operculum is horny and elliptic in shape. Distribution: the same with the last species.

18. *Gemmula granosa* (HELBLING)

The shape and sculpture are similar to those of *G. cosmoi*, but this is larger in size and the siphon is comparatively shorter. The presence of two notches on the outer lip is also common to both species. The posterior notch is deep and slit-like. It is dirty white in ground color, and surrounded by rows of brown spots on the shoulder keel and on spiral ribs. Distribution: the same with the preceding species.

19. *Thatcheria mirabilis* ANGAS

This is an endemic species of Japan that has a singularly shaped and large shell, thin in texture. The whorls bear a sharp keel on the acutely angled shoulder. The side of whorls is almost straight, both above and below this keel, so that the spire quite resembles screw-stairs. The body whorl tapers sharply toward the anterior end of the shell. The outer surface is smooth and weakly glossy, bearing faint spiral threads only over the anterior side of the keel. The aperture is very widely open, and bordered by the smooth, curved columella and the thin margin of outer lip. The color of the shell is white inside, and pink outside, but the beautiful tone readily fades away. Distribution: Pacific coasts of central Honshû and Shikoku, at 80–100 fathoms depth.

[PLATE 37]   Conidae

Family Conidae (1)

This is the family of cone shells, which are called in Japan ' tuber shells ' because of the resemblance of their outline with the tuber of taros, one of the oldest tuber crops in Japan. The shells are usually cone-shaped, with a low or flat spire and a well developed last whorl tapering toward the pointed anterior end. The aperture is slit-like and long, and fringed by parallel lips. They have a small and horny operculum of narrow shape. Cone shells are ornamented all over the outer surface by various beautiful patterns and diversified coloration attractive to collectors, but a thick epiderm frequently conceals the surface patterns. The animals are often armed with sharp arrow-like teeth and a poisonous gland, and their bites are occasionally fatal even to mankind. Many species inhabit warm waters of the world.

1. Lithoconus tessulatus (BORN)

This is a typically cone-shaped shell having a low spire and the carinated shoulder. This bears checkered patterns of cinnabar or brownish red on its white ground color. Sometimes the square spots are longitudinally connected each other into wavy lines. The anterior end of the body whorl is colored in violet. Such coloration of the anterior tip of cone shells is one of the important characters to discriminate the species. Distribution: Bôsô Peninsula of Kantô District and farther south, at 5–10 fathoms depth.

2. Lithoconus eburneus (HWASS)

Resembling the first species, this is larger in size, and wider in outline, and the shoulder carination is somewhat rounded. The exterior of the body whorl is nearly smooth, except several spiral furrows at the base. Black spots are sparsely and more or less regularly scattered all over the white surface. Distribution: south of the Ryukyus, 5–10 fathoms in depth.

3. Lithoconus litteratus (LINNÉ)

The outline is more elongated than that of the preceding species. The spire is flat. This shell is often confused with an immature specimen of *L. pardus*, but can be distin-

guished from the latter by 3 spiral bands of light orange on the surface. Black spots on the white background are regularly arranged, and each maintain comparatively regular square-shape. Distribution: the same with the preceding species.

4. Lithoconus pardus [RÖDING]

This shell is even more elongated and heavier than the last species. The surface is covered by many spiral rows of bluish black spots, which are less clear-cut and more irregular in shape than those of *L. litteratus*. No orange-colored bands are present. Distribution: the same with the foregoing two species.

5. Rhizoconus sugimotonis (KURODA)

The body whorl is slender especially in its anterior half, and the side-slope is somewhat concave. The spire is low, but the apex is pointed and elevated. Spiral sculptures are found on the surface of spire, but they become less distinct on the side of body whorl. Fold-like growth lines are clearly marked. The columellar end is constricted by a well developed fasciole. It is white all over the surface, without any color patterns. Distribution: deep zones of the Pacific along southern Honshû and Shikoku, at 100–120 fathoms depth.

6. Conus marmoreus (LINNÉ)

The shoulder line of whorls is waved, owing to tubercles it bears. The whorls are covered by regularly arranged, spiral threads. The outer surface is marked by scale-shaped, triangular, white spots, and the rest is black in color. A light brown epiderm covers the surface. Distribution: south of the Ryukyus, 2–5 fathoms in depth.

7. Conus bandanus (HWASS)

The outline of this shell is almost the same with that of *C. marmoreus*. The triangular spots on the surface are, however, light pink in color and their size is heterogeneous. The inside of aperture shows pink tone. Distribution: the same with the last species.

8. *Rhombus imperialis* (LINNÉ)

This is larger than the former two species. The side surface is white in ground color, and many spiral rows of black bars and brown dots are marked over it. Three wide zones of orange brown also encircle the surface of body whorl. The anterior end of the shell is colored in grayish brown. Distribution: south of Amami Islands, 5–10 fathoms deep.

9. *Virroconus ebraeus* (LINNÉ)

A stubby and heavy shell of small size. The spire is moderately tall, and ends in an obtuse apex. The tubercles on the shoulder of whorls are only weakly developed. The body whorl bears 4 rows of large quadrilateral black spots on its white surface, and its fore-end is colored black. Distribution: southern Honshû and farther south, at 2–5 fathoms depth.

10. *Virroconus coronatus* (GMELIN)

The spire is a little taller than that of the last species, and the shoulder of whorls bears only small granules. This is purplish white in ground color, bearing rows of small brown spots in two spiral zones. Distribution: south of southern Kyûshû, at 2–5 fathoms depth.

11. *Virroconus chaldeus* [RÖDING]

This shell is close to *V. ebraeus* in appearance, but is smaller. The spire bears small granules along the suture. Black spots on the outer surface are longitudinally joined together into zigzag lines, contained in two broad spiral zones. Distribution: south of southern Honshû, at 2–5 fathoms depth.

12. *Virroconus sponsalis* (HWASS)

This is also a small shell. The spire bears a spiral row of indistinct granules, and a few granulated ribs surround the basal part of the shell. The white exterior surface is encircled by a row of small brown spots on the shoulder, and by two zones of oblique brown patterns on the middle and the basal part of body whorl, of which the fore-end is dark purple in color. White specimens having no color patterns and those somewhat

elongated in outline have been respectively named *nanas* SOWERBY and *czylonensis* BRUGUIÈRE, but they are no more than the varieties of this species. Distribution: south of Amami Islands, 2–5 fathoms deep..

13. *Virroconus fulgetrum* (SOWERBY)

This is a medium-sized cone shell, with a row of distinct tubercles along the shoulder line. The exterior is marked by fine spiral threads, and covered by a fine network of light brown lines on the white background. Distribution: south of central Honshû, 5–10 fathoms in depth.

14. *Puncticulis arenatus* (HWASS)

The tubercles covering the spire are weaker than those of the above species. The body whorl is more inflated, and its anterior end is wider. Minute dots of purplish brown are densely marked over its white surface in longitudinal and zigzag-shaped stripes. The dots are especially dark-colored on two spiral zones around the body whorl. Distribution: south of Amami Islands, 5–10 fathoms deep.

15. *Puncticulis pulicarius* (HWASS)

This is close to the last species in shape, having a slightly less inflated body whorl. Black spots are rather sparsely scattered over the white ground color. Distribution: the same with the last species.

16. *Chelyconus catus* (HWASS)

The shell is fairly short, the body whorl steeply tapering toward the anterior. No granules are formed on its spire, but the side of body whorl is distinctly sculptured by spiral ribs bearing small granules. Brown cloud patterns cover the gray background of outer surface. Distribution: southern Kyûshû and farther south, at 2–5 fathoms depth.

17. *Chelyconus boeticus* (REEVE)

The outline is somewhat more slender than that of the preceding species. The outer surface is of a gray-white ground color, on which two broad spiral bands of light chestnut-brown are marked. The central part of body whorl between the two bands as

[PLATE 37]   Conidae

well as the shoulder part of whorls bears scattered spots of chestnut-brown. Distribution: south of Amami Islands, 2–5 fathoms deep.

18. Chelyconus fulmen (REEVE)

This shell is moderately large and thick. The spire is fairly tall, with a pink-colored apex. The last whorl is slightly inflated, bearing indistinct spiral threads on its exterior surface, which become somewhat stronger near the columellar end. It is marked by irregular dark brown blotches over its yellowish background. Specimens collected from deeper waters, that tend to have a more rounded shoulder and to bear dark spots only on the surface of spire, are named subsp. *kirai* KURODA. Distribution: south of Bôsô Peninsula, Kantô District, at 5–20 fathoms depth.

19. Rhizoconus rattus (HWASS)

This is a medium-sized shell, with a somewhat swollen spire bearing alternately brown and white radial patterns. The body whorl is surrounded by faint spiral threads on the outer surface, bearing dark brown cloud patterns all over the gray-white ground. In addition, white blotches of irregular size are spirally arranged on the shoulder and the middle part of the last whorl. Distribution: south of Amami Islands, 5–10 fathoms deep.

20. Pionoconus magus (LINNÉ)

The shell is fairly large and elongated. The flat spire is only slightly elevated at the apex. Spiral threads on the outer surface are very weakly sculptured. In ordinary specimens, brown longitudinal streaks are marked against the white ground in two wide spiral zones. The patterns are, however, very variable. Distribution: southern Kyûshû and farther south, below the tide line down to 5 fathoms.

21. Leptoconus generalis (LINNÉ)

This is a quite slender shell, with a flat spire. Only the apex is pointed and protruding. The shoulder of whorls is sharply angled, and the side-wall of the last whorl is almost straight. The outer surface is nearly smooth, only bearing several spiral threads near the base. Two reddish brown bands encircle the white surface of body whorl, and the rest of the surface is marked by dark brown zigzag lines and fine brown spiral bands. The anterior end of the shell is purplish brown in color. Distribution: south of the Ryukyus, at 5–10 fathoms depth.

22. Dauciconus vitulinus (HWASS)

The outline resemble that of *L. generalis*, but is somewhat broader especially at the anterior end of the shell. Spiral threads are more distinct; each one in every few threads is stronger than others, and those near the base bear granules. The surface patterns also resemble those of the last species, but are generally darker in color. The fore-end of the body whorl lacks any special coloration. Distribution: south of Amami Islands, at 5–10 fathoms depth.

23. Rhizoconus miles (LINNÉ)

This shell is wide at the shoulder, and sharply declines in width toward the anterior end. The spire is moderately developed, and furrowed along the suture. Spiral threads are raised on the basal part, while the surface of body whorl is smooth. The outer lip margin is especially thin. The ground color is light brown, and is marked by two dark brown bands encircling the middle and basal parts. Fine, wavy, longitudinal, and brown lines densely fill up the spaces not covered by the brown bands. Distribution: southern Honshû and southwards, at 15–20 fathoms depth.

24. Dauciconus striatellus (LINK)

The spire is small. The body whorl is slightly inflated on its sides. Faint spiral ribs on the outer surface are more strongly raised on the basal part, where they bear sparse, but distinct granules. Two spiral bands and irregular longitudinal stripes of brown are marked on the white ground color. This closely resembles a related species, *D. planorbis*, but differs from the latter in the broader shell and also in the different surface sculpture. Distribution: the Ryukyus and farther south, in subtidal zone down to 5 fathoms.

PLATE 37

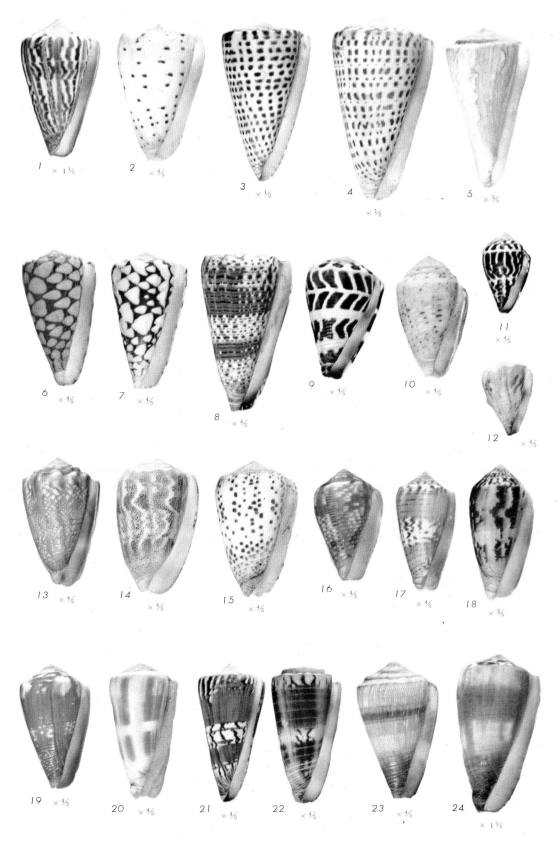

1   × 1 1/5

2   × 4/5

3   × 1/2

4   × 1/2

5   × 3/5

6   × 4/5

7   × 4/5

8   × 4/5

9   × 4/5

10   × 4/5

11   × 4/5

12   × 4/5

13   × 4/5

14   × 4/5

15   × 4/5

16   × 4/5

17   × 4/5

18   × 3/5

19   × 4/5

20   × 4/5

21   × 4/5

22   × 4/5

23   × 4/5

24   × 1 1/5

PLATE 38

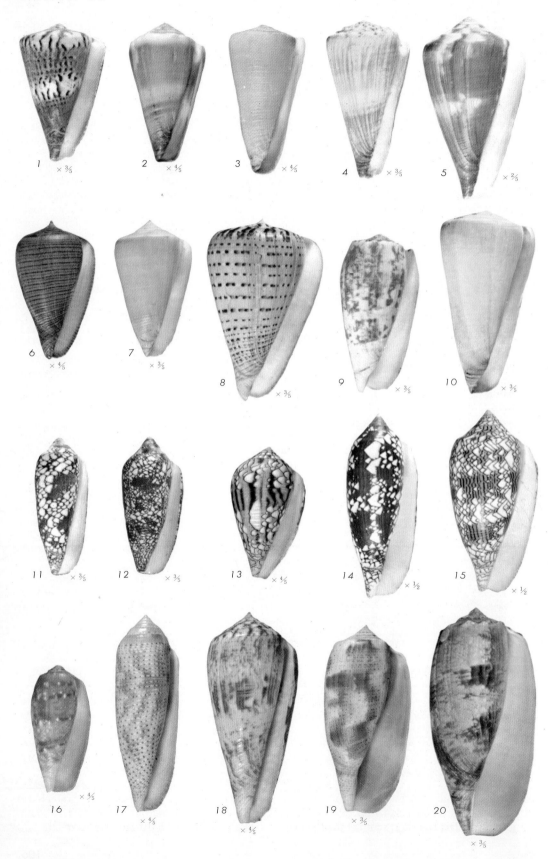

1 × 3/5

2 × 4/5

3 × 4/5

4 × 3/5

5 × 2/5

6 × 4/5

7 × 3/5

8 × 3/5

9 × 3/5

10 × 3/5

11 × 3/5

12 × 3/5

13 × 4/5

14 × 1/2

15 × 1/2

16 × 4/5

17 × 4/5

18 × 4/5

19 × 3/5

20 × 3/5

Family Conidae (2)

1. Rhizoconus capitaneus (LINNÉ)

The shell is medium-sized, and wide at the shoulder part, and sharply tapers. ·The apex is slightly raised above the low spire, which is radially colored in alternate brown and white. The aperture is fairly wide, and bordered by the thin outer lip. The body whorl bears two broad spiral zones of orange-yellow or gray-brown, in which small brown dots are arranged in spiral rows. Other parts of the side surface is white, and longitudinally marked by irregular dark brown streaks. Distribution: central Honshû and farther south, at 2–5 fathoms depth.

2. Virgiconus lividus (HWASS)

This resembles the preceding species in appearance, but differs in the more slender shape, the higher spire and the lack of dark patterns. The exterior surface is white on the shoulder and middle part of body whorl, while the rest is covered by spiral zones of dark brown. Besides, 2 fine brown lines encircle the lower middle part. The color of the fore-end of the shell is purplish brown. Distribution: south of southern Honshû, 5–10 fathoms deep.

3. Virgiconus emaciatus (REEVE)

This is a slender, cone-shaped shell, whose body whorl is slightly emaciated at its central part. It is light orange all over the surface, with two vague zones of darker tone encircling the side surface. The anterior end is tipped with purplish brown. Distribution: the same with V. lividus.

4. Virgiconus distans (HWASS)

The shell is fairly large and slender. The spire is slightly elevated, bearing weak granules along the shoulder line. The side slope of the body whorl is almost straight, but barely constricted at the middle part, on which a light-colored band encircles. The areas above and below this band are brown, and the anterior end is colored purplish brown. The surface of spire is fasciated by brown between the shoulder granules. Distribution: south of the Ryukyus,

5–10 fathoms deep.

5. Rhizoconus vexillum (GMELIN)

This shell is rather thin in texture in spite of its large size. The spire is moderately tall, and furrowed on its surface. The aperture is fairly broad. The surface of spire is alternately colored in white and brown along the spiral, whereas the side surface is generally brown, except vague white zones surrounding the shoulder and the middle part. Distribution: south of central Honshû, 5–10 fathoms deep.

6. Cleobula minima (LINNÉ)

This is a heavy shell of medium size. The spire is slightly raised at the pointed apex. The body whorl is somewhat inflated and rounded at the shoulder, and is nearly smooth, bearing spiral threads only on the basal area. The apical surface is dark brown, while the side is ornamented by fine, dark brown, spiral lines all over the lighter ground color. Distribution: south of Tanegashima, southern Kyûshû, at 5–10 fathoms depth.

7. Cleobula quercina (SOLANDER)

The shoulder of this shell is slightly carinated. Otherwise, the shape is not so much different from that of the preceding species. It is light yellow all over its surface, occasionally bearing a white spiral band. The epiderm is velvet-like and thick. Distribution: south of Shikoku, from the tide line down to 5 fathoms.

8. Cleobula betulina (LINNÉ)

This is a large and heavy shell, resembling Cl. minima in outline. Spiral threads are seen only on the basal part of body whorl. The ground color is light reddish yellow. It is faintly lustrous on the surface, and encircled by some 15 rows of dark brown dots, more or less varying in size. The surface of spire is fasciated by brown stripes. This shell is famous for its beautiful coloration. Distribution: south of the Ryukyus, 5–10 fathoms in depth.

[PLATE 38]   Conidae

9. Dendroconus striatus (LINNÉ)

The shell is large, thick and somewhat cylindrical in shape. The sutural zone is raised, but the suture line itself is grooved. The body whorl is densely sculptured over its outer surface by fine spiral threads, and bears a remarkably developed fasciole. The surface of spire is marked by orange-brown fasciations, and the apex bears reddish tone. The ground color of side surface is white or pinkish, and clouded by purplish brown blotches composed of very fine lines. Distribution: south of the Ryukyus, from the tide line to 5 fathoms.

10. Virgiconus virgo (LINNÉ)

A large, thick shell with a low spire and a slender body whorl. The surface looking almost smooth is faintly marked by feeble spiral threads. This is light flesh-colored all over its outer surface, with a violet spot on the fore-end. Distribution: south of the Ryukyus, at 5–10 fathoms depth.

11. Darioconus episcopus (HWASS)

This shell is medium- or large-sized. The spire is moderately steep, having a rounded apex. The body whorl is inflated, and considerably long. Spiral threads are somewhat sparsely marked. The ground color is white, but a coarse network of brown lines covers the whole surface, leaving many, white, triangular spots of various sizes. Distribution: the Ryukyus and farther south, below the tide line.

12. Darioconus magnificus (REEVE)

The shell resembles the last species in outline. The apex is blunt, but not rounded, and spiral threads on the exterior surface are dense, unlike those of D. episcopus. The network of reddish brown more finely covers the pinky white background. Blotches of the same color are more or less spirally arranged in two zones around the side surface. Distribution: south of southern Honshû, from the tide line to 5 fathoms depth.

13. Darioconus retifer (MENKE)

This is smaller, and more stocky in outline

than the preceding two species of Darioconus. The spire is tall, ending in a pointed apex. Spiral threads cover the outer surface, which is pinky white in ground color, bearing 2 orange, spiral zones on the middle and basal part of body whorl. Triangular and white spots, which are relatively large in size, are formed by a brown network overlaid on the entire surface. Distribution: south of the Ryukyus, below the tide line down to 5 fathoms.

14. Darioconus (Regiconus) aulicus (LINNÉ)

A large and narrowly elongated shell, more or less cylindrical in the outline of the last whorl. The spire is tall, and pointed. The reddish brown surface is filled up by numerous triangular colorless spots of varying sizes. Distribution: the same with the last species.

15. Darioconus textile (LINNÉ)

This is a pretty shell, large in size and heavy in construction. The spire is moderately tall and pointed. The surface of well inflated body whorl is glossy, and faintly marked by fine, slender, spiral threads. The aperture is fairly wide. Three orange-yellow bands, containing fine, longitudinal and wavy lines of dark brown, surrounds the side surface. Besides, it is covered all over its surface by mosaics of white triangular spots. Distribution: central Honshû and farther south, between the tide line and 5 fathoms depth.

16. Textilia bullata (LINNÉ)

This is like D. striatus in its outline. The glossy surface bears spiral threads only on the base of body whorl, clouded all over by purplish red, and scatteredly spotted by white. The inside of aperture is beautifully colored in pink. Distribution: south of southern Honshû, from the tide line to 5 fathoms depth.

17. Hermes nussatella (LINNÉ)

This medium-sized shell is cylindrical, fairly long and narrow in outline. The spire is tall and pointed. The surface of body whorl anterior to the shoulder is entirely covered by coarse spiral ribs, on which brown-colored granules are linearly arranged. The whitish ground is also ornamented by light brown cloud patterns. Distribution: south of Tanegashima, southern Kyûshû, 5–10 fathoms in depth.

18.   Chelyconus kinoshitai (KURODA)

Though this resembles *Ch. fulmen* in shape, the body whorl is more elongated, and its anterior part is narrower. The outer surface is faintly shining, and almost smooth. The ground color is purplish white, bearing brown, irregular patterns in 3 zones around the side surface. Like *Ch. fulmen*, this shell also tends to lose dark surface patterns, owing to the increase of depth of its habitat. Distribution: southern Honshû, 10–20 fathoms deep.

19.   Gastridium tulipa (LINNÉ)

This is a medium-sized cone shell, resembling *D. striatus* in outline, though rather thin in texture. The spire is pointed, bearing low tubercles. The exterior surface is slightly glossy and smooth, only encircled by spiral threads on the basal area. The aperture is wider than in *D. striatus*. It bears brown cloud patterns and many spiral rows of small brown dots over its purplish white background. Distribution: south of the Ryukyus, in subtidal zone down to 5 fathoms.

20.   Gastridium geographus (LINNÉ)

The shell is similar to the last species in shape, but is larger. The spire bears tubercles along the shoulder, which are especially prominent on the last whorl. Spiral threads are very weakly marked on

the faintly shining surface. The aperture is wide, and the columella is curved inward. Brown clouds and networks cover the pinky white surface. Distribution: the same with the last species.

Gastridium spp., *Dendroconus striatus*, *Darioconus textile*, *Darioconus aulicus*, etc. are known for their fatal bites and venomous glands. Most snails have a radula, or regularly arranged rows of fine teeth in their mouth, by which the animals grate their food. In cone shells, some teeth are tubular and arrow-like in shape, and their base is connected with the poison gland, as shown in the textfigure. Collectors should be cautious not to grasp the living animals carelessly by hand.

The opercula of some cone shells are also illustrated here. They are usually degenerate and so small that they can not even cover the narrow aperture of the shells. It is likely that the animals may use the operculum as a hook or fulcrum in their movement, as already stated in the section of the conch shells (p. 38).

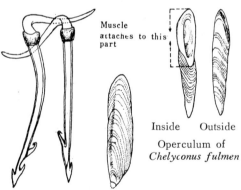

Muscle attaches to this part

Inside   Outside

Operculum of *Chelyconus fulmen*

Poison teeth of cone shells

Operculum of *Asprella sieboldi*, nuclear part missing

[PLATE 39]   Conidae, Terebridae

Family Conidae (3)

1. Asprella (Conasprella) cancellata (HWASS)

This shell is relatively small for the genus which is characterized by a tall, pointed and tower-shaped spire. The fore-end of the shell is rather abruptly narrowed. Distinct growth lines and spiral threads cross on the surface of spire, while the side surface of body whorl is covered by coarse spiral ribs. The outer lip margin is acute, and thin. The color of the outer surface is white, bearing brown fasciations and 2 spiral zones of irregular brown blotches on the spire and the body whorl, respectively. Distribution: south of southern Honshû, 30–50 fathoms in depth.

2. Asprella (Endemoconus) ione (FULTON)

This is slightly larger than the preceding species, and thin in texture. The spire is moderately tall. The surface of body whorl is almost smooth, except some spiral ribs near the anterior end. The ground color of the exterior surface is light purple, on which 2 interrupted bands and many rows of small dots are spirally marked in light brown color. Distribution: southern Honshû and farther south, at 50–80 fathoms depth.

3. Asprella (Conasprella) ichinoseana KURODA

This medium-sized shell has a tall and somewhat stepped spire. Each whorl except the last one bears granules on the shoulder. On the spire surface, growth lines are clearly seen, while spiral threads are only slightly marked. The side surface is sculptured by punctured, fine grooves, which are indistinct near the shoulder but grow deeper anteriorly. The aperture is narrow, and the outer lip bears an acute margin. Three rows of brown spots and a few intervening rows of smaller dots encircle the body whorl over its white ground color. Only the uppermost row on the shoulder extends over the spire. Distribution: Pacific coasts of Shikoku, 80–100 fathoms deep.

4. Asprella (Endemoconus) sieboldi (REEVE)

The shape and structure of the shell resemble those of A. ione, but this has a taller and sharply pointed spire, which is slightly stepped due to the carination of whorls at the shoulder. No granules are seen on the shoulder line. Spiral grooves are on the basal part of body whorl. The exterior is white in ground color, and usually marked by 3 interrupted, brown bands, but the number of the bands may be 2, 1, or even 0 in different individuals. Distribution: south of central Honshû, as deep as 30–50 fathoms.

5. Asprella orbignyi (AUDOUIN)

Resembling A. ichinoseana in shape, this differs from the former in the following points. The granules along the shoulder line are distinct on all whorls including the body whorl. Spiral furrows are distinctly marked all over the outer surface, and do not cross with growth lines. The side surface is wholly covered by disconnected brown lines, and some of them are especially dark in color, forming 3 vague, spiral zones. Distribution: the same with A. sieboldi.

6. Asprella australis (HOLTEN)

The spire is tall, but scarcely stepped. The outer surface is clearly sculptured by coarse spiral furrows. Longitudinal lines of dark brown are irregularly marked on the surface. The anterior end of the shell is tipped with orange color in aged specimens. Distribution: the same with the last species.

Family Terebridae (1)

The shells belonging to this family are called the auger shells, and are slender and very elongated in shape, having a tall spire and numerous whorls. The whorls are flat-sided, and generally encircled immediately below the suture by a zone that is more or less distinctly demarcated and bears particular sculptures (subsutural zone). The aperture is small and very short, compared with the total shell length. The anterior canal forms a notch, and the columella lacks folds on it. The operculum is horny. Many species are found mostly in warm waters of the world. See also supplementary illustrations in Plate 71.

7. Cinguloterebra stearnsii (?) PILSBRY

This slender shell is fairly long, reaching 150 mm or more in length, but is only 1/10 as wide at its maximum diameter. The apical end is usually lost, but the number of whorls may probably be more than 50. The subsutural zone is remarkably raised, and divided by a spiral groove into the wider posterior zone and narrow anterior zone. Other parts of the surface bears a few spiral threads. The columellar end is truncated. The anterior canal is short, but deeply notched. It is yellowish white in ground color, and marked by a spiral row of brown spots on the subsutural zone and by brown longitudinal stripes on the anterior half of whorls. Distribution: central Honshû and Shikoku along Pacific coasts, at 80–100 fathoms depth.

8. Myurella pretiosus (REEVE)

This is somewhat shorter than the preceding species in the total length of shell. The length of each whorl is, however larger. The subsutural zone is only weakly raised, and bears granules in earlier whorls. Later whorls are slightly inflated, and marked by reticulate sculpture formed by spiral threads and curved longitudinal folds crossing each other. The aperture is larger than that of the preceding species. This is dirty white in ground color, and surrounded by a broad, brown band on each whorl. Distribution: south of central Honshû, 50–80 fathoms deep.

9. Triplostephanus triseriatus (GRAY)

An extremely elongated and narrow shell comprising some 50 whorls. This will reach 100 mm in length, but is only about 7 mm wide. Somewhat raised subsutural zone is divided into two subzones, bearing a row of granules. Granulated, spiral threads and longitudinal lines cover the anterior part of whorls, showing a fine reticulate sculpture. The aperture is very small and short, containing a reflexed anterior canal.

Distribution: the same with the last species.

10. Dimidacus babylonia (LAMARCK)

The shell is more stout, as compared with the foregoing 3 species. The whorls are 24–25 in number, bearing a slightly raised subsutural zone, which is granulated on earlier whorls but only grooved on later whorls. Other parts of the whorls' surface are sculptured by a coarse network of spiral and longitudinal grooves. The aperture is short, and the anterior canal is reflexed. The ground color is flesh-brown, while the raised parts of surface sculpture are whitish. Distribution: south of the Ryukyus, from the tide line to 5 fathoms depth.

11. Noditerebra (Pristiterebra) bifrons (HINDS)

The shell is even shorter, and composed of about 15 whorls. The subsutural zone is scarcely raised, and the whorls are slightly constricted along its anterior margin. The surface sculpture, consisting of weak spiral threads, longitudinal lines and granules on their intersection points, is very faintly marked. The aperture is rather long, containing a reflexed anterior canal. It is simply dark brown all over the surface. Distribution: south of central Honshû, 5–10 fathoms deep.

12. Acuminia lanceata (LINNÉ)

This is a slender shell, composed of 17–18 whorls that lack the subsutural zone. The outer surface is smooth and beautifully glossy, bearing longitudial folds only on initial several whorls. The aperture is small, but fairly elongated. The whorls are sparsely marked over the white surface by brown, longitudinal lines. Distribution: south of Amami Islands, 5–10 fathoms in depth.

13. Cinguloterebra monilis (QUOY et GAIMARD)

The shell is rather stout, comprising about 20 whorls. The subsutural zone bears granules, and is distinctly raised and white-colored, whereas other parts of outer surface are marked by reticulate sculptures and flesh-brown in color. The aperture is short,

[PLATE 39]   Conidae, Terebridae

containing a reflexed anterior canal. Distribution: southern Honshû and farther south, 5–10 fathoms deep.

14. Brevimyurella lischkeana (DUNKER)

This is a short auger shell that consists of some 17 whorls. The subsutural zone is not raised, but is bordered by a spiral groove. Fine, longitudinal folds cover the entire surface, and faint spiral threads are barely visible through a magnifying glass. It is light brown all over, and surrounded by a brown band along the suture. Distribution: Pacific coasts south of Honshû, from the tide line down to 5 fathoms.

15. Hastula diversa (SMITH)

This is even shorter and narrower than the preceding species. The whorls are only 14 or so in number. The subsutural zone can not be distinguished by the surface sculpture, but a white zone containing a row of brown spots encircles the whorls subsuturally. The upper part of each whorl bears longitudinal folds, while spiral sculptures are not seen. The exterior is shining and purplish brown, and only the protoconch is white-colored. Distribution: the same with the preceding species.

16. Subula crenulata (LINNÉ)

The shell is large and stout in construction, comprising about 20 whorls. On earliest whorls, the subsutural zone is bordered by a groove and bears granules, but on later whorls the groove tends to disappear, and the granules are gradually transformed into longitudinal folds and then into pointed nodules. No other surface sculptures are seen. The fore-end of the shell bears a fasciole, and the anterior canal is reflexed. Rows of tiny brown dots surround the whorls on the light flesh-brown background. Distribution: south of Amami Islands, from the tide line to 10 fathoms depth.

17. Subula dimidiata (LINNÉ)

This resembles the last species in shape, but the subsutural zone is not raised but bordered by a distinct groove. The exterior is smooth, except a spiral row of

granules and longitudinal furrows on the apical part of spire. This has also a fasciole and a reflexed anterior canal. The operculum is horny and elliptic, with concentric lines around an eccentrically situated nucleus. The surface is lustrous and reddish brown in color, and is sparsely marked by longitudinal white streaks. Distribution: south of Amami Islands, below the tide line down to 5 fathoms.

18. Subula areolata (LINK)

The size, shape and sculpture are almost the same with those of *S. dimidiata*, but the ground color of outer surface is white. The surface is marked by rows of brown, square-shaped spots. Distribution: Amami Islands and farther south, from the tide line down to 10 fathoms.

19. Terebra subulata (LINNÉ)

This is nearly of the same length with the preceding shell. The whorls are shorter and larger in number (about 30), and are slightly inflated at the subsutural zone. The outer surface lacks any distinct sculpture and is smooth and glossy, bearing spirally arranged, large, quadrilateral blotches of dark brown over the white or light fleshy ground color. Distribution: south of Shikoku, from the tide line to 5 fathoms depth.

20. Terebra guttata [RÖDING]

The shell is slightly thicker than that of *T. subulata*. A spiral row of granules, longitudinal folds and a furrow bordering the subsutural zone are seen on initial whorls near the apex, but they disappear on later whorls. So, most of the outer surface is smooth and faintly glossy. Only fine, thread-like growth lines are marked. Two rows of white spots encircle the body whorl on the pinky flesh-colored surface, and one of them extends on other whorls. The shell surface is somewhat raised or swollen under the white spots. Distribution: south of the Ryukyus, between the tide line and 5 fathoms depth.

21. Subula (Oxymeris) maculata (LINNÉ)

This shell is very large, stout and thick.

PLATE **39**

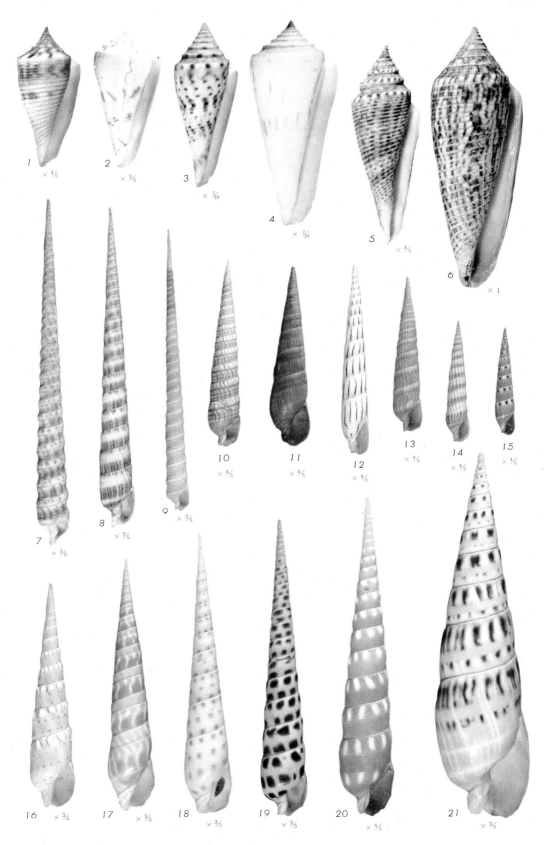

1
× 4/5

2
× 3/5

3
× 7/10

4
× 7/10

5
× 4/5

6
× 1

7
× 3/5

8
× 3/5

9
× 3/5

10
× 4/5

11
× 4/5

12
× 4/5

13
× 4/5

14
× 4/5

15
× 4/5

16 × 3/5

17 × 3/5

18 × 3/5

19 × 3/5

20 × 4/5

21 × 3/5

PLATE **40**

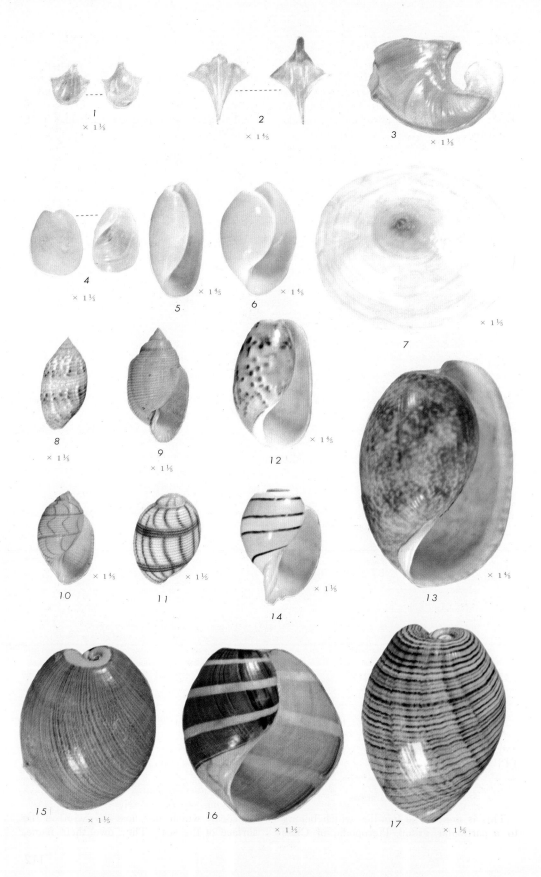

1
× 1 ⅕

2
× 1 ⅘

3
× 1 ⅕

4
× 1 ⅕

5
× 1 ⅘

6
× 1 ⅘

7
× 1 ⅕

8
× 1 ⅕

9
× 1 ⅕

12
× 1 ⅘

13
× 1 ⅘

10
× 1 ⅘

11
× 1 ⅕

14
× 1 ⅕

15
× 1 ⅕

16
× 1 ⅕

17
× 1 ⅕

The spire tapers rather steeply toward its apex, and consists of about 15 whorls. The change of surface sculpture from initial to later whorls is as described in the preceding species. The fasciole is strongly developed. The glossy exterior surface is white or light flesh-brown in its ground color, and marked by a row of longitudinal stripes of dark brown and by another disconnected, narrow band of the same color. It is frequently used as a material of shell-works. Distribution: the same with *S. areolata.*

[PLATE 40]

Family Cavolinidae

This is one of the families which belong to a particular group, Pteropoda, of Class Gastropoda. The animals of this group have two wing-like feet as shown in the text-figure, by which they float and swim on the surface of the sea. They owe their name, sea-butterfly as they are often called, to this way of living. The shells are not spirally shaped, but are like honey-comb, cylindrical or needle-shaped. The number of the species are not so large, but certain species are said to swarm in such a great amount as to partly change the color of water surface.

Living animal of
Diacria trispinosa
(after TRYON)

1. Diacria trispinosa (BLAINVILLE)

The shell is depressed and quadrilateral in shape, with two lateral spines and a tubular protrusion at its anterior end. The length and width of the shell are about 8 mm and 4 mm, respectively. This is entirely or half transparent, showing brown tone around the opening of its aperture. The central part of the shell bears folds on its surface.

2. Clio pyramidata LINNÉ

The shell is transparent, and the texture is like cellophane. It is irregularly rhombic in outline and approximately 11 mm × 8 mm in its size. The aperture is widely open anteriorly, the posterior end is sharply pointed, and the central part of the shell is swollen, so that the whole shell is somewhat funnel-shaped.

Since the animals of this group are planktonic or floating in their life, the shells are washed ashore after the gale anywhere along sea-coasts of Japan.

Family Aplysiidae

This is the family of sea-hare, one of the groups of sea-slugs having no shells around their body. In some species, however, a kind of calcareous shell is formed within their body, of which one example is illustrated here.

3. Dolabella auricularia (SOLANDER)

The animal is a large, light brown-colored sea-hare reaching 140 mm in its body length. The shell is formed inside the body, being a twisted plate, about 45 mm in length and 35 mm in maximum width. It has a round apex showing a somewhat spiral structure, from which the plate extends gradually increasing its width. The plate is white and covered by a brown film over the surface. Distribution: the animals live among seaweeds, near 1 meter depth in subtidal zone, south of Honshû.

Family Philinidae

4. Philine kurodai HABE

The animals of this family have a soft body with a head like a shield in its shape, and have a thin shell within it covered by the mantle and situated posteriorly to a notch at the center of the head. The shell of this species is oval in shape, white, semi-transparent and very thin. It is just like a shallow cup in appearance, having the spirally rolled apical part and a widely open aperture. It has no vertex, and is characterized by a constriction on the neck-part. The surface bears growth lines. Distribution: south of Honshû, in subtidal zone.

A related species, *Ph. argentata* GOULD is distinguished from the former by the lack of constriction on the shell.

Family Haminoeidae

5. Aliculastrum cylindricum (HELBLING)

This shell is oblong elliptic in outline, thin in texture, and opaque. Since the whorls are rolled inside, the spire is concealed. The central part of the outer surface is smooth and faintly lustrous, and both ends are marked by fine spiral furrows. The aperture is elongated and widened in its anterior part. The posterior canal is twisted, and extends over the apical end. The shell is pure white in color and covered over the exterior by a thin gray epiderm. Distribution: south of Honshû, below the tide line.

6. Atys naucum (LINNÉ)

The structure of this shell is not essentially different from that of the last species, but its outline is wide and oval, owing to the inflation of the last whorl. The surface sculpture is also similar to that of *A. cylindricum*, but the spiral furrows develop all over the entire surface in some individuals. This is white in color, and covered by a thin epiderm bearing sparse, longitudinal stripes of brown. Distribution: south of central Honshû, below the tide line.

Family Umbraculidae

7. Umbraculum umbraculum (HUMPHREY)

The animal of this species has a large cylindrical body that looks just like a dark rock-mass. The limpet-like shell lies above the upper side of the body, posteriorly to the antennae, like a small coolie-hat. It is a white disc, slightly elongated in outline, having an apex protruding at the center. On the outer side of the shell it bears growth lines around its apex, marked with a round, brown spot and covered by a yellowish brown epiderm. The inner side is somewhat concave. Distribution: south of Honshû, at 20–30 fathoms depth.

Family Acteonidae (8, 9, 12, 13)

8. Solidula sulcata (GMELIN)

This is a thick, cylindrical shell with a small, pointed spire composed of about 7 whorls. The outer surface of the large body whorl is entirely covered by distinct spiral ribs. The aperture extends anteriorly. It has folds on its columella, of which the foremost one is deeply notched into the columellar axis. It is white in ground color, and bears small irregular patterns of dark brown or greenish gray. Distribution: south of Amami Islands, in subtidal zone.

9. Punctacteon kirai (HABE)

The shape of this shell resembles that of *P. sulcata*, but this differs from the preceding species in its reticulate sculpture on the shell surface, produced by the intersection of

spiral ribs with longitudinal growth lines. Only one, weak fold is seen on the columella. Distribution: central Honshû and southwards, as deep as 50–80 fathoms.

Family Bullidae

10. Bullina lineata (GRAY)

The shell is small, thin, and elliptic in outline. The spire is small, comprising about 5 whorls, while the last whorl is large and inflated. Fine spiral threads crossing with growth lines cover the outer surface. The columella is slightly twisted. It is white in color, bearing 2 spiral lines and sparse, longitudinal, zigzag lines. Both lines are red in color. Distribution: Honshû and farther south, in subtidal zone.

11. Bullina nobilis HABE

Having a shape similar to the preceding species, this is considerably larger in size. The surface sculpture is finely reticulate, consisting of fairly thick, round, spiral ribs and longitudinal growth threads. Two or three spiral lines are clearly marked in red against the white background, together with a number of longitudinal lines of the same color. Distribution: central Honshû and southwards, at 50–80 fathoms depth.

Family Hydatinidae

12. Bulla orientalis HABE

The spire is concealed under the well developed body whorl, and a pit-like depression is seen on the apical end. The outline is cylindrical, with the elongated aperture that widens anteriorly. The outer lip margin is acute, and its central part is almost straight. The outer surface is smooth and purplish brown in ground color, and is marked by scattered, triangular, small spots of lighter color as well as by 4 interrupted zones of dark brown encircling the body whorl. Distribution: south of the Ryukyus, below the tide line.

13. Bulla vernicosa GOULD

Closely resembling the preceding species, this is larger in the size of shell and of

114

apical pit. The last whorl is more inflated, and the outer lip margin is slightly curved in its central part. The brown ground of exterior surface is flecked by light-colored spots and dark brown blotches arranged more or less zonally. Distribution: south of Honshû, in subtidal zone.

14. Aplustrum amplustre (LINNÉ)

An oval bubble shell, thin in texture. The spire is composed of 5 whorls so, and very low. The columellar end is somewhat extended anteriorly, and twisted together with the parietal callus. The large body whorl is smooth, white, and faintly glossy on its surface, and is marked by 2 broad, spiral, color bands of pink, which are respectively bordered by fine black lines on both sides. Distribution: south of Kyûshû, below the tide line.

15. Hydatina (Hydatoria) zonata (SOLANDER)

This globular shell is large, very thin and fragile in texture. The number of whorls are less than 4. The spire is depressed especially along the suture. The body whorl is well inflated, and very large. The aperture is broadly open. A thin callus widely develops over the inner lip. This is smooth and glossy on the outer surface, on which fine, longitudinal lines of black are densely marked all over the light yellowish brown background, except on the anterior and posterior ends of whorls. Distribution: south of Honshû, below the tide line.

16. Hydatina (Hydatoria) albocincta (VAN DER HOEVEN)

The structure and texture of this shell are alike to those of H. zonata, but the body whorl is more strongly swollen. Four black zones encircle the whorls on the light yellow background. Distribution: the same with H. zonata.

17. Hydatina physis (LINNÉ)

The shell is subgenerically distinguished from the preceding two bubble shells, having an umbilicus and a weakly developed fasciole. It is also different in the coloration of outer surface: many fine spiral lines of black densely cover the entire surface which is buff in ground color. Distribution: the same with the preceding two species.

Class Scaphopoda

The molluscs of this group have a single tubular shell, approximately round in cross-section and tapering toward the posterior end. It is curved like a tusk of the elephant, the concave side being the dorsal side. The shell has openings on both ends, of which the anterior one is larger. The animals have a pointed foot and a poorly developed head, having neither eyes nor antennae. They live half-buried on sandy bottom of the sea, with their posterior end exposed above the sand. This class is taxonomically placed between Gastropoda and Pelecypoda, because this is related to the former in having a single shell and radula, while the pointed foot and undeveloped head are common to the latter.

Family Siphonodentaliidae

1.   Dischides belcheri (PILSBRY et SHARP)

A minute elephant tusk shell, about 9 mm in length and 1.2 mm in diameter. The shell is only slightly curved and circular in its cross-section, bearing only growth lines on the outer surface. The apical end is characteristically forked, owing to the wedge-shaped notches on both dorsal and ventral sides. This is semi-transparent, and milky white in color. Distribution: central Honshû, below the tide line.

2.   Gadila (Platyschides) novilunata (KIRA)

This small tusk shell is about 16 mm long and 2.3 mm in maximum diameter. Unlike other species, the shell tube reaches its maximum thickness at its middle part, tapering toward both ends. The aperture is compressed dorso-ventrally, and elliptic in outline. The surface bears no sculpture and is somewhat translucent and milky white. Distribution: Tosa Bay of Shikoku, 80–100 fathoms deep.

3.   Entalina majestica KIRA

This is a little larger than the preceding species, about 16.9 mm and 2.3 mm in length and diameter respectively. This bears 2 carinated ridges, respectively on dorsal and ventral sides, so that the cross-section of tube is like a trapezoid with its base on the ventral side. On the outer surface a number of fine, longitudinal threads is also seen. The shell is white in color, but opaque. Distribution: central Honshû and Shikoku, at 30–50 fathoms in depth.

4.   Gadila kikuchii (KURODA et HABE)

The tube of this minute tusk shell rapidly increases its width from the apex to the aperture, and is only slightly curved, and, somewhat compressed dorso-ventrally, being elliptic in cross-section. It is also semi-transparent, and milky white in color. Distribution: Toyama Bay of central Honshû, as deep as 100 fathoms.

Family Dentaliidae

5.   Episiphon candelatum (KIRA)

This is a small tusk shell, about 10.7 mm long and 2.1 mm wide, and only weakly curved. The tube maintains nearly the same thickness from the top to the base. The apical opening lacks a notch, and is closed by a septum, from the center of which rises a fine tube (0.2–0.4 mm thick) like a candlewick. The surface is smooth and white. Distribution: Tosa Bay of Shikoku, at 80–100 fathoms depth.

6.   Antalis weinkauffi (DUNKER)

A medium-sized and bent shell, round in its cross-section. It is approximately 75 mm × 6.6 mm in size. The outer surface is smooth, and slightly lustrous, bearing weak longitudinal ribs only on its apical part. The posterior end of the shell is double-tubed, with a slit-like notch on its ventral side. This is usually white, but may be light yellow or pink in color. Distribution: south of Honshû, 5–10 fathoms deep.

7.   Dentalium (Paradentalium) octangulatum hexagonum GOULD

8.   Dentalium (Paradentalium) octangulatum DONOVAN

These two forms have a curved shell,

[PLATE 41]   Siphonodentaliidae, Dentaliidae

bearing several sharp ridges longitudinally on the surface. The cross-section is thus polygonal. Interspaces are irregularly marked by interstitial, longitudinal threads. They lack the apical notch, and are white in color. The two forms are separated based on the difference in the number of longitudinal ridges, 6 in the former and 8 in the latter. On examining many individuals, however, one find that the number is variable, ranging from 5 to 8. Therefore, the specific distinction seems not to be reasonable. Distribution: south of Honshû, below the tide line.

9. Laevidentalium crocinum (DALL)

The shell is moderately large, and bent like a bow. It has a circular cross-section, and glossy smooth surface, and lacks the apical notch. The exterior is beautifully colored in fleshy brown. Distribution: central Honshû and farther south, at 30–50 fathoms depth.

10. Fissidentalium hungerfordi (PILSBRY et SHARP)

This is also moderately large and nearly straight. Only the apical part is slightly curved, and bears a deep slit on its ventral side. The cross-section is dorso-ventrally compressed, and elliptic in outline. The outer surface is finely sculptured by many longitudinal threads, and is yellow in ground color, with a few rings of orange-red near the aperture. Distribution: the same with the preceding species.

11. Pictodentalium formosum hirasei (KIRA)

This pretty shell is stout, thick and heavy in construction. This is slightly bent, and the double-tubed posterior end bears a notch. The exterior surface is weakly shining, but uneven owing to strong longitudinal ribs (15–18 in number) and interstitial threads. Ring patterns of reddish purple, greenish and light brown alternately ornament the surface like a rainbow spectrum. Distribution: southern Honshû and southwards, near 20 fathoms depth.

12. Fissidentalium yokoyamai (MAKIYAMA)

The shell is long, nearly straight and thinner in texture than the last species. The white-colored surface is marked by many longitudinal ribs of different thickness, which are crossed by fine lateral lines. It has a round cross-section with the wrinkled margin. A deep slit occurs on the apical end. Distribution: Tosa Bay of Shikoku, 80–100 fathoms deep.

13. Fissidentalium vernedei (SOWERBY)

This is the largest of Japanese tusk shells. The tube is moderately curved, round in cross-section and doubled at the apical end bearing a notch. The surface of this thick shell is densely covered by fine longitudinal threads, which are somewhat weaker than those of the last species. The exterior is white in ground color, with or without ring patterns of light brown or yellow. Distribution: south of central Honshû, at 10–20 fathoms depth.

PLATE **41**

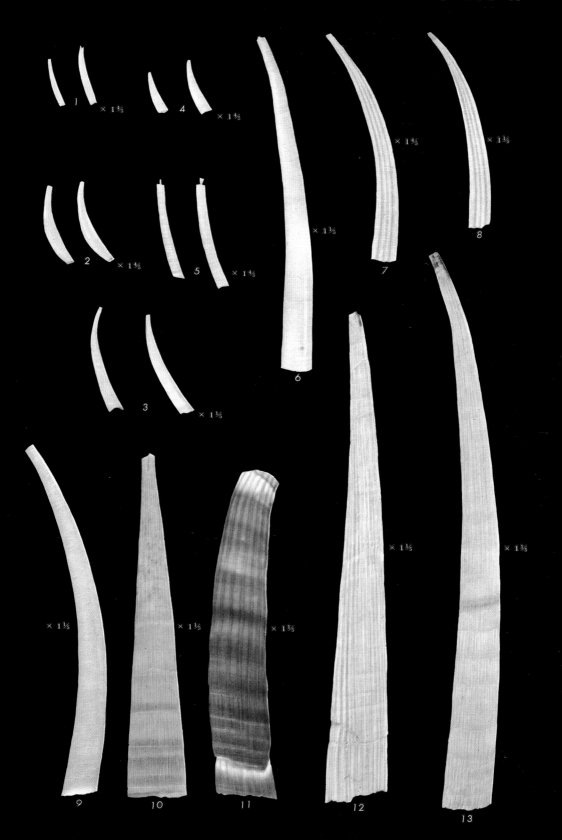

1

× 1⅘

4

× 1⅘

× 1⅘

× 1½

2

× 1⅘

5

× 1⅘

7

8

× 1½

3

× 1½

6

× 1½

× 1½

× 1½

× 1½

× 1½

9

10

11

12

13

PLATE 42

1 × 1⅕

2 × ⅘

3 × 1⅕

4 × 2½

8 × 1⅕

9 × 1⅕

a, b,

5 × 1⅕

10 × 1⅕

11 × 1⅕

12 × 1⅕

a, *6* b,

× 1⅕

13 × 1⅕

7 × 1⅕

14 × 1⅕

Class Pelecypoda

The animal enclosed between two mantle lobes lacks a head as well as jaws and radular teeth, and is protected by a couple of shelly valves, secreted from the mantle lobes. The valves are connected by a horny ligament and resilium. Moreover, they usually bear 2 muscle scars on the inner surface of the valve, on which the adductor muscles are attached, connecting both valves. But, the oysters possess only one posterior adductor muscle scar. The outer surface of the valve is smooth or sculptured, and is covered with an epiderm or periostracum. The foot is adapted for burrowing and generally wedge-shaped, and sometimes bears a gland secreting a byssus by which the animal attaches itself to other objects. Two siphons lead into the mantle cavity; the lower inhalant one conducts water to gills, and the upper exhalant one carries water away from the cavity. Foods are taken with the aid of two ciliated gills, which are also respiratory organs. This class of bivalves comprises far less number of species as compared with Gastropoda. But the bivalves are generally more important as a food-resource of mankind, and some of them are even artificially raised on a large scale in Japan. They are the dwellers of marine, brackish and fresh waters.

Family Solemyidae

This family is characterized by the polished, brown periostracum extending well beyond the margin of the valves. Though the shells are somewhat allied to those of Solenidae in shape, they are thin, with a toothless hinge and gaping at both rounded ends. See also Plate 72.

1. *Solemya (Acharax) joponica* DUNKER

The shell is small and covered with a polished, purplish brown periostracum, extending over the margin. The surface bears faint broad grooves radiating from the umbo to the margin. The beak is very low, and situated near the posterior end, and the external ligament is situated behind the umbo. Hinge bears no tooth. Distribution: rather common in shallow waters from Honshû to Kyûshû.

2. *Solemya (Acharax) tibai* KURODA

This giant awning clam reaches about 90 mm in length, and is thin, fragile and elongate, tapering toward the posterior end. The surface is sculptured by broad but shallow grooves runing from the umbo to the margin, and covered with a blackish thick periostracum extending over the shell margin with finger-like fringes. The interior is white and somewhat porcellaneous. The beak is very close to the posterior end, on which the external ligament is seen. This has no teeth. Distribution: rarely found off Cape Erimo of Hokkaidô, near 250 fathoms depth.

Family Nuculidae

The shells of this family are small to medium in size, trigonal ovate and equivalved, with 2 rows of numerous teeth meeting below the umbo and separated by a pit for a resilium or chondrophore. The interior is pearly, and the ventral margin is smooth or crenulated. The mantle line is entire.

3. *Ennucula niponica* (SMITH)

This is a large, rather inflated nut shell, trigonal oval in outline. The surface is shiny blackish green in color, and shows a faint concentric sculpture of growth lines. The interior is pearly white. The hinge plate is narrow, and two series of teeth are separated by the projecting chondrophore. Distribution: from northern Honshû to Kyûshû, at 50 fathoms depth.

4. *Ennucula tenuis* (MONTAGU)

This species has a small, thin shell. The periostracum is glossy and pale yellowish olive in color. The interior is shiny nacreous. The beak is more prominent and more triangulate than that of the preceding species, and is located near the anterior end. Distribution: common on fine sandy bottom of 50 fathoms depth, northern Honshû and northwards.

[PLATE 42]   Solemyidae, Nuculidae, Nuculanidae

5. *Acila divaricata* (HINDS)

The shell is medium in size, thick ovate, and shortly rostrated posteriorly. The outside of the shell is decorated with a divaricating sculpture forming angles along a line from the umbo to the midpoint of ventral the margin. The periostracum is smooth, polished and yellowish or blackish brown. The interior is pearly, and the margin is not crenulated. Distribution: Honshû and southwards, at 10–100 fathoms depth.

6. *Acila schencki* KIRA

This resembles the preceding species, but the shell is larger, with a coarser sculpture, and more angularly rostrated posteriorly than the preceding species. Distribution: south of central Honshû, 50–80 fathoms deep.

7. *Acila divaricata vigilia* SCHENCK

This form is more compressed and larger than the real form. The posterior rostrum is weak, and the divaricating grooves are also shallow. Distribution: northern Honshû and Hokkaidô, at 80–100 fathoms depth.

Family Nuculanidae

The shells are comparatively oblong, and usually rounded at the anterior end, and prolonged at the posterior. The periostracum is yellowish brown, and the interior is porcellaneous. They have 2 series of teeth, separated by an oblique pit for the ligament. These species are chiefly dredged from deep sea bottom, and are often got from the stomach of the flatfish.

8. *Nuculana (Robaia) robai* (KURODA)

This is a small, slightly inflated shell, with a straight posterior prolongation. The anterior end is regularly rounded, and a ridge extends from the umbo to the posterior end, by which a narrow escutcheon is produced along the dorsal margin. The surface is fairly smooth, glossy and greenish brown, with only faint concentric lines. Distribution: commonly found in the Japan Sea, at 80–100 fathoms depth.

9. *Nuculana (Thestyleda) acinacea* HABE

The shell is small, elongate, slightly inflated, rounded anteriorly, greatly prolonged posteriorly, slightly upturned, and truncated at the hinder end. The surface bears numerous very fine concentric lines, which are strengthened in the area between the 2 ridges runing from the beak to the posterior end. Distribution: Tosa Bay of Shikoku, as deep as 80–100 fathoms.

10. *Saccella confusa* (HANLEY)

This shell is ovate, rounded in front, pointed behind, and somewhat inflated. The surface is sculptured by distinct concentric ridges, and its color is pale yellowish brown. The beak is situated almost at the middle of dorsal margin. Distribution: Honshû and southwards, in shallow waters.

11. *Portlandia (Portlandella) japonica* (ADAMS & REEVE)

A thin and inflated shell, with the ends rounded anteriorly and bluntly pointed posteriorly. The glossy surface bears very fine concentric lines, and is colored in yellowish brown. Distribution: from Honshû to Kyûshû, on muddy bottom at 5–50 fathoms depth.

12. *Yoldia (Cnesterium) notabilis* YOKOYAMA

The shell is medium-sized, ovate in shape and compressed. The surface bears distinct concentric lines crossing with oblique lines on its posterior part, and is blackish brown in color. The beak is situated at the posterior end. Distribution: northern parts of Japanese coasts, in shallow waters down to 50 fathoms.

13. *Yoldia (Cnesterium) johanni* DALL

The shell is quite thin and compressed ovate in shape. The posterior end is pointed and upturned, while the anterior end is rounded. The surface is sculptured by concentric and oblique lines only on its posterior part, not marked by growth lines, but covered by a vernicose, yellowish brown periostracum. The interior is white, but not pearly. The beak is situated almost at the middle of dorsal margin. Distribution: from northern Honshû to Hokkaidô, in shallow waters.

14. Yoldia (Megayoldia) thraciaeformis STORER

This is large, somewhat resembles the blade of an axe in shape, and is upturned at the posterior end. An obtuse fold runs from the umbo to the posterior ventral margin. The surface is scarcely sculptured, and grayish brown in color. The ligament pit below the umbo and chondrophore between 2 series of teeth are large and spoon-like. Distribution: on both coasts of the north Pacific as far south to Hokkaidô and Oregon, rather common at 20–100 fathoms depth. It is often found in the stomach of fish.

[PLATE 43]   Arcidae

Family Arcidae (1)

The ark shells of this family vary from small to large size and are mostly elongate or squarish in shape. The surface is sculptured by radial ribs and covered with a thick velvety periostracum. The interior is china-white. The beaks are hooked and usually apart from each other, forming a wide ligamental area between them, and the straight hinge line posseses numerous small teeth. The animal often has the byssus by which it attaches itself to rocks or other substrata. Some of them are cultured for food in Japan.

1. Striarca (Spinearca) interplicata (GRABAU et KING)

The shell is small, solid and inflated, roundly squarish in shape. The surface is decussately sculptured by radial cords and growth lines, forming beads at the crossing points. The pale brown periostracum is velvety. The interior is white and the margin is crenulated. The ligamental area is narrow and covered with a black ligament. Distribution: from Honshû to China, on muddy bottom below the low tide mark.

2. Bentharca xenophoricola (KURODA)

This is a small and rather inflated shell, the left valve being larger than the right one. It is trigonal ovate, broadly truncated at the posterior end and acuminate at the anterior end. The surface is reticulated and somewhat granulated by radial and concentric lines. A narrow gape is seen at the ventral margin from which the byssus is projected. The beak is close to the anterior end, and forms a narrow ligamental area. Distribution: from central Honshû to Kyûshû, attaching to rocks or other shells such as *Xenophora*.

3. Barbatia (Ustularca) cruciata (PHILIPPI)

The shell is medium in size, and somewhat elongated toward the posterior end. The surface bears numerous radiating costae and concentric lines, producing a faint network, and is covered with radially arranged fibrous periostracum, which is blackish or dark purplish brown in color. The interior is brown. Hinge teeth are slightly curved. Distribution: from central Honshû to the Ryukyus, in shallow waters.

4. Barbatia (Savignyarca) virescens (REEVE)

The shell is elongate, rather flat, and somewhat extending toward the posterior end. The surface bears fine rays, which grow coarser on the posterior part, and is covered with a fibrous periostracum. The interior is pale bluish white. The animal attaches to rocks by the byssus, that passes through a narrow gape. Distribution: common on rocks of open sea coasts of Japan, in intertidal zone.

5. Striarca (Galactella) oyamai HABE

A small, squarish and very inflated shell. The surface is finely decussate, and covered with a velvety periostracum. The beaks are fairly well elevated and make a wide ligamental area, and the hinge line is straight with numerous teeth. The inner margin is not crenulated. Distribution: common among gravels between tide marks in bays of Japan.

6. Acar plicatum (DILLWYN)

This is a moderately elongate, solid and inflated shell. The anterior end is short and rounded, while the shell is slightly elongated toward the posterior. The surface is reticulated by elevated radial ribs and concentric lines, bearing scales on the posterior part of the ridge which runs from the umbo to the post-basal margin. Distribution: central Honshû to the Ryukyus, common in shallow waters.

7. Arca arabica PHILIPPI

This shell is solid, inflated and somewhat squarish, and medium in size. The surface is sculptured by radial ribs and concentric lines. It is easily identified by the prominent ridge running from the beak to the posterior end. Distribution: from Honshû to the Ryukyus, common on rocks in tidal zone and down to 40 fathoms.

PLATE **43**

1   × 1⅕

2   × 1⅘

3   × 1⅕

4   × 1⅕

5   × 1⅕

6   × 1⅕

7   × 1⅕

8   × 1⅕

9   × 1⅕

10   × 1⅕

11   × 1⅕

12   × 1⅕

13   × 1⅕

14   × 1⅕

15   a,

b,

× 1⅕

PLATE 44

a   b

1

× 2/5

2

× 3/5

3

× 3/5

4

× 3/5

5   × 1 1/5

6   × 1 1/5

7   × 1 1/5

8   × 1 1/5

9

× 4/5

10   × 3/5

11   × 4/5

12

× 4/5

13   × 4/5

14   × 4/5

8. Striarca (Didimacar) tenebrica (REEVE)

The shell is small, inflated and slightly elongate toward the anterior, and both ends are round. The surface is decussately marked by radial threads and concentric lines, and coated with a velvety brown periostracum. The beak is close to the anterior end, forming a narrow ligamental area behind it. This species is allied to *St. interplicata* and *St. oyamai*, but differs in its narrow ligamental area and reticulated outer surface. Distribution: from central Honshû to Kyûshû, among gravels near the low tide level.

9. Barbatia (Barbatirus) cometa (REEVE)

The shell is small, rather flat and somewhat elongate oval. The surface is sculptured by radial ribs and concentric lines, which are lamellated on the posterior part. This is easily distinguished by its sculpture from allied species. Distribution: from Kyûshû to the Ryukyus, near the low tide mark.

10. Pseudogrammatodon dalli (SMITH)

This is a medium-sized, rather flat shell, rounded at both ends. The surface is decussate and covered with a fibrous periostracum. The hinge teeth are horizontally arranged in the posterior part. It is somewhat like *B. lima* and *B. bicolorata*, but differs in having the horizontally arranged hinge teeth, unlike those of the latter species which are vertically aranged. Distribution: Inland Sea of Japan, attaching to submarine rocks with the byssus.

11. Barbatia (Savignyarca) virescens obtusoides (NYST)

The shell is rather flat and oval in outline, and expands toward the posterior end. This is closely related to the typical form of *B. virescens*, but its radial ribs are not so coarse as in the latter, and the fibrous epiderm is finer. It seems to be an ecolog-

ical form of the typical form. Distribution: abundant on rocks of tidal zone, along Japanese coasts.

12. Barbatia lima (REEVE)

This shell is medium in size, rather flat and oval, and rounded at both ends. The surface is reticulated by numerous radial riblets crossing with growth lines, and covered with a brownish fibrous epiderm which grows radially along the riblets. Distribution: common on rocks in tidal zone of Japanese coasts.

13. Barbatia lacerata (BRUGUIÈRE)

A large, solid and slightly inflated shell, which expands toward the posterior. Radial riblets and concentric lines cross on the surface, growing coarser posteriorly. The periostracum is thick and has laminated hairs. This is easily distinguished from allied forms by its sculpture and coloration. Distribution: from Amami Islands to the Philippines, in shallow waters.

14. Barbatia (Ustularca) bicolorata (DILLWYN)

This species resembles *B. lima* in shape, but the shell is round at both ends, and fasciated by two white color bands on the purplish brown background. Distribution: from Honshû to the Philippines, common between the tide line and 100 fathoms depth.

15. Arca boucardi JOUSSEAUME

This medium-sized shell is elongate and inflated. The surface is sculptured by rough radiating ribs and concentric lines, forming a reticulated sculpture, and covered with a hairy periostracum. The beaks are elevated and hooked, producing a wide and flat ligamental area between them, on which chevron-shaped ligamental grooves are marked. Distribution: from Hokkaidô to Formosa, under rocks in subtidal zone.

[PLATE 44]   Arcidaé

Family Arcidae (2)

1. Arca navicularis BRUGUIÈRE

The outline is elongated squarish and inflated. The surface is sculptured by strong radiating ribs and faint intercalated riblets between the ribs, which are somewhat de-cussated with growth lines. This species is more or less like A. boucardi, but differs in having broader radial ribs and in its coloration. Distribution: southern Honshû and southwards, below the low tide mark.

2. Arca ventricosa LAMARCK

The shell is large, inflated and somewhat irregular in shape. The surface is faintly reticulated by fine radial riblets and con-centric lines. It is closely related to the preceding species in the feature of liga-ment and hinge teeth, but differs in having a larger shell and faint decussate sculp-ture, and the beak is closer to the posterior end. Distribution: from central Honshû to the Philippines, on rocks in tidal zone.

3. Trisidos (Epitrisis) semitorta (LAMARCK)

This large and elongate shell is weakly twisted. The surface is covered by a pale yellowish periostracum, under which fine radial riblets cross with growth lines. The beaks are close to each other, forming a narrow ligamental area between them. This species is remarkable in its twisted shape of the shell, and distributed around Formosa and southwards, below the low tide mark to 100 fathoms depth.

4. Trisidos tortuosa kiyonoi (MAKIYAMA)

The shell is peculiarly twisted, large, elongate and inequivalved. The left valve is slightly larger and more strongly twisted than the right one. The surface is sculp-tured by radial riblets and covered with a thick, grayish, velvety periostracum. This is closely related to the preceding species, though its shell is more elongate and more strongly twisted. Distribution: from north-ern Kyûshû to central Honshû, on muddy bottom between the low tide mark and 20 fathoms depth.

5. Anadara (Scapharca) troscheli (DUNKER)

A thin, inflated and rounded squarish shell, medium in size. The surface is covered by a hairy periostracum. Though this is somewhat like A. subcrenata and is sometimes confused with juvenile shells of the latter species, the radial ribs number about 24 in this species instead of 32 in the latter. Distribution: central Honshû, on muddy bottom of shallow waters.

6. Anadara (Tegillarca) nodifera (VON MARTENS)

This differs from A. granosa bisenensis in having a transversely elongate shell. Somewhat angulated and granulated radial ribs are 22 in number. Distribution: For-mosa and southwards, below the tide line.

7. Anadara (Scapharca) subcrenata (LISCHKE)

The shell is inflated, rounded squarish in shape, and medium-sized. The surface bears a blackish periostracum. The ribs of the left valve are granulated nears the summit. It differs from A. broughtonii in having a smaller solid shell, which bears about 28–32 radial ribs. Distribution: this species inhabits shallow muddy bottom of bays from Honshû to the Ryukyus, where it is cultured for food. Pulverized shells are used as a painting material.

8. Anadara (Tegillarca) granosa bisenensis SCHENCK et REINHART

This ark shell is solid, rather inequi-valved, and medium in size. The surface bears some 20 radial ribs which are strongly elevated and granulated. Its flesh is also eaten by the Japanese and the Chinese. Distribution: southern part of Honshû and China, common on muddy bottom of shallow waters.

9. Cucullaea granulosa JONAS

The shell is large in size, prominently inflated, squarish and inequivalved. The left valve is larger than the other. The surface is reticulated by a number of faint radial and concentric lines, and covered with a dark yellowish velvety periostracum. The interior has a projecting septum for the posterior adductor muscle, and dark purplish red in color. The hinge teeth are horizontally arranged and elongate at both ends. Distribution: central Honshû and southwards, on muddy bottom about 20–100 fathoms deep.

10. Anadara (Scapharca) satowi nipponensis (Pilsbry)

The shell is thin and roundly inflated, and medium in size. The periostracum is brownish and somewhat fibrous. This closely resembles *A. subcrenata*, but has more inflated valves bearing 37–38 radial ribs. The distribution, habitat and use in Japan are the same with those of *A. subcrenata*.

11. Anadara (Diluvarca) tricenicosta (Nyst)

This shell is medium-sized, somewhat elongate, solid and inflated. The surface has about 28 broad radial ribs, which are slightly granulated, and is covered with a blackish, rather thick periostracum. The ligamental area is flat and wide, with the chevron grooves on it. Distribution: from central Honshû to Kyûshû, in shallow waters.

12. Anadara maculosa (Reeve)

A solid, equivalved shell, with the extended postero-ventral part. Under the cover of a velvety periostracum, the surface bears 38 radial ribs. This shell is somewhat allied to the preceding species, but it is thicker and larger, and the hinge teeth are coarser. It was formerly called *A. scapha* (Mauschen). Distribution: south of Amami Islands to the Philippines, in shallow waters.

13. Anadara (Scapharca) satowi (Dunker)

The shell is solid, inflated and squarish, and large in size, exceeding 100 mm in length. The valve is slightly extended at the postero-ventral side, bearing radial ribs, about 40 in number. Distribution: this edible species is commonly found on muddy bottom in shallow waters of Japanese coasts.

14. Anadara (Scapharca) broughtonii (Schrenck)

The shell is thin, inflated, squarish and large, attaining more than 150 mm in length. This is closely related to the preceding species, but its surface is sculptured by 42 radial ribs instead of 40 in the preceding species, and the beak is lower. It has very delicious flesh. Distribution: from Honshû to Kyûshû, common on shallow muddy bottom.

[PLATE 45]   Limopsidae, Glycymeridae

Family Limopsidae

The shells of this family are rather small, solid, and the posterior part is obliquely oval in outline. The surface is covered with a velvety brown periostracum. The interior is porcellaneous and the margin is smooth or crenulated. The straight hinge line is somewhat like that of Glycymeridae, but the ligamental area is small and trigonal in shape. A pit for the resilium is seen beneath the umbo. They are mostly found on muddy bottom of deep waters.

1.   Oblimopa forskalii (A. ADAMS)

The shell is small, rather flat and rotundate. The surface is reticulated with faint radial riblets and growth lines under the cover of a brown hairy periostracum. The interior margin is slightly crenulated. Distribution: from central Honshû to Kyûshû, on muddy bottom 50–100 fathoms in depth.

2.   Limopsis tajimae SOWERBY

Resembling the preceding species, this shell is elongated toward the posterior end and its margin is not crenulated. The surface is weakly sculptured by radial threads. The periostracum is hairy and brown. Distribution: from Honshû to Kyûshû, on muddy bottom at 80–100 fathoms depth.

3.   Limopsis uwadokoi OYAMA

The shell is medium in size, rather flat and somewhat rotundate. The outer surface is covered with a thick hairy periostracum, while the interior is porcellaneous. The hinge line is longer than those of the allied species, and the teeth are large in number. This and the preceding species are closely related, but this shell is less elongate. Distribution: northeastern Honshû and Hokkaidô, on sandy bottom of 50–100 fathoms depth.

4.   Limopsis tajimae emphaticus KIRA

This subspecies closely resembles the real form, but its shell is thicker and more elongated toward the posterior end and more inflated than the three species above described. Distribution: Tosa Bay, Shikoku, at 80–100 fathoms depth. This seems to be

no more than a form of *L. tajimae.*

Family Glycymeridae

These shells are medium to large in size, and thick, usually orbicular and equivalved. The surface is sculptured by radial ribs or smooth, and covered with a soft velvety periostracum. The interior is porcellaneous with an entire mantle line connecting 2 large muscle scars. The margin is crenulated. The beaks are closely situated, forming a narrow triangular ligamental area which bears chevron-shaped ligamental grooves. They live on muddy or sandy bottom in shallow waters.

5.   Glycymeris imperialis KURODA

The shell is medium in size, rotundate and prominently inflated. The surface is weakly sculptured by faint radial ribs and growth lines, and covered with a brownish velvety periostracum. Distribution: Pacific coasts of central Honshû, on sandy bottom near 50 fathoms depth.

6.   Glycymeris (Veletuceta) reevei (MAYER)

This shell is close to the preceding species in shape, though this is less inflated, and the radial ribs are coarser than those of the preceding species. The surface is usually dyed in two different tones, the anterior part being white and the posterior dark brown. Distribution: Amami Islands and southwards, common in shallow waters.

7.   Tucetona auriflua (REEVE)

This shell is medium in size, thick and rather inflated. The surface bears prominently elevated radial ribs and growth lines. The beak is close to the posterior end, and the hinge teeth are large and curved. This differs from the last species in having elevated ribs. Distribution: Amami Islands and southwards, in shallow waters.

8.   Glycymeris rotunda (DUNKER)

The surface is covered with a brownish periostracum. Though the shell is similar to *Gl. imperialis* in shape, it differs in having less inflated valves which extend at the

PLATE 45

PLATE 46

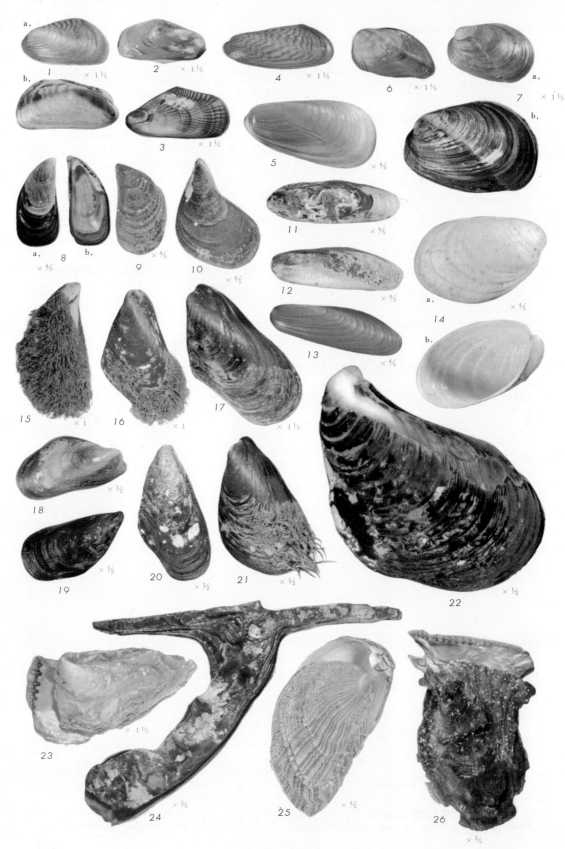

a,

1 × 1⅕

2 × 1⅕

4 × 1⅕

6 × 1⅕

a,

7 × 1⅕

b,

3 × 1⅕

5 × ⅘

b,

a,   *8*   b,

× ⅘

9 × ⅘

10 × ⅘

11 × ⅘

a,

× ⅘

14

b.

12 × ⅘

13 × ⅘

15 × 1   *16* × 1

17 × 1⅕

18 × ½

19 × ½

20 × ½

21 × ½

22 × ½

23 × 1⅕

24 × ⅗

25 × ⅘

26

× ⅗

postero-ventral margin when fully matured. Distribution: from Honshû to Kyûshû, on muddy bottom of 10–50 fathoms depth.

9. Glycymeris (Veletuceta) fulgurata (DUNKER)

The shell is rotundate, thick, solid and rather large in size. Broad radial ribs and growth lines cover the surface under a thin velvety periostracum. The beak is somewhat elevate. Usually it has zigzag patterns. Distribution: south of Kyûshû, on shallow sandy bottom.

10. Glycymeris yessoensis (SOWERBY)

The shell is medium-sized, thick and rather flattened. The surface is alternately sculptured by low ridges and grooves, and covered with a brownish rough periostracum. The interior is porcellaneously white, and the margin is strongly crenulated. This is separated from the resembling species, Gl. rotunda, by the slightly elevated radial ribs, each of which consists of 3–4 fine radial lirae. Distribution: northern Honshû to Hokkaidô, on sandy bottom in shallow seas.

11. Glycymeris vestita (DUNKER)

A thick shell, medium in size. The surface is slightly sculptured by radial riblets and concentric lines. The periostracum is dark brown and velvety. The interior margin is strongly crenulated. The beaks are close to each other, forming a narrow ligamental area with chevron-shaped ligamental grooves. This species somewhat resembles Gl. imperialis, but differs in having a much larger and less inflated shell. Distribution: central Honshû to Kyûshû, chiefly on shallow muddy bottom.

12. Glycymeris (Veletuceta) albolineata (LISCHKE)

This large and thick shell is rather elongated oval in its outline. The surface sculpture consists of radial ribs, each composed of about 10 radial lirae. Immature shells of this species look like the allied species, but differ in having the pale brown interior and the outer surface with distinctive radial series of small pits or punctures. Distribution: from Honshû to Kyûshû, on shallow muddy bottom.

[PLATE 46]

Family Mytilidae

The shells of this mussel family vary from small to large in size and are thin, equivalved and mostly rounded trigonal or elongated oval in shape. The surface is covered with a smooth or hairy periostracum, and sometimes sculptured by radial ribs. The interior is pearly and

[PLATE 46]   Mytilidae, Isognomonidae

glossy with an entire mantle line. The beak is sharply elevated with a ligament behind it. Some members burrow in soft wood or clay, but the majority are fastened to the substratum by the byssus. A few species are used for food.

1. Musculus (Musculista) senhousia (BENSON)

This has a small, thin shell, elongate trigonal in shape. The surface is nearly smooth, with a few radial cords on the anterior part, and marked by narrow, reddish, radial bands against the pale yellowish green background on the postero-dorsal part. They fasten each other with the byssus, and build a nest made of mud and byssal threads. Distribution: all over Japan, and China, on muds in tidal zone.

2. Brachidontes setiger (DUNKER)

The shell is thin and oval, extending toward the posterior, and medium in size. The surface is sculptured by radial ribs, and the interior margin is crenulated. It differs from the above species in having a much larger shell with the fine radial sculpture. Distribution: from central Honshû to Kyûshû, in tidal zone.

3. Hormomya mutabilis (GOULD)

The surface is prominently sculptured by divaricating radial ribs. The interior is pearly and glossy, and the margin is not crenulated. The beak is very close to the anterior end and a few denticles are seen beneath it. Distribution: from central Honshû to Kyûshû, on rocks of tidal zone.

4. Musculus (Musculista) japonica (DUNKER)

The shell is thin, elongate, narrow and small in size, with fine reddish-colored radial cords on the postero-dosal area. There are no hinge tooth, and no marginal crenulation except for the anterior end and the dorsal margin just behind the hinge. This species differs from M. senhousia in its elongate and narrow shell that lacks

radial ribs on the anterior part. Distribution: from southern part of Hokkaidô to Kyûshû, on muddy bottom of tidal zone.

5. Musculus (Amygdalum) watsoni (SMITH)

The shell is fragile and medium in size, and rotundate anteriorly and broadly prolonged posteriorly. The hinder end is roundly truncated. It is somewhat like M. senhousia, but is more elongate, and its surface is smooth and glossy, and orange yellow in color. The interior margin is not crenulated. Distribution: central Honshû to Kyûshû, in shallow waters.

6. Musculus (Reynella) cupreus (GOULD)

The shell is trigonal oval and somewhat roundly inflated. The surface is divided in three distinct areas, and sculptured with radial lirae at both ends, while the median part is smooth and slightly concave. The beak is prominently elevate. Distribution: central Honshû and southwards, below the low tide level embedded in the testa of ascidians.

7. Musculus laevigatus (GRAY)

This is closely related to the preceding species, but is larger in size and more elongate toward the posterior end, and less inflated. The sculpture on the anterior and posterior area is not so prominent as in the preceding species. Also the beak is low. Distribution: north of northeastern Honshû, in tidal zone.

8. Septifer (Mytilisepta) virgatus (WIEGMANN)

The shell is somewhat trigonal in shape, extending toward the posterior end. The surface is marked by growth lines and a few divaricating broad radial ribs which are mostly eroded, and covered with a purplish periostracum. The interior has a small shelly septa, which is the most distinct feature of this genus, beneath the umbo, and is pearly and glossy. The margin is irregularly crenulated. The beak is situated at the anterior end. Distribution: from Japan to Australia, in tidal zone forming a gregarious mass on rocks.

9. Septifer bilocularis pilosus (REEVE)

This shell is fairly thick, trigonal ovate in shape and small in size. The surface is sculptured by numerous divaricating radial lirae and coated with a hairy brownish periostracum. The interior is regularly crenulated at the margin and has an anterior septa. This subspecies differs from the real form in having the remarkably hairy periostracum. Distribution: central Honshû and southwards, on rocks in intertidal zone.

10. Septifer bilocularis (LINNÉ)

The shell is thick, trigonal or elongate oval in shape and rather small. The surface bears numerous fine divaricating cords. The greenish brown periostracum is not so hairy as in the preceding form. The interior is purplish or bluish brown and has a prominent anterior septa, with the crenulated margin. Distribution: Shikoku and southwards, attaching to rocks of tidal zone.

11. Lithophaga (Leiosolenus) curta (LISCHKE)

This species is the commonest rock-borer found on Japanese coasts. It is a fragile and elongated cylindrical shell, rounded posteriorly and gently tapering anteriorly. The surface is smooth and covered by a brownish periostracum, usually with a thin calcareous crust. The interior is pearly and somewhat glossy. The beak is close to the anterior end and has a narrow ligamental area behind it. Distribution: from Honshû to the Ryukyus, below the tide mark, boring in hard sand-stones and even the shells of such big bivalves as Chama.

12. Lithophaga (Leiosolenus) lima (LAMY)

Though the shell closely resembles the preceding species in shape, it differs in having a posteriorly elongated dorsal margin and a calcareous layer on the surface pseudo-sculptured by a few fine rays near the posterior end. Distribution: south of central Honshû, in intertidal zone.

13. Lithophaga zitteliana DUNKER

This shell is thin, inflated, cylindrical and prominently elongate, and rather large in size. The surface is sculptured by growth lines and numerous fine divaricating radial cords. The periostracum is thin and light yellowish brown in color. The interior is somewhat pearly and glossy. This species is similar to the preceding two species in general features, but differs in lacking calcareous layer on the outer surface. Distribution: southern Honshû to the Ryukyus, below the low tide level.

14. Solamen saccosericatum HABE

The shell is very thin, oval, roundly inflated and medium in size. The silvery white surface is sculptured by fine radial striae and growth lines which are elevated at intervals. The interior is white and glossy, and the margin is minutely crenulated. The beak is elevate and somewhat prosogyrate. This species differs from a related species, S. diaphana (DALL), in its larger and more elongated shell, bearing a slight angle at the postero-dorsal margin. Distribution: Tosa Bay. Shikoku, to East China Sea, on deep muddy bottom at 100–150 fathoms.

15. Trichomya hirsuta (LAMARCK)

The shell is trigonal and inflated, and medium in size. The surface is covered by numerous fine radial cords and growth lines. The periostracum is hirsute and brownish. The interior is white or bluish brown in color and the margin is crenulated. The beak is close to the anterior end, and a few denticles occur beneath it. Distribution: central Honshû and southwards, on rocks of intertidal zone.

16. Modiolus nipponicus (OYAMA)

The surface is covered with a somewhat hirsute epiderm, and is colored reddish brown on the middle part and brownish on the dorsal and ventral parts. The interior is nacreous, and the margin is not crenulated. This shell is like the preceding species, but the shell is less inflated and has a radial sculpture, and its hirsute periostracum is thinner. It also differs from the following species in its ventral margin which is not twisted but gaping. Distribution: from Honshû to Formosa, on rocks of intertidal zone.

[PLATE 46]   Mytilidae, Isognomonidae

17. Modiolus agripeta IREDALE

This shell is thin, trigonal, broadly extending toward the postero-ventral part, and roundly truncate at its end. Closely resembling the preceding species, its beak is not so close to the anterior end as in that species, and its posterior margin is more extended. Distribution: southern Honshû to Australia, clinging to rocks by the byssus in intertidal zone.

18. Modiolus philippinarum (HANLEY)

The surface sculpture consists of numerous fine concentric lines under a light brownish periostracum. The interior is pearly and dyed in white and purplish red, and the margin is not crenulated. It is larger in size and more elongated toward the posterior end than the above mentioned two species. Distribution: central Honshû and southwards, below the low tide level down to 20 fathoms.

19. Mytilus edulis LINNÉ

This blue mussel is thin, elongate trigonal and large in size. The surface is deep bluish black and smooth with a thin, brownish periostracum. The beak is close to the anterior end and has a few teeth just inside the umbo. This is a feature that distinguishes this from the allied species. The margin is not crenulated. This common mussel has a nearly world-wide distribution in cooler waters and used for food in Europe. It is believed to have immigrated and become native to Japan only in recent years.

20. Mytilus corscum GOULD

General features are alike in this and the preceding species, so it is difficult to distinguish them especially in the young stage. But this shell is thick even in its young stage, and is covered with a vernicose periostracum. There are about 3 strong hinge teeth and several minute crenulations on the ventral margin near the apex. This was formerly well known as M. crassitesta LISCHKE. Distributoin: southern Hokkaidô to Kyûshû, common on rocks of inter- and subtidal waters.

21. Modiolus difficilis (KURODA et HABE)

The shell is thin, somewhat trigonal and large in size when fully grown. The surface is covered by a periostracum bearing long and strong bristles on the posterodorsal area, and smooth and vernicose on the remaining area. It is like M. nipponicus, but differs in having a larger shell and bristled periostracum. Distribution: from northern Honshû to the Kuriles, on muddy bottom below the low tide mark.

22. Mytilus grayanus DUNKER

This is a thick, large shell, not so elongate in shape as in M. corscum. It can be distinguished from M. corscum and M. edulis by the longer series of minute crenulation on the antero-ventral margin, olivaceous blackish periostracum, and larger muscle scar. Distribution: from northern Honshû to the Kuriles, clinging to rocks by the byssus below the low tide level.

Family Isognomonidae

The shells of this family are thin, flat and strongly compressed and the size varies from medium to large. The surface is sometimes sculptured by numerous radial cords and covered by a thin periostracum. The interior is pearly with only one muscle scar. The beak is close to the anterior end with a narrow byssal gape. Hinge line is straight, and one or numerous parallel resilifer grooves exsist perpendicularly to the dorsal margin of the valve. The family includes a few species which attach to rocks in shallow waters.

23. Isognomon legumen (GMELIN)

The shell is very thin, fragile and irregular in shape, and mostly elongated towards the ventral side, and rather small in size. The white surface is marked by irregular growth lines, and covered with a thin, brownish periostracum. The interior is pearly and glossy. The beak is close to the anterior end with a few resilifer grooves on its hinge plate. Distribution: south of central Honshû, common on rocks of intertidal zone.

24. *Malleus malleus* (LINNÉ)

The shell is rather thick, large in size, and irregularly T-shaped, extending the wings toward the anterior and posterior ends. The surface is purplish black in color with irregular growth lines. The interior is nacreous and somewhat glossy. Hinge line is straight and a large resilifer pit is situated at the median part of it. The allied species, *M. albus* (LAMARCK), has a regularly shaped shell and is white in color. Distribution: southern part of Japan and southwards, in shallow sea. *M. albus* is found to the south of central Honshû.

25. *Vulsella vulsella* (LINNÉ)

This is medium in size, thick, rather flat and prolonged to the ventral end, and somewhat irregular in outline. The surface sculpture is coarsely decussate with growth lines and fine radial cords, under a brownish periostracum. Brown radial stripes are distinctive on the outside, and the interior is nacreous. The beaks are elevate and close to each other, forming a narrow resilifer pit. Distribution: central Honshû and southwards, embedded in sponge colonies below the low tide level.

26. *Isognomon isognomun* (LINNÉ)

The shell is moderately thick and large in size, and projects a narrow wing, which is sometimes obscure, toward the posterior end. The surface is somewhat rugose and purplish red in color. The interior is pearly and 16–20 pallarel resilifer grooves exsist perpendicularly to the hinge line. Distribution: from southern Kyûshû to Australia, below the low tide level.

[PLATE 47]

Pteriidae, Anomiidae, Pinnidae, Placunidae

Family Pteriidae

These shells of the pearl oyster family are fragile, fairly thin and small to large in size. The left valve is larger and more inflated than the right one that has a byssal notch at its anterior end. The interior is pearly white and glossy, and bears one or two small denticles which fit into shallow sockets on the opposite valve. Hinge line is straight and its posterior end is considerably elongated. Some species are used as mother shells for the cultured pearl. See also Plate 72.

1. Electroma japonica (DUNKER)

The shell is thin, slightly inflated and oval, extending toward the postero-ventral end, and medium in size. The surface is sculptured by only growth lines and marked with reddish brown radial rays on the pale brown background. Hinge line is straight, and there is no denticulation. Distribution: southern part of Honshû and southwards, below the tide level.

2. Pinctada maculata (GOULD)

A thin, fragile and medium-sized shell. The surface only bears growth lines, forming lamination which extends beyond the margin, and is white with greenish rays. The periostracum is thin and light yellowish. The interior is pearly and glossy. The shell is somewhat like the following species, but differs in having the smaller and greenish shell. Distribution: the Ryukyus and farther south, in tidal zone.

3. Pinctada martensii (DUNKER)

This shell is medium in size, rather inflated and fragile. There is a byssal notch at the anterior end and a wing slightly projects toward the posterior end. The surface is covered with lamellae extending well beyond the margin. The interior is highly pearly and glossy, and the margin is thin and fragile. The shell is like the preceding species, but differs in having the larger and more inflated shell. This is the mother shell of the famous Japanese cultured pearl. Distribution: from central Honshû to the Ryûkyûs, commonly attaching

to rocks by the byssus in intertidal zone.

4. Pteria (Austropteria) loveni (DUNKER)

The shell is inflated, strongly rounded at the ventral side and medium in size. It forms an anterior rostrum and a posterior wing which is elongated and tapering at its distal end. The outline is thus somewhat like a bird. The surface has only growth lines and is covered with a brownish periostracum. The interior is nacreous and the margin is thin and fragile. Distribution: central Honshû to the Ryukyus, epiphytic on sea-fans below the low tide mark.

5. Pteria (Austropteria) brevialata (DUNKER)

Another bird-shaped shell, which is thin, rather inflated and somewhat large in size. As in the preceding two species, the relative length of the posterior wing in proportion to the total shell size decreases with the growth of shell (see textfigure). The surface is sculptured by numerous fine growth lines and covered with a brownish periostracum. A few pale brownish rays are marked against the purplish background. The shell differs from the preceding species in its larger size and wider tail. Distribution: the same with the preceding species.

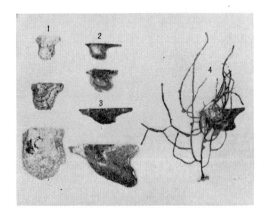

Young (upper) and matured (lower) shells of some species of Pteriidae

1. *Pinctada martensii*
2. *Pteria loveni*
3. *Pteria brevialata*
4. A specimen of *Pt. brevialata* clinging to a sea-fan

6. Pteria (Austropteria) cypsellus (DUNKR)

The margin extends roundly toward the ventral part and is rostrrated at both ends. The shell feature closely resembles the preceding two species, but differs in having sharp beaks on both the ventral and posterior ends. The color is blackish, and sometimes several yellowish oblique rays exsist. Distribution: from Shikoku to the Ryukyus, in shallow waters.

7. Pinctada fucata (GOULD)

The shell is medium-sized, thin and fragile. The surface is covered with a laminated sculpture and reddish brown in color. This species is closely related to *P. martensii* in shell features, and they seem to be the same species.

Family Anomiidae

These are thin, inequivalved shells, irregular in shape owing to their adherent life, more or less translucent, and medium to large in size. The left valve is rather inflated, while the right one is flat and thin and has a large perforation as the byssal opening. The surface is sculptured by numerous growth lines and sometimes with radial ribs. The interior is pearly and glossy. They attaches to some solid objects by the calcified byssus, with which the animal is tightly fixed on the substrata. There are no hinge teeth. See also Plate 72.

8. Anomia chinensis (PHILIPPI)

This pearly saddle oyster is thin, flat, irregularly rounded in shape, and medium-sized. The left valve is somewhat inflated, with 3 scars on the inside at its center and one beneath the umbo. Its outer surface is sculptured by numerous growth lines and irregular radial cords. The right valve is thin and flat, with a rounded large perforation. The interior is pearly and glossy. Distribution: southern Honshû and southwards, in tidal zone.

9. Monia macroschisma (DESHAYES)

This is thin, rather flat and medium in size. The surface is irregularly sculptured by radial ribs and numerous growth lines. The interior is pearly and usually tinged with green. This species is different from the preceding species in having 2 scars inside at the center of the left valve instead of 3 in *A. chinensis*, and also in the larger size. Distribution: northeastern Honshû and northwards, in subtidal zone.

Family Pinnidae

The members of this family have a medium- or large-sized shell, which is fragile, thin and wedge-shaped. The posterior end is broadly truncated and gaping. The surface is sometimes sculptured by radial ribs which set erect spines or decussate with growth lines. The interior has a large muscle scar at the center of the valve. The beak is located at the anterior end, and the dorsal magin is long and straight, having a narrow but long ligament behind the umbo. There are no hinge teeth. They have the large and powerful byssus. Some members grow to a length exceeding 600 mm and have edible flesh.

10. Atrina (Servatrina) pectinata (LINNÉ)

The shell is thin, large, attaining about 300 mm in length, trigonal in shape, and gaping at the posterior end. The surface is smooth in typical form, but is often sculptured by radial ribs, which are serrated and strengthened on the postero-dorsal area, but are reducing on the postero-ventral area. Various kinds of intermediate forms between the two types are found even in the same locality. Distribution: from Honshû to the Philippines, standing by the byssus on shallow muddy bottom of bays. Its flesh is eaten by the Japanese.

11. Atrina (Servatrina) kinoshitai HABE

This shell is rather small in size for this group, thin and trigonal, extending posteriorly, and gaping and broadly truncated at the posterior end. The ventral margin curves beneath the umbo, but runs parallel to the straight dorsal margin at its posterior part. The surface bears numberous, erect, tubercular spines. The interior is

[PLATE 47]   Pteriidae, Anomiidae, Pinnidae, Placunidae

somewhat pearly and has a large muscle scar in the center. The coloration is yellowish brown with the purplish black umbonal area. This species is closely related to *A. penna* (REEVE), but differs in having a less elongated shell even in the young stage, as well as in its characteristic serrate sculpture. Distribution: central Honshû and Shikoku, on muddy bottom of rather deep waters.

12. *Streptopinna saccata* (LINNÉ)

This medium-sized shell is irregular in shape and somewhat twisted, owing to its life embedded in sponges. The posterior end is truncated and gaped. It is also thin and semi-translucent. The surface is sculptured with irregularly arranged radial ribs and growth lines. The interior is pearly and white to purplish in color. Distribution: Indo-Pacific areas as far north to central Honshû, in subtidal zone.

Family Placunidae

The shells of this family are large, fragile and very flat or twisted. The surface is covered with a fine laminated sculpture. The interior has a muscle scar at the center. These are distributed in tropical or subtropical seas, chiefly in China, Formosa, New Guinea and northern Australia.

13. *Placuna (Placuna) placenta* (LINNÉ)

The shell is large, round, very flat and semi-translucent. The surface is pearly and white in color. The interior is also nacreous and glossy, and has a muscle scar at the center. This is the most flat shell of all bivalves and sometimes used as a substitute for window glass in China. The allied species, *Placuna ephippium* (RETZIUS) differs from this species in having a large, twisted and saddle-shaped shell. Distribution: from Formosa to Australia, in shallow waters.

PLATE 47

1
× 1⅕

2
× 1⅕

4
× 1

5
× ⅘

6
× ⅘

3
× 1⅕

8
× 1⅕

7
× ⅘

9
× 1

10
× ⅖

11
× ½

12
× ⅗

13
× ⅗

PLATE 48

× 1⅓

× 1⅓

× 1⅓

1

2

3

Family Pectinidae (1)

The shells of this scallop family range from small to large size, and are suborbicular or regular. The right valve is strongly convex with a byssal notch below the front ear, and the left valve is usually flat or slightly concave. Some species are, however, almost equivalved. The surface is usually sculptured by radial ribs or fine lirae, which sometimes bear numerous erect spines. The interior bears a large muscle scar in the center and is slightly nacreous. The beak is centrally situated. The hinge line is straight and united by a narrow ligament. The shells have ears at both ends, and the anterior ear is rather large, while the posterior one is a little oblique. Juvenile shells attach to the rock with the byssus, whereas adult shells generally swim freely by rapidly opening and closing their valves. The animal has a row of tiny eyes fringing the mantle edge. The scallops are rich in species, and often ornamented by splendid colorations. A few members have edible flesh. See also Plate 72.

1. Pecten (Notovola) sinensis SOWERBY

The shell is of medium size, thin and inequivalved. The outline is subcircular and almost equilateral except for ears. The right valve is roundly convex, and marked with broad, square, flat-topped, radial ribs, and the interspaces are narrow, channeled and about one third of the ribs in width. In addition, the surface is slightly sculptured by numerous fine radial striae and growth lines. The left valve is somewhat concave and sculptured by narrow, rather square, radial ribs, 11–12 in number, and the interspaces are broad and minutely lamellated with growth lines. These ribs and interspaces fit into those on the opposite valve.

The coloration is reddish purple to orange, with white maculations on the right valve, and zigzag dark reddish brown lines on the left valve, the right one being more highly and beautifully colored.

The ears are slightly unequal in size. The anterior one is trigonal in shape, has a byssal notch, and is sculptured by fine radial lirae and growth lines. The posterior one is sculptured in the same way. The interior is slightly nacreous and somewhat glossy, and a large muscle scar is seen in the center. The beak is placed behind the mid-length, and the hinge is straight and long.

This closely resemble the following two species, but differs in having a roundly convex right valve, and also the larger number of radial ribs. This was formerly known as *P. puncticulatus* DUNKER. Distribution : from southern Hokkaidô to Kyûshû, on shallow sandy bottom.

2. Pecten (Notovola) excavatus ANTON

The shell is rather thin, and suborbiclar, the height and length being almost equal. The right valve is moderately convex and colored reddish orange with white markings, while the left valve is sculptured by 9–11 radial ribs. The interior is white and glossy, tinged with reddish brown in part on the left valve. The beak is situated at the mid-point of the hinge line which is straight and rather long, and connected with a narrow ligament which is separated by a resilium pit beneath the umbo.

The shell is of similar shape and color to the preceding species, but is larger, the right valve is less convex, and the left valve is less concave than those of the preceding species. This also differs from the following species in having more inflated right valve, having beautiful coloration, and in the number of radial ribs. Distribution : southern part of Japan, Formosa and southern China, in shallow waters.

3. Pecten (Notovola) albicans (SCHRÖTER)

The shell is rather large, and the length is somewhat larger than the height. The right valve is sculptured by broad, flat-topped, low, radial ribs, and the interspaces are broad. It is reddish brown to white in color. The left valve bearing 8 radial ribs is almost flat, and reddish brown. The interior is clearly marked by radial ribs as in the former two species, and tinged with reddish brown on the white background. The beaks are situated at the mid-point of the hinge line, and united with a narrow ligament which is separated by a resilium pit beneath the umbo. One or two narrow ridges are almost horizontally arranged inside the ears beneath the hinge line.

This species is separated from the preced-

[PLATE 48]

Pectinidae

ing two species by the least convex right valve, least number of radial ribs on the left valve, and less beautiful coloration. Distribution: southern Hokkaidô to Kyûshû, on sandy bottom of shallow waters. This has edible and delicious flesh.

Family Plicatulidae

The shells of this small family are small to medium in size, rather flat and trigonal or spathate in shape. They attach to rocks or other shells with the right valve. The surface is sculptured by broad, divaricating, radial ribs, which are sometimes set with erect tiny spines. Hinge line is short, with a narrow condrophore which is wedged between vertically arranged ball and socket.

1. Plicatula simplex (GOULD)

This small shell is thick, slightly inflated, and somewhat like a rat's paw in shape. The surface is sculptured by prominently elevated, broad, radial ribs which are about 6 in number, and the interpaces are deep, channelled and marked with growth lines. It is creamy white outside with brownish rays. The right valve is sculptured and colored in the same way. The interior is white and somewhat glossy, and a large muscle scar is situated at the postero-ventral end with an entire mantle line. The margin is rippled and alternately stained with white and reddish brown. The hinge line is short, with a pair of narrow ball and socket on both valves. Distribution: central Honshû and southwards, below the low tide line.

2. Plicatula australis LAMARCK

The shell is small, less inflated than the preceding species, and irregular but mostly rounded in shape. The surface is sculptured by numerous, fine, divaricating, radial ribs bearing tiny erect spines. The interspaces are narrow and finely marked with growth lines. It is marked by a number of maculated, blackish brown spots on the white background. The interior is somewhat pearly and glossy, and the margin is waved. Distribution: southern Honshû and southwards, on rocks below the low tide mark.

3. Plicatula muricata SOWERBY

The shell is small, rather flat, thin and trigonal ovate in shape. The surface sculpture consists of lamellated growth lines and divaricating, narrow, radial ribs, which are set with long and erect semi-tubular spines. The interspaces are fairly broad. It is white

with irregularly arranged brownish radial rays on both valves. The interior is pearly and rather glossy, the margin is rippled, and a somewhat large muscle scar is situated near the postero-dorsal end. It attaches to the substrata only with its umbonal area. Distribution: south of central Honshû, common in shallow waters.

4. Plicatula plicata (LINNÉ)

This has a larger shell than the preceding three species. It is flat, trigonal and well extends toward the ventral margin. The surface is sculptured by a few, rather broad, divaricating, low, radial ribs and greenish white in color. The interior is pearly, with the slightly rippled margin. Distribution: southern Honshû and southwards, below the low tide level.

Family Pectinidae (2)

5. Pecten (Serratovola) tricarinatus ANTON

The shell is rather small for the group, rather flat, thin, suborbicular and equilateral except for the ears. The right valve is moderately convex and sculptured by squarely elevated, flat-topped, radial ribs which are about 19 in number, and somewhat lamellated with numerous, regular, growth lines, and tinged with reddish purple on the white background. The left valve is rather flat and slightly convex near the umbo, and sculptured by finely serrated radial ribs, 18 in number, and finely lamellated with growth lines, and dotted everywhere with pale red. The ears are somewhat unequal, the anterior ear of the right valve has a shallow byssal notch, and both of them are marked with a few fine radial ribs. The interior has a large muscle scar on the postero-dorsal area. Hinge line is straight and united with a narrow ligament, which is separated by a chondrophore at the mid-point beneath the umbo. Distribution: central Honshû and southwards, in shallow waters.

6. Chlamys quadrilirata (LISCHKE)

This small scallop is thin, slightly inflated and equivalved except for the ears. The valves are marked with somewhat elevated radial ribs which are 12 in number, each one of which is usually composed of narrow riblets. The coloration is variable, but mostly pale purple with concentric white bands. The interior is white and tinged with pale purple, with its margin irregularly crenulated. The ear is distinctly unequal and finely rayed with somewhat imbricated cords, the anterior ear being larger and bearing a deep byssal notch on the right side. This differs from the next species in having a less inflated shell, bearing smaller number of ribs. Distribution: from central Honshû to Kyûshû.

7. Chlamys asperulata (ADAMS et REEVE)

The shell is thin, somewhat triangulate orbicular, resembling the last species in appearance. The surface is strongly sculptured by radiating ribs which are very irregular in size and about 18 in number, bearing prickly serrated scales. The outer surface is whitish to yellowish, tinged with violet near the margin and vermilion-red at the umbo. The front ear is large and rather flexuous. Distribution: northern Kyûshû to Korea, attaching to rocks in shallow waters.

8. Chlamys jousseaumei BAVAY

This is also a similar small, thin shell, nearly orbicular in outline, and a little higher than wide. The valves are rather compressed and almost equivalved. The surface is finely sculptured by densely radiating striae which are serrated throughout. It is whitish to yellowish, and concentrically stained with rose and scattered with light brownish blotches. This is also known as *Chl. mollita* (REEVE). Distribution: from central Honshû to Kyûshû, in shallow seas.

9. Chlamys lemniscata (REEVE)

The surface is marked by numerous irregularly radiating cords with erect tiny spines, and the interspaces are minutely squamated. It is stained with dark reddish brown maculations on the pale rosy-red surface. The ears are with coarse, squamous striae; the front ear is large and has a deep byssal notch. Distribution: southern Honshû and southwards, 20–30 fathoms deep.

10. Chlamys schmeltzii (KOBELT)

The shell is small, flat, thin, orbicular and somewhat fan-shaped. The surface bears broad, roundly elevated, radial ribs, which are 15 in number and each finely ribbed in turn. The outside is alternately stained with white and brown maculations. The ears are unequal and rayed with fine, somewhat serrated cords. Distribution: south of central Honshû, in shallow waters.

11. Chlamys asperulata pelseneeri DAUTZENBERG et BAVAY

The shell is small, thin, and fairly inflated. Roundly elevated radial ribs are about 18 in number, set with erect tiny spines and gradually intercalated with narrow ridges on both sides of each rib. It is fasciated or maculated with reddish brown on the pale yellow background. The ears are prominently unequal and sculptured by squamous radial striae. This is a form of *Chl. asperulata* with various intermediate forms. Distribution: southern Honshû and southwards.

12. Chlamys (Coralichlamys) madreporarum (SOWERBY)

This small, thin shell is flat, inequivalved and inequilateral. The right valve is slightly more convex than the left one, and somewhat obliquely elongated at the posteroventral side. Its surface is sculptured by numerous, fine, faintly serrated, radial cords and there are secondary and tertiary intercalation between the ribs. The left valve is stained with radially arranged, dark brown dots on the creamy white background, while the right one is cream-yellow. The ears are unequal and rayed with squamous, fine striae. This species somewhat resembles *Chl. jousseaumei*, but differs in having a flat and rather inequivalved shell. Distribution: from Amami Islands to Australia, on coral reef below the low tide mark.

13. Chlamys inaequivalvis (SOWERBY)

The shell is small or medium in size, thin, inequivalved, nearly round and a little expanded posteriorly. The left valve is almost flat, a little raised toward the umbo and rayed with 18–20 elevated, slightly angulated

PLATE 49

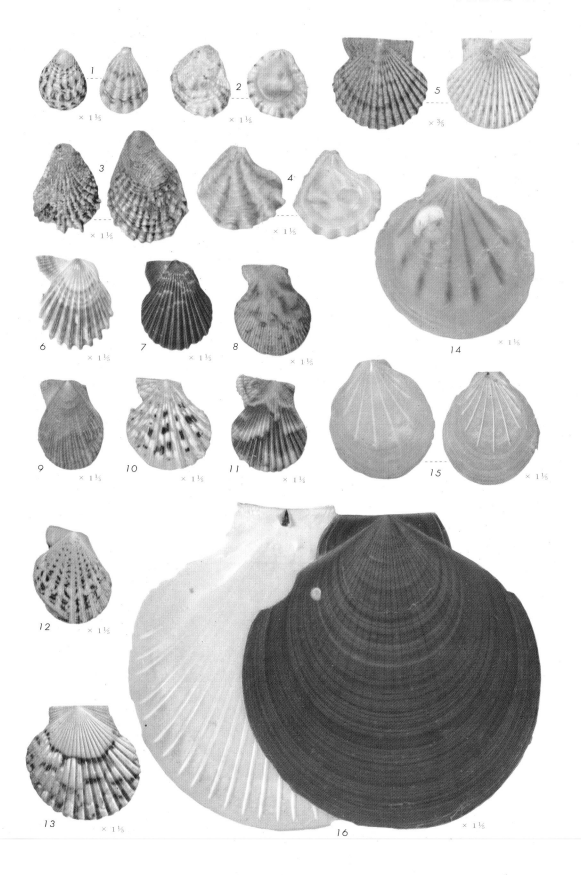

PLATE 50

1   × ½

2   × ½

3   × ⅗

4   × ⅗

5   × ⅗

6   × ⅘

7   × ⅘

8   × ⅘

9   × ⅘

10   × ⅗

11   × ⅗

12   × ⅗

13   × ⅘

14   × ⅗

15   × ⅗

16   × ½

cords, and obliquely streaked with dark gray and marked with a few white spots. The right valve is prominently convex and ventricose, sculptured with 18 rather broad radial ribs and stained with pale gray-brown spots on the white background. Distribution: central Honshû and farther south.

14. *Luteamussium sibogai* (DAUTSZENBERG et BAVAY)

The shell is medium in size, thin, fragile, rather flat and almost orbicular and semitransparent. Both valves are marked with faint concentric lines on the smooth, yellowish brown surface. The left valve is somewhat deeply colored. The interior is sculptured by somewhat elevated, reddish yellow, radial ribs, which are 7 in number and seen through the shell from the outside. The ears are almost equal and small. Hinge line is short and straight, and united by a thin ligament which is separated at its mid-point by a condrophore beneath the umbo. Distribution: southern Honshû and southwards, in deep waters near 100 fathoms.

A white scar under the front ear seen on the plate is the trace of a parasitic limpet, *Capulus tosaensis* OTUKA.

15. *Parvamussium (Flavamussium) caducum* (SMITH)

This species is closely related to the pre-ceding species in coloration and other features, but has a smaller, oval shell with prominently elevated radial ribs on its inside, which are 8–9 in number and white in color, and somewhat intercalated on the left valve. The outer surface is more distinctly sculptured by numerous fine concentric lines. Another related species, *Bathyamussium jeffreisi* (SMITH), differs from this in having a finely decussate sculpture on the left valve. Distribution: south of central Honshû, near 100 fathoms depth.

16. *Amusium pleuronectes* (LINNÉ)

The shell is medium in size, nearly orbicular, rather thin, flat, equilateral, and equivalved, a little gaping on both sides. The left valve is nearly smooth with numerous fine concentric striae. It is pale reddish purple and rayed with fine bluish lines. The right valve is white, faintly reticulated with numerous fine radial and concentric striae. The interior is white in color and rayed with 11–12 pairs of ribs which grow prominent at the margin. The ears are equal and relatively small in size. This species differs from *A. japonicum* (Plate 72) in its smaller shell and pale reddish purple color of the left valve. Distribution: Formosa to Australia, common on shallow sandy bottom.

[PLATE 50]

Family Pectinidae (3)

1. *Cryptopecten vesiculosus* (DUNKER)

The shell is medium in size, orbicular and nearly equilateral except the ears. The right valve is somewhat more inflated than the left one. The surface is sculptured by prominently elevated, flat-topped, radial ribs, which are about 14 in number and smooth or serrated. The interspaces are marked with

[PLATE 50]   Pectinidae

fine radial striae and concentric, erect lamellae. Its coloration is variable, but mostly white with reddish purple maculations. The ears are unequal and rayed with serrated cords; the anterior ear is larger and has a deep byssal notch. Distribution: from Honshû to Kyûshû, on muddy bottom near 20 fathoms depth.

2. Excellichlamys spectabilis (REEVE)

This is a thin, fan-shaped scallop, equilateral but inequivalved. The left valve is flat, but slightly convex near the umbo, and sculptured by 12, somewhat irregular, prominently elevated, radial ribs which are covered with numerous concentrically imbricated scales. The right valve is convex and sculptured in the same way with the left valve. The interstices on both valves are deeply channeled, and marked by lamellated growth lines. The ground color is white, and the ribs are alternately tessellated or spotted with black and vermilion. The ears are large and rayed with squamous cords and dotted with red. The anterior ear has a large byssal notch on the right valve. Distribution: southern Honshû and southwards, in shallow waters.

3. Chlamys irregularis (SOWERBY)

The shell is medium in size, thin, rather flat and equivalved. It extends toward the ventral side, and is somewhat angulate at the posterior end. The surface bears numerous, irregular, imbricate, fine, radial cords which are sometimes serrate or smooth. The coloration is variable, but usually yellow to reddish. The ventral and dorsal halves are often differently colored. The interior is rather nacreous. The ears are distinctly unequal, the anterior being larger, and has a deep byssal notch. Distribution: south of central Honshû, common in shallow waters.

4. Chlamys squamata (GMELIN)

This shell is medium-sized, thin, rather fllat, nearly equivalved and somewhat triangularly orbicular. The valve is sculptured by 7 or more, rounded, radial ribs which are sparsely set with large erect scales. The interstices between the ribs are more or less broad and marked by 2–3 radial cords. This is pale orange in color, and stained with light brown maculations. The anterior ear is slightly larger than the posterior one. The interior is pearly and partly tinged with reddish brown, and the margin is irregularly crenulated. Distribution: central Honshû and southwards.

5. Chlamys larvata (REEVE)

A moderately large, thin, and flat shell, rather ovate and higher than wide. The surface is alternately rayed with serrated ribs and fine, smooth cords. The ears are unequal and radially bears squamous, fine cords. This is somewhat like *Chl. irregularis*, but differs in having the larger shell and alternate sculpture of serrated and smooth ribs. Distribution: Amami Islands and southwards.

6. Decatopecten striatus (SCHUMACHER)

This peculiar shell is medium in size, thick, rather inflated and trigonal ovate in shape. The surface is sculptured by broad, rounded, radial ribs which are about 5 in number. The ribs become narrower and more deeply carved toward the umbo, and the whole surface thus looks like a cloth bag fastened at its mouth. Many fine radial cords are also seen all over the surface. The interior is finely crenulated. The anterior ear is somewhat larger and has an extremely shallow byssal notch. Hinge line is straight, having a pair of ball and socket on its plate. Distribution: central Honshû and southwards, in shallow waters.

7. Volachlamys hirasei awajiensis
(PILSBRY)

The shell is medium-sized, thin, moderately inflated, and somewhat trigonal ovate. Radial ribs are prominently elevated, smooth and round-topped, and growth lines are finely lamellated in the interspaces. The coloration is white, with pale purple or purplish brown maculations. The ears well extend toward both ends, and are nearly equal in size. The byssal notch is narrow and rather deep. It is closely related to the following real form, but differs in having prominently elevated radial ribs. Distribution: from central Honshû to Kyûshû, in shallow waters.

8.   Volachlamys hirasei (BAVAY)

The outline of this shell is similar to the preceding form. The surface is nearly smooth or only slightly ribbed, and sometimes finely sculptured with radial cords. It is colored from dark purple to orange-yellow with white dots. The ear is large, trigonal and rayed with fine striae. Distribution : southern Honshû.

9.   Chlamys islandica hindsi (CARPENTER)

This shell is medium in size, thin, inequivalved and inequilateral. The right valve is moderately convex, and sculptured by irregular, narrow, radial ribs, which are finely serrated by growth lines, and also intercalated by fine radial cords. The left valve is rather compressed, and marked with moderately elevated, broad, radial ribs, which are the assemblage of 2–3 radial cords and bear serrated fine scales. The interstices have a few intercalated cords. The ears are prominently unequal and rayed with a few squamous striae; the anterior one is large and the byssal notch is rather deep. The surface is white or pinkish in color. Distribution : in cold waters from Hokkaidô to Alaska.

10.   Gloripallium pallium (LINNÉ)

This is a splendid, medium-sized shell, which is thick, orbicular, equivalved and nearly equilateral. The surface is sculptured by some 14, prominently elevated, radial ribs, which are very densely and beautifully set with imbricated, tripartite scales. The scales are more or less lamellated and erect. The interspaces also contain fine, serrated cords. The outer surface is deep orange-vermilion or violet or purple-red, and more or less checkered with white concentric maculations. The interior is white and tinged with orange and purple near the margin. The ear is thick, unequal and rayed with a few, wart-like squamate cords. The byssal notch is rather deep and narrow.

This species is easily distinguished from allied species by its tripartite sculpture and beautiful coloration. Distribution : from southern Honshû to Australia, below the low tide level.

11.   Chlamys farreri nipponensis KURODA

The shell is fairly large, thin, moderately inflated and equivalved. The surface is radially sculptured by many, low, rather irregular, serrated ribs, some of which are stronger than others. The surface coloration is variable and mostly purplish brown, but in some specimens it is orange, yellow or white. The ears are unequal and rayed with squamous cords ; the larger anterior ear has a rather deep byssal notch on the right side. A related form, Chl. farrei akazara is a northern race which has numerous subequal radial ribs, and there are intermediate forms between the two. Distribution : southern Hokkaidô to China Sea, in subtidal zone.

12.   Chlamys (Mimachlamys) nobilis (REEVE)

Resembling the above species in size and shape, this shell is somewhat less inflated. Radial ribs number 20 or more, and are regularly arranged, elevated, round-topped and set with concentrically arranged erect scales. The interstices are rather broad, channeled and finely lamellated with growth lines. The surface is purple to yellow or orange in color, sometimes with white dots. The ears are distinctly unequal and rayed with squamous cords. Distribution : central Honshû and southwards, in shallow waters.

13.   Chlamys islandicus erythrocomata (DALL)

The shell is larger than subsp. hindsi, moderately convex, rather thin, equivalved and nearly equilateral. The surface is sculptured by irregularly elevated, radial ribs which are finely and very closely imbricated with tiny erect scales. The interspaces have a few intercalated cords. The right valve is nearly white, and concentrically marked by rose-red bands. The left valve is salmon-pink with dark red rings. The ears are unequal and rayed with a few broad, squamous cords. This differs from subsp. hindsi in having the larger, equivalved and salmon-pink-colored shell. Distribution : the Kuriles and northwards.

14.   Chlamys (Swiftopecten) swifti (BERNARDI)

This shell is large, rather thick, moderately inflated, equivalved, and characterized

[PLATE 50]

Pectinidae

by a few, broad but low, radial ribs bearing somewhat large nodules at intervals. Moreover it is rayed with fine cords all over the surface. The outer surface is mostly white or reddish purple, while the interior is white and somewhat glossy. The ears are distinctly unequal and rayed with a few striae. The byssal notch is not so prominent. Distribution: from northern Honshû to Alaska, attaching by the byssus to rocks below the low tide mark.

15.   Comptopallium radula (Linné)

A moderately large, thick, and flat shell, somewhat triangularly ovate in outline. The right valve is more convex, while the left valve is peculiarly compressed at the umbo. The valves are strongly sculptured by 12 broadly round, elevated, radial ribs which are finely ribbed over again and set with numerous, densely and finely imbricated scales. The interspaces are broad and finely rayed with imbricately serrated cords. The coloration is yellowish, the left valve

being spotted with reddish black. The ears are nearly equal; the byssal notch is shallow and obscure. Distribution: south of southern Honshû.

16.   Patinopecten yessoensis (Jay)

This is the largest of Japanese Pectinidae, exceeding 160 mm in length. It is orbicular and equilateral. The right valve is more convex than the left one, and sculptured by broad, low, rather smooth, radial ribs, and yellowish white in color. The left valve is rayed with narrow, radial cords and finely lamellated with numerous growth lines. The interspaces are prominently broad and reddish purple in color. The interior is white and somewhat glossy. The ears are almost equal-sized and finely lamellated, and the byssal notch is extremely shallow. It is one of the economically important shells and cultured for its delicious flesh in Hokkaidô. Distribution: from northern Honshû to the Kuriles, in shallow waters.

Family Spondylidae

The shells are medium or large in size, solid and irregular in shape. The right valve is strongly convex, having a characteristic, triangular face at the umbo, and firmly attaches to the rock. The left valve is usually flat. The surface is sculptured by radial ribs, usually armed with erect spines or scales. The interior is porcellaneous or slightly pearly, and the margin is mostly crenulated. The ears are small and sometimes obscure. The resilifer pits are large, and situated between a pair of large hinge teeth. They have no byssus.

1. Spondylus anacanthus MAWE

The shell is medium-sized, irregular but mostly elongate triangular in shape and swollen toward the umbo. The left valve is densely sculptured by radiating striae which are nearly smooth and sometimes set with attenuate, irregular spines near the margin. The right valve is covered with a few lamellae. The coloration is bright scarlet, and generally rayed with separated white lines. The ear is rather large, and almost smooth. This species is distinguished from *Sp. sanguineus* by its elevated gibbous shell and the absence of scales. Distribution: central Honshû and southwards, in shallow waters.

2. Spondylus nicobaricus SCHREIBERS

This shell is medium in size, elongate ovate and thick. The surface is radially sriated and bears over it erect spines, which are more prominent than those of the preceding species. This is white, partially stained with purplish brown, and dotted with purple-black around the umbo. This is closely related to the preceding species, but differs in its dotted coloration and spines. Distribution: south of Shikoku, below the low tide level.

3. Spondylus candidus LAMARCK

The large shell is irregular but usually somewhat orbicular in shape. The surface is coarsely and radially ribbed, and the ribs are irregular in size and set with small granulous spines and sometimes with short scuta. The interspaces are somewhat finely and imbricately striated. It is purplish red, and sometimes tinged with bright rose. The ear is small and finely lamellated. This species can easily be identified by its imbricated striae and granulous spines. Distribution: central Honshû and southwards, in shallow waters.

4. Spondylus sinensis SCHREIBERS

The outline of this large shell is irregular, rather depressed and somewhat triangularly orbicular. The surface is sculptured by several elevated, broad, radial ribs bearing a few, long, flatly palmated scales, which are often twisted. The interspaces are finely and imbricately striated. The coloration is variable and usually pale fulvous or purplish red, bearing orange-red color around the umbo and white on the scales. This species is easily distinguished by its palmately scaled sculpture. Distribution: southern Honshû and southwards, in subtidal zone.

5. Spondylus versicolor SCHREIBERS

The shell is large, elongate oval and rather ventricose. Numerous, irregularly elevated, radial ribs are irregularly set with many, rather short, narrow, spines and somewhat broad scales, which are usually well developed near the margin. It is orange-red or pale purple, somewhat faded at the umbo, and the scales are usually colorful. This species differs from the next one in its scaled sculpture and larger shell, and also from *Sp. barbatus* in having a less sculptured shell. Distribution: southern Honshû and farther south, below the tide line.

6. Spondylus cruentus LISCHKE

The shell is medium in size, irregular, but mostly more or less orbicular, with somewhat extended antero-ventral margin. The surface is sculptured by irregular, fine, somewhat imbricated, radial ribs which bear a few, short spines. The coloration varies from scarlet to purplish brown. It is characterized by a rather small shell with its finely spined sculpture. Distribution: central Honshû and southwards, near the low tide level.

[PLATE 51]   Spondylidae

7.   *Spondylus barbatus* REEVE

The shell is medium to large in size, and quite irregularly shaped. The left valve is conspicuously and radially ribbed and striated, and the ribs bear broadly and narrowly squamated, flat, petal-like scales, which are densely imbricated toward the margin. The right valve is somewhat lamellated at the margin. The coloration is variable, mostly light reddish purple, more or less stained with flesh-rose and dotted near the umbo with deep red. This closely resembles the preceding species, but is characterized by the presence of flattened scales. Both the species are, however, hardly distinguishable due to the occurence of various intermediate forms. Distribution: Honshû and southwards, common below the tide line.

8.   *Spondylus sanguineus* DUNKER

This is a rather small shell, elongate oval, and broadly compressed triangular in out-

line. The surface is sculptured by numerous finely imbricated, radial striae which are very finely scaled, and the scales are sometimes almost obsolete. It is rose-colored but sometimes whitish, and rayed with vermilion. This species is easily distinguished by its beautiful coloration and scarcely scaled sculpture. Distribution: central Honshû and farther south, in shallow waters.

9.   *Spondylus regius* LINNÉ

This splendid shell is large, ovate, ventricose and almost equivalved. The surface bears a few, broad, prominently elevated, radial ribs and numerous minutely serrated ridges. The ribs bear prominently long, erect, solid spines, which are the most characteristic feature of this species. The outer surface is purplish rose, and the spines are sometimes whitish. Distribution: southern Honshû and southwards, 20–30 fathoms deep. It is found in shallower waters in the Ryukyus.

PLATE 51

1 × 3/5

2 × 3/5

3 × 4/5

4 × 3/5

5 × 3/5

6 × 1 1/5

7 × 3/5

8 × 1 4/5

9 × 1/2

PLATE **52**

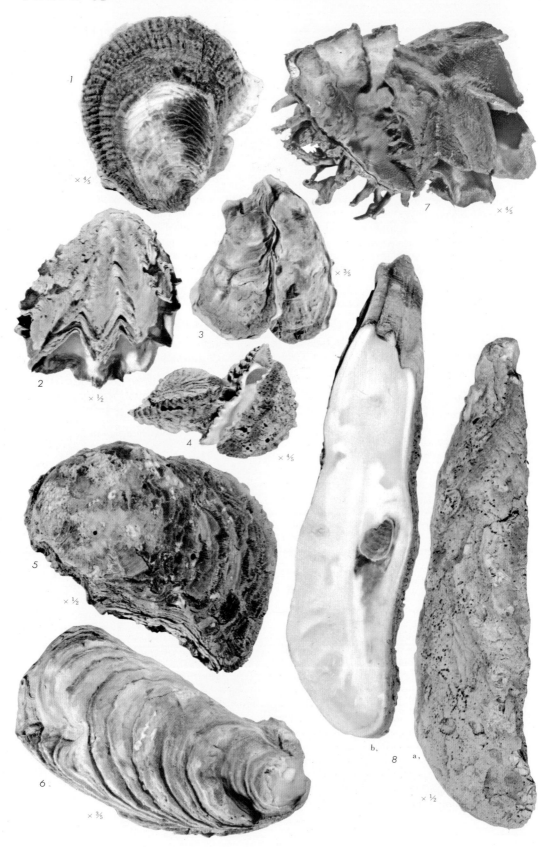

1

× ⁴⁄₅

2

× ½

3

× ³⁄₅

4

× ⁴⁄₅

5

× ½

6

× ³⁄₅

7

× ⁴⁄₅

b, *8* *a,*

× ½

Family Ostreidae

The oyster shells are usually irregularly deformed, owing to the adherent life to rocks and other objects. The attaching left valve is more convex, and somewhat larger than the free right one. The posterior muscle scar is large and circular, and is located nearly at the center of the inner surface which is usually white. The anterior muscle scar is reduced away. The hinge possesses a distinct ligamental impression, and with or without teeth on each side of it. This family is not so large, but includes the edible species relished by peoples of the world.

1. *Ostrea denselamellosa* LISCHKE

This is a large oyster, whose shell is usually ovate in shape, and compressed. The surface bears foliated growth lines and radial low ribs all over the surface. This feature is very characteristic of this species. The hinge bears several small crenations on each side of a ligamental impression. Distribution: central Honshû to Kyûshû, attaching to pebbles in shallow waters of bays. The delicious flesh is favored by the inhabitants.

2. *Dendostraea hyotis* (LINNÉ)

The shell is large and solid. The surface is purplish brown, and sharply folded along several radial ridges, and imbricated. Distribution: Amami Islands and southwards, clinging to rocks below the tide line.

3, 8. *Crassostrea gigas* (THUNBERG)

This is commercially the most important oyster cultured as a major source of food in Japan, the seeds of which are exported to the west coasts of U. S. A. and Canada every year. The shell is of various shapes, but usually elongate. The surface bears somewhat lamellate growth lines, and purplish brown radial rays on its whitish background. No crenation is seen on both sides of the hinge. The shells from Hokkaidô are so large, solid, and elongate, reaching about 400 mm in height, that we call them "Nagagaki" meaning a long oyster (Fig. 8). This

is the common intertidal species native to Japan, and some ecological forms have been reported under the names of *O. tailenwanensis* CROSSE, *O. laperousi* SCHRENCK and *O. shikame* AMEMIYA. Distribution: throughout Japan, Korea, China and Siberia. This tends to live in somewhat brackish waters.

4. *Saxostrea mordax* (GOULD)

This very solid oyster is an adherent on rocks between tide marks, of which the surface is stained in purple and is sculptured by furcated, stout ribs, accompanied by deep but narrow grooves. The margin is dentate, corresponding to the ribs on the surface. Small denticulations are seen on each side of the ligamental impression. Distribution: central Honshû and farther south.

5. *Crassostrea nippona* (SEKI)

This is very close to the large form of *O. gigas* in its general features, but the shell is not so elongate as that of *O. gigas*. It is very thick and solid. The surface bears brown foliated growth lines and numerous narrow radial cords. The ligamental hinge is broad. This lives in much saltier water than *O. gigas*. Distribution: central Honshû to Kyûshû.

6. *Crassostrea rivularis* (GOULD)

This has a large and rather flat shell, of which the surface bears very coarse and widely spaced concentric lamellae. This is cultured in Ariake Bay of Kyûshû for food. Distribution: central Honshû to Kyûshû, Korea and China.

7. *Lopha cristagalli* (LINNÉ)

A large shell with a strongly dentate margin. The surface is colored in purplish brown, never in white, strongly folded and covered by a granulated texture. In adherent life, it clings to the substratum with a prong-like projection on the lower valve. Distribution: Amami Islands and southwards, uncommon below the tide mark. This is an unique species, well known as cockcomb oyster.

Family Limidae

These shells are usually white, obliquely ovate in shape and rather compressed. The anterior side is rather straight with an excavated lunule and a gape, while the posterior is rounded, with a gape. Between the umbo elevated on the dorsal margin and the straight hinge line, a triangular flat area is formed. The small ear is on each side of the umbo, the anterior ear being smaller than the posterior. The surface bears radial ribs. The hinge plate is usually edentulous. The interior bears a monomyarian muscle scar.

1. Lima fujitai OYAMA

The shell is rather small for this genus, glassy white but solid, rather compressed and semicircular in shape, having the rather long straight anterior margin and the rounded posterior one. About 28 ribs radiate on the surface, and bear many erect spines. This rather commonly attaches to pebbles by its byssus on the bottoms of 20 –50 fathoms depth. Distribution: throughout Japan except Hokkaidô.

2. Mantellum orientalis (ADAMS et REEVE)

The shell is thin, white, and obliquely ovate, gaping at both ends. The surface bears many narrow but sharp radial threads, and the interspaces are wider than the ribs. This mollusc can swim by flapping its valves and marginal tentacles tinted with fleshy orange. Distribution: widely distributed in the Indo-Pacific areas up to Hokkaidô, on the bottom of shallow waters.

3. Mantellum fragilis kiiense (OYAMA)

The shell is thin, elongate oval, oblique antero-ventrally, compressed and widely gaping at both ends. The almost flat surface bears distantly placed weak radial threads. It is glassy white, but covered by a light brown periostracum. Distribution: central Honshû to Kyûshû, under pebbles below the low tide mark.

4. Mantellum hirasei (PILSBRY)

This is very similar to the preceding species in general features, but the shell is obliquely ovate, with many faint radial threads. Distribution: central Honshû to Kyûshû, not uncommon among pebbles near the low tide mark.

5. Ctenoides annulatus (LAMARCK)

The shell is oval, white and covered by a thin brownish periostracum. The surface has many radial ribs crossed by growth lines, forming series of granules on them. Distribution: Amami Islands and southwards, in subtidal zone.

6. Ctenoides japonica (DUNKER)

This closely resembles the preceding species, but the surface sculpture consists of numerous weaker radial threads only. Distribution: south of Honshû, attaching to rocks below the low tide level.

7. Acesta smithi (SOWERBY)

This shell is large, exceeding 100 mm in height, and light yellowish white. The surface has numerous low radial ribs, with narrow interspaces. The posterior ear is distinctly larger than the anterior. The ligamental impression is situated posteriorly on the triangular area between the umbo and the straight hinge line. Distribution: uncommonly collected from 50–100 fathoms depth, south of central Honshû.

8. Lima zushiensis YOKOYAMA

This is a beautiful medium-sized shell, which is characterized by the reddish brown coloration with darker concentric bands. The surface sculpture consists of about 26 prickly ribs, broader than their interspaces. Distribution: central Honshû to Kyûshû, uncommon in shallow waters.

9. Lima sowerbyi DESHAYES

A white, solid, and ovate shell, resembling the last species in appearance. The surface has about 21 strong, scaly ribs. The anterior slope is rather long and straight. Distribution: widely found in the Indo-Pacific areas up to Honshû, common between tide marks attaching to rocks by the byssus. In the Japanese form, the interspaces between two ribs are somewhat wider than those of the typical form of this species, named *nippona* OYAMA.

10. Acesta goliath SOWERBY

This giant species reaches approximately 150 mm in the height of shell, whose surface is white, rather smooth and polished in fully grown specimens. But in young specimens, the shell is light yellow, and roundly ovate, and its surface bears radiating narrow grooves. Distribution: uncommonly collected from deep bottoms in the Japan Sea and the Pacific, north of central Honshû, near 100 fathoms depth.

Family Crassatellitidae

The shells of this family are trigonally ovate, shortly rostrated and truncated posteriorly, solid and compressed. The surface usually bears concentric ribs. The resilium is internal, and placed on the chondrophore behind the cardinal teeth on the hinge plate. The mantle line is entire.

11. Crassatellites adamsi (KOBELT)

The shell is small, rather thin, compressed, and ovate in shape. The surface is covered with a brownish periostracum. The inner margin is minutely crenulated. Distribution: central Honshû to Kyûshû along Japan Sea coasts, on muddy bottom of 20–50 fathoms depth.

12. Crassatellites japonicus (DUNKER)

This is rather close to the preceding species in general features, but the shell is somewhat larger and more solid. The surface is covered with a yellowish brown periostracum with reddish brown radial rays. Distribution: central Honshû to Kyûshû, common on fine sandy bottom of shallow waters.

13. Crassatellites nanus (ADAMS et REEVE)

This resembles the preceding two species in its young stage, but the adult shell is larger in size and rostrated posteriorly, constricted at the hinder part of ventral margin,

and is sculptured by concentric sulci on the surface. Distribution: central Honshû to Kyûshû and Korea, very common on fine sandy bottom of 5–50 fathoms depth.

14. Crenocrassatella foveolata (SOWERBY)

The shell is solid, moderately convex, transversely elongated oval and rostrated toward the obliquely and shortly truncated posterior end. Strong sulci are marked over the surface covered with a brownish periostracum. Distribution: Formosa and southwards, on sandy bottom below the low tide mark.

Family Carditidae

The shells are rather solid, and orbicular to elogated oval in outline. The umbo varies in its position from the anterior to the middle of dorsal margin. The sculpture consists of radial ribs. The ligament is external, and located posteriorly to the umbo. The hinge teeth consist of two cardinals and sometimes 1–2 laterals. Ventral margin is more or less crenulated, and the mantle line is simple. Only a small number of Japanese species is included in this family.

15. Cardita nodulosa LAMARCK

The shell is cream-yellow, rather solid, and elongate ovate in shape. The surface is marked by strong, rather narrow, elevated, radial ribs, which are narrower than the interspaces and each bear a series of spiny processes. The number of the ribs is about 11. Distribution: common on gravely bottom south of central Honshû, 10–100 fathoms deep.

16. Cardita leana DUNKER

This shell is rectangularly ovate, solid, and dull white, with dark brown spots on the carinated ribs which radiate from the anterior umbo to the margin. The ribs are stronger on the posterior surface than on the anterior. Interspaces between the ribs are narrow and deep. Distribution: from Honshû to Formosa and Korea, common in tidal zone attaching to rocks and pebbles by the byssus.

[PLATE 53]

17. Cardita variegata BRUGUIÈRE

This is closely related to the preceding species, but the shell has rounded radial ribs, is maculated with black and crossed by somewhat lamellate growth lines. Distribution: south of Amami Islands, in the same habitat with the last species.

18. Venericardia (Megacardita) ferruginosa (ADAMS et REEVE)

The shell is solid, rectangularly ovate in shape, and rather convex. The anterior dorsal margin is short and steeply inclined, while the posterior dorsal margin is long and slightly curved. The posterior end is obliquely truncated. The surface is covered with a thick blackish periostracum and bears about 15, stout, low ribs. The cardinal teeth are very strong, and the posterior lateral tooth is long. The inner margin is scalloped, corresponding to the outer ribs. Distribution: central Honshû to Kyûshû, rather common on sandy bottom in shallow waters.

19. Venericardia (Megacardita) ferruginosa kiiensis (SOWERBY)

This is a form of the preceding species, and slightly differs from that in having the interspaces wider than ribs. Distribution: Pacific side of central Honshû.

20. Glans hirasei (DALL)

The shell is rather solid, very inflated, and quadrilateral in shape. The umbo is strongly elevated, curved and coiled forwards. The surface is covered by about 30, high, radial ribs on which tubercular spines are arranged. It is colored in yellowish brown, with large reddish brown blotches. Distribution: central Honshû to Kyûshû, rarely found at 20–100 fathoms depth.

21. Cyclocardia paucicostata (KRAUSE)

This is a very solid, rather inflated, orbicular shell, whose surface has about 18 stout but low ribs and very narrow grooves, radiating from the umbo to the margin, and is covered with a thick, velvety, black periostracum. The interior is white, and the hinge plate is large and wide, bearing 2 strong cardinal teeth. The inner magin is strongly crenulated. Distribution: northern Honshû and northwards, on muddy bottom in shallow waters.

Family Astartidae

The shells are usually ovate, and moderately compressed. The surface is smooth or with concentric ridges, and is covered with a thick periostracum. The interior is white, and the mantle line is simple. The ligament is external. A stout cardinal tooth is seen on the broad hinge plate of the right valve and two on the left. This family includes a small number of species living in cold seas.

22. Astarte (Tridonta) borealis (SCHUMACHER)

The shell is solid, rather compressed, and trigonal ovate. The surface is covered with a thick brownish periostracum, and marked by concentric growth lines, which are strong near the umbo and weakened toward the margin. This is a cold water element, very common on muddy bottom in shallow waters. Distribution: northern Honshû to Alaska, and arctic seas.

Family Glossidae

The shells of this small family are medium or large in size, moderately solid, and rounded or angularly ovate, with a strong carina running from the umbo to the postero-ventral corner. They are with or without the periostracum on the smooth or grooved surface. They have a hinge, 2 elongated cardinal teeth more or less parallel to each other, and a long posterior lateral tooth. Mantle line is simple. See also Plate 72.

23. Meiocardia lamarckii (REEVE)

The shell is rather thin but solid, and subquadrate in shape. When both valves are conjoined, the cross-section through the umbo is heart-shaped. It has a strongly incurved umbo, from which a carina runs to the sharply pointed postero-ventral corner. The surface is cream yellow and polished, but undulated by growth ridges. This is very close to the following species in general features, and should be a form of that species. Distribution: central Honshû to Shikoku and China, 50–100 fathoms in depth.

24. *Meiocardia tetragona* (ADAMS et REEVE)

It is difficult to find discriminative features between this and the preceding species, except a larger shell size in this species. This is also closely related in shape to *M. vulgaris* (REEVE) from China. It may be concluded that these belong to the same species covering their individual variations. Distribution: over the Indo-Pacific areas up to central Honshû, rather common on muddy bottom of 30–100 fathoms depth.

Family Trapeziidae

These shells are medium- or large-sized, rather solid, compressed, trapezoidal to ovate in shape, and whitish or yellowish. The surface bears rough growth lines with or without faint radial threads. The ligament is externally situated behind the umbo. This has a hinge plate with 2 cardinal teeth, and a long posterior and a short anterior lateral tooth. The interior is whitish or with purplish tinge posteriorly. Mantle line is simple.

25. *Trapezium bicaricatum* (SCHUMACHER)

The shell is elongated square-shaped and rather compressed. The surface bears an obtuse angle running from the umbo to the postero-ventral corner, and is marked by somewhat rough growth lines and radial threads forming a fine reticulation. The color is light yellow, except on the purplish posterior part. Distribution: central Honshû and farther south, below the tide line.

26. *Trapezium oblongum* (LINNÉ)

This resembles the preceding species in shape, but the shell is more inflated and increases in height toward the posterior margin. The surface has numerous radial ribs. Distribution: south of Amami Islands, uncommon in subtidal zone.

27. *Coralliophaga coralliophaga* (GMELIN)

The shell is thin, inflated and elongated ovate, narrowly gaping at the posterior end. The white surface is marked by fine ribs radiating from the umbo situated near the anterior end of dorsal margin, and covered with a thin yellowish periostracum. This is a coral borer and commonly found in coral masses washed ashore. Distribution: widely distributed in the Indo-Pacific areas, south of southern Honshû.

28. *Trapezium (Neotrapezium) sublaevigatum* (LAMARCK)

Closely resembling the following species in shape, this shell differs from the latter in lacking the strong keel along the posterior dorsal margin. Distribution: over the Indo-Pacific areas up to central Honshû, usually in rock crevices below the low tide mark.

29. *Trapezium (Neotrapezium) liratum* (REEVE)

The shell is solid, compressed and quadri-angular in shape. The surface with rough growth lines is marked by purplish rays against the dull white background, and is usually stained on its posterior part with purple. This commonly attaches to rocks or in cervices by its byssus in waters of low salinity. Distribution: Indo-Pacific areas south of Honshû.

Family Ungulinidae

The shells are usually orbicular, much inflated and white. The ligament is external, and only 2 cardinal teeth are seen on the narrow hinge plate. The surface is usually smooth, but sometimes sculptured. The mantle line is simple.

30. *Phlyctiderma japonicum* (PILSBRY)

The shell is circular, much inflated like a ball, solid and pure white in color. The surface is sculptured by concentric rows of small and elongate pimples, especially on its anterior half. This is a characteristic feature different from allied species. This bores in coral or limestone between tide

148

[PLATE 53]

marks. Distribution : throughout Japan and Korea.

31. *Felaniella usta* (GOULD)

This is one of the characteristic species of cold waters. The shell is circular, moderately inflated, and rather thin. The surface is covered with a smooth and olivaceous periostracum, and bears weak concentric growth lines. Distribution : northern Honshû and northwards, Korea and Siberia,

common on shallow sandy bottom.

32. *Joannisiella nomurai* HABE

The shell is very close to the preceding species in shape, but this is rather thick, somewhat more inflated, and covered with a yellowish periostracum. *J. cumingii* (HANLEY) from southern Japan is an allied species having a very inflated thin shell. Distribution : Honshû to Kyûshû, uncommonly collected from shallow bottom.

PLATE 53

1   × ⁴⁄₅
2   × ⁴⁄₅
3   × ⁴⁄₅
4   × ⁴⁄₅
5   × ⁴⁄₅
6   × ⁴⁄₅
7   × ⁴⁄₅
8   × ⁴⁄₅
9   × ⁴⁄₅
10 × ³⁄₅
11 × ⁴⁄₅
12 × ⁴⁄₅
13 × ⁴⁄₅
14 × ⁴⁄₅
15 × ⁴⁄₅
16 × ⁴⁄₅
17 × ⁴⁄₅
25 × ³⁄₅
22 × ⁴⁄₅
18 × ⁴⁄₅
19 × 1
20 × 1
26 × ½
23 × ⁴⁄₅
24 × ⁴⁄₅
30 × ⁴⁄₅
31 × ⁴⁄₅
21 × ⁴⁄₅
27 × ⁴⁄₅
28 × ⁴⁄₅
29 × ⁴⁄₅
32 × ⁴⁄₅

PLATE **54**

1 × ⅗

a,

3

b,

2 × ⅗   × ⅗

4 × ⅗

5 × ⅗

6 × ⅗

7 × ⅗

8 × ⅗

9 × ⅗

10 × ⅗

11 × ⅗   12 × ⅗   13 × ⅗

16 × ⅘

14 × ⅗

15 × ⅗

17 × ⅘

Family Lucinidae

The shells of this family are of small to large size, usually orbicular, compressed or inflated, and generally white. The lunule in front of the umbo is small and deeply impressed. The surface is smooth or with concentric or radial sculptures. The ligament is deeply sunken between both valves. The hinge plate is usually with 2 cardinal teeth and 2 lateral teeth on the right valve. The anterior muscle scar is long and narrow. The mantle line is simple.

1. Ctene divergens (PHILIPPI)

This is a small, solid, rather flat and circular shell. Radiating ribs on the surface become denser on its middle part, and somewhat divaricate on both anterior and posterior parts. Growth lines cross the ribs, forming a granulated sculpture on the surface. The inner margin is crenulated corresponding to the ribs. Distribution: central Honshû and southwards, rather common on sandy bottom in shallow waters. *C. delicatula* (PILSBRY) is an allied species, but has a smaller shell with a coarser sculpture on its surface.

2. Lucinoma annulata (REEVE)

The shell is circular, rather compressed, and white. The sculpture consists of distantly placed and sharply raised concentric lamellae. The periostracum is thin and yellowish. Two cardinal teeth are accompanied with a small anterior lateral tooth. The interior is smooth. Distribution: Kyûshû to Hokkaidô, fairly common on muddy bottom, 10–150 fathoms deep. *L. spectabilis* YOKOYAMA differs from this species in having the larger and flatter shell, with more distantly placed concentric lamellae.

3. Codakia paytenorum IREDALE

This shell is of medium size, thick, rather flat, and circular. The surface is sculptured by radial and concentric ribs forming a reticulation. It is light yellowish white on the outer surface, and yellow, marginated with rosy red, on the inner surface. Distribution: throughout tropical Pacific areas up to Amami Islands, rather common on shallow sandy bottom.

4. Fimbria soverbi (REEVE)

The shell is moderately large, thick, rather inflated, ovate, longer than high, and widely rounded posteriorly. The surface is marked with distinctly lamellate growth lines crossed by narrow radial ribs, forming a reticulated sculpture. It is colored white with light rosy rays. The interior is light yellow except the light rosy margin. Distribution: south of Amami Islands, below the tide line.

5. Codakia tigerina (LINNÉ)

This is a large, thick, compressed, and circular shell, whose surface is white and reticulated by narrow radial ribs and concentric cords, accompanied with nodules at the points of intersection. The interior is light yellow. Distribution: central Honshû and southwards, uncommon on sandy bottom in shallow waters.

6. Anodontia edentula (LINNÉ)

A thin, strongly inflated, white shell, which is sphaerical when the valves are conjoined. The hinge plate is edentulous. The surface is dull white with weak concentric growth lines. Distribution: Amami Islands and southwards, rather common on shallow muddy bottom.

7. Anodontia stearnsiana (OYAMA)

This differs from the preceding species in having a larger shell with somewhat alate anterior and posterior dorsal margins. The shell is circular, inflated and chalky white. The hinge plate is without teeth. Distribution: from Kyûshû to Honshû, very common on muddy bottom in bays.

8. Codakia punctata (LINNÉ)

This is a large, solid, compressed and circular shell, whose surface is white around the margin and yellow near the umbo. The surface has broad, flattened, radial ribs, rather irregularly placed. The interior is yellow with the reddish margin. Distribution: Amami Islands and southwards, common on sandy bottom of shallow waters.

[PLATE 54]　　　　　　　　　　　　　　Lucinidae, Chamidae, Cardiidae

Family Chamidae

These shells are inequivalved, very solid and irregular in shape owing to the adherent way of living, but are usually suborbicular. They attach to the substratum usually with the left valve, which is larger and more convex than the rather flat opposite valve. The umbo is subspiral. The surface is sculptured by concentric lamellae which are often fimbriate or laciniate. The hinge plate has 2 very stout elongate cardinal teeth on the right valve and another on the left. The ligament is external. The mantle line is simple.

9.　Chama (Pseudochama) retroversa (LISCHKE)

This is the only species of the subgenus *Pseudochama* in Japan. The shell is elongate ovate, solid and colored dull white or purple. The attaching left valve is larger than the flat right. The umbo is turning from right to left. Distribution: Honshû to Kyûshû, rather commonly found on rocks between tide marks.

10.　Chama reflexa REEVE

The shell is rather small, solid, orbicular and whitish or reddish. The surface of the free right valve bears undulating rows of short, irregularly imbricate spines. The umbo turns sinistrally. Distribution: Formosa to Honshû, very common on rocks and pebbles between tide marks.

11.　Chama reflexa jukesi REEVE

This is very close to the preceding species, but this varietal form has numerous whitish tubercular spines on the surface. Distribution: Amami Islands and southwards.

12.　Chama dunkeri LISCHKE

The shell is elongated oval, narrowing toward the ventral margin and is colored red especially on its posterior part. Distribution: from central Honshû down to the Ryukyus, rather common in tidal zone attaching to rocks with the left valve.

13.　Chama ambigua LISCHKE

The shell is solid and circular. The attaching left valve is deep, while the free right valve is flat. The surface has foliaceous growth lamellae. The surface color is whitish. Distribution: central Honshû to Kyûshû, fairly common on rocks near the low tide mark.

14.　Chama iostoma CONRAD

This is characterized by its inner margin tinted with deep purple. The surface is marked by lamellate growth lines which bear spiny processes on the marginal area. Distribution: Amami Islands and southwards, and Hawaii Islands.

15.　Chama brassica REEVE

This species resembles *Ch. ambigua* in shape, but has a much larger shell, whose surface has radially arranged, tubercular processes and is colored white to light rose. Distribution: central Honshû and farther south.

Family Cardiidae (1)

The shells range from small to large size, and are inflated, usually rounded or ovate and higher than wide. The sculpture consists of many radial ribs, sometimes reduced in number or entirely lacking in certain species, and often ornamented with scales or lamellae. The ligament is external. The hinge plate has 2 cardinal teeth and one lateral tooth on each side of them. Mantle line is simple. The inner margin is crenulated or serrated. See also Plate 72.

16.　Vasticardium burchardi (DUNKER)

The shell is moderately large, solid, somewhat compressed and ovate with a rather straight, long, posterior dorsal margin. The large ligament is situated behind the umbo. The surface has about 43, strong, scaly ribs. Deep interspaces between them are narrower than the rib. The surface is covered with a yellowish periostracum, with chestnut-brown tinge and spottings on the umbonal area. The margin is strongly serrated. Distribution: Kyûshû to Honshû, rather common on sandy bottom in offshore waters.

17. *Vasticardium enode* (SOWERBY)

This shell is oblong ovate, solid, and inflated. Strong ribs on the surface are about 39 in number, and bear rather distantly spaced scales on their tops. The interspaces are deep, and narrower than the ribs. It is white, and spotted with reddish brown on the umbonal area. The margin is strongly serrate as in the preceding species. Distribution: central Honshû and southwards, rather common on sandy bottom in shallow waters.

[PLATE 55]   Cardiidae

Family Cardiidae (2)

1. *Fulvia hungerfordi* (SOWERBY)

The shell is rather small, thin, fragile, inflated, roundly ovate, and truncated and narrowly gaping at the posterior end. The surface is shiny and has several radial ribs on the posterior part. It is usually reddish brown. Distribution: from China to Japan, except northern Honshû and Hokkaidô, very abundant on shallow muddy bottom of sheltered waters.

2. *Laevicardium undatopictum* (PILSBRY)

This is a thin, rather small, inflated and almost circular shell resembling the preceding species. The surface is shiny, and bears numerous, weak, narrow, radial threads which grow stronger toward the posterior part. The inner margin is minutely crenulated. The color varies from white to reddish brown, usually with darker brown mottlings over the surface. Distribution: central Honshû to Kyûshû, very common on sandy bottom of offshore waters, a few fathoms in depth.

3. *Fulvia bullata* (LINNÉ)

This shell is thin, inflated, roundly ovate, rounded anteriorly, and somewhat rostrated and gaping posteriorly. The surface is marked with radial ribs which become stronger posteriorly. The periostracum grows series of radially lamellate erect hairs. The exterior is mottled with purplish red and white blotches are also seen. Distribution: central Honshû and southwards, uncommon on shallow muddy bottom of bays.

4. *Fulvia australis* (SOWERBY)

This closely resembles the preceding species in shape, but has a more inflated and circular shell, lacking the posterior rostration. The surface bears numerous broad but low radial ribs, and maculated with yellowish blotches on the light yellowish ground color. Distribution: south of central Honshû, rather common on muddy bottom in shallow waters.

5. *Afrocardium ebaranum* (SOWERBY)

This shell is small, rather thin and ovate. The beak is oblique anteriorly and is located near the anterior end. Carinate radial ribs on the surface are crossed by growth lines forming small scales on their tops. This is white to reddish brown, with darker blotches on the postero-ventral area. The margin is strongly crenulated corresponding to the ribs on the surface. Distribution: central Honshû to the Ryukyus, in crevices of pebbles and among rots of organisms in offshore waters.

6. *Trifaricardium nomurai* KURODA et HABE

The shell is thin, strongly convex at the umbonal area and quadriangularly ovate. The white surface has many narrow radial ribs, which are crossed by growth cords forming a reticulated sculpture, except on the irregularly undulating and beaded small anterior area. The interspaces are as wide as the ribs. One in every 3 interspaces contains a row of small tubercular spines, while other two are intersected by growth cords. Distribution: Tosa Bay of Shikoku, uncommon at 80–150 fathoms depth.

7. *Frigidocardium eos* (KURODA)

This shell is somewhat like the preceding species in shape, but is decorated by narrow radial ribs all over the surface, with interspaces narrower than them. Slender, prominently elevated tubercles rise in every third interspaces. The surface is white to orange red and sometimes rayed with white and red. Distribution: central Honshû to the China Sea, on fine sandy bottom of 20–150 fathoms depth.

8. *Frigidocardium exasperatum* (SOWERBY)

This is a white shell closely allied to the preceding species, but is characterized by the alternation of 2 granulated ribs and a row of slender tubercular spines on the surface. Distribution: central Honshû to the China Sea, uncommon on fine sandy bottom at 20–100 fathoms depth.

9. Nemocardium (Keenaea) samarangae (MAKIYAMA)

The shell is medium in size, thin, inflated and somewhat quadriangularly circular in shape. The posterior one fourths of the surface is marked by both radial and concentric riblets, and distinctly separated from the remaining finely striated area. It is dull white, and radially rayed with orange red. The surface is covered with a thin yellowish periostracum. The interior is dull white and crenulated at the margin. Distribution: south of Honshû, fairly common on muddy bottom, 10–150 fathoms in depth.

10. Microfragum festivum (DESHAYES)

This is a small shell which is rather inflated, ovate in shape, truncated posteriorly, and rounded anteriorly. About 40 ribs radiate on the surface, raising scales on the flat tops. The interspaces between the ribs are narrow but deep. A thin periostracum covers the dull white shell which is sometimes tinted with rose on its posterior part. Distribution: south of Amami Islands, rather common on sandy bottom in shallow waters.

11. Fragum bannoi OTUKA

The shell is small, white, solid, and almost trapezoidal in shape, with a widely truncated posterior end forming an angular postero-ventral corner. The sculpture consists of about 16 strong ribs bearing distantly placed scaly granules. The periostracum is thin and light yellow. Distribution: from Honshû to Formosa, common on fine sandy bottom between tide marks. This is often confused with the southern species *Fr. carinatum* LYNGE, but differs from the latter in lacking a strong carina running from the umbo to the postero-ventral corner.

12. Fragum mundum (REEVE)

The shell is small, solid, inflated, elongated trapezoidal, and widely truncated at the long posterior margin. The umbo is prominent and very oblique anteriorly. There is a strong keel that runs from the umbo to the acutely angulated postero-ventral corner. Posteriorly to this keel,

the surface is almost flattened, while it is inflated anteriorly. The surface is marked by rather strong but flattened radial ribs about 28 in number, which are separated by narrow impressed grooves and rendered nodulose by regularly disposed concentric threads. The exterior is yellow and mottled by orange red on the postero-dorsal area. Distribution: south of Amami Islands, rather common on sandy bottom in shallow waters.

13. Fragum loochooanum KIRA

This is closely related to *Fr. bannoi*, but differs in having about 24 radial ribs instead of about 16 in the latter species. Distribution: Amami Islands and the Ryukyus, on shallow sandy bottom.

14. Fragum fragum (LINNÉ)

The shell is medium-sized, inflated and ovate with a strongly serrate long posterior truncation. The umbo is somewhat prominent and oblique anteriorly. A keel runs from the umbo to the postero-ventral corner, separating the rather flat posterior area from the inflated anterior part. Strong radial ribs number about 24 and ornamented by regularly arranged nodules bending ventrally on their flat tops. This is plainly colored in yellowish white, and the inner margin is intensely crenulated. Distribution: Amami Islands and southwards, common on sandy bottom in shallow waters.

15. Lunulicardia subretusa (SOWERBY)

This is a white and solid shell. The surface is crossed by a strong keel from the umbo to the postero-ventral corner. A lunule in front of the umbo is strongly incurved forwards, and is small but deeply impressed. The surface bears low and flat ribs, each bearing a series of granules. Narrow punctuated grooves are seen between each pair of the ridges, and intersected by growth lines. Distribution: widely found in tropical Pacific areas up to Amami Islands, uncommon on shallow sandy bottom.

16. Lunulicardia retusa (LINNÉ)

The shell is very solid, quadriangular in

[PLATE 55]   Cardiidae

shape, with an obtuse keel running from the umbo to the postero-ventral corner that separates the very inflated anterior area from the rather flattened posterior part. The surface is sculptured by flat and low ribs with a series of granules on their tops. The interspaces are narrow. The preceding species is very close to this, but the former can be distinguished by the sharply angulated keel on its surface. Distribution: southern Honshû to tropical Pacific areas, rather rare on shallow sandy bottom.

17.   *Fragum unedo* (LINNÉ)

This closely resembles *Fr. fragum* in shape, but the shell differs in having a more solid shell with about 30 strong ribs, which are separated by deep but narrow grooves and are decorated with purplish red scales distantly placed on their flat tops. The inner margin is strongly serrated. Distribution: widely distributed in tropical Pacific areas up to Amami Islands, very common on shallow sandy bottom.

18.   *Nemocardium bechei* (REEVE)

The shell is fairly large, solid, circular and very convex at the umbonal area. The surface is covered with a golden brown periostracum and sculptured by conspicuously serrated radial ribs on the posterior one fourth and by weak radiating threads on other three fourths. The ground color is light reddish. The interior is white and minutely crenulated at the margin. Distribution: tropical Pacific areas up to central Honshû, uncommon on sandy bottom in offshore waters.

19.   *Discors lyratum* (SOWERBY)

This shell is large, solid, strongly swollen, and rounded in shape. The surface has distinct two types of sculpture. The posterior half bears radiating ribs which are weaker and closer to the anterior, while transversely oblique distant ridges cover the anterior half of the shell. The color is purplish red. Distribution: the same with the preceding species.

PLATE **55**

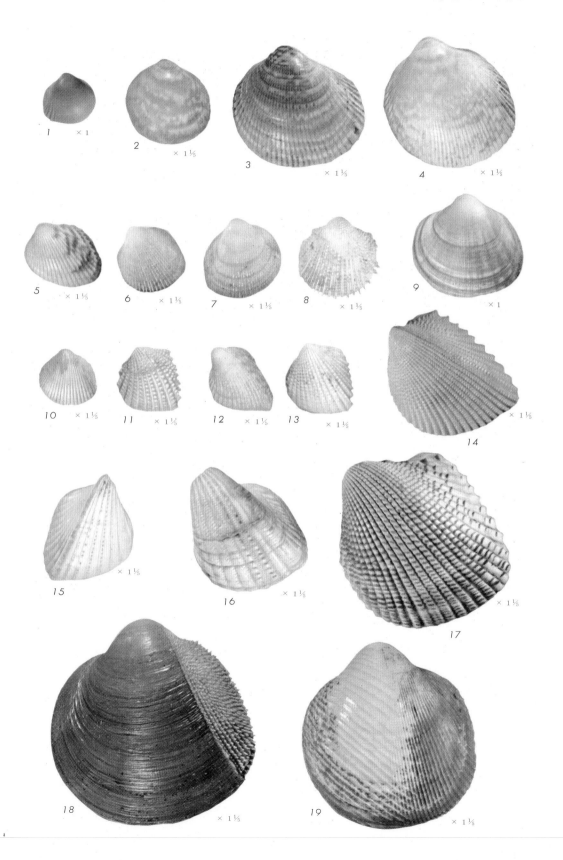

PLATE 56

1   × ³⁄₅

2   × ³⁄₅

3   × ³⁄₅

4   × ³⁄₅

5   × ³⁄₅

6   × ³⁄₅

7   × ³⁄₅

8   × ³⁄₅

9   × ³⁄₅

10   × ³⁄₅

11   × ³⁄₅

15   × ³⁄₁₀

a,

16   × ½

b,

12   × ⁴⁄₅

13   × ⁴⁄₅

14   × ½

17   × ½

18   × ²⁄₅

Family Cardiidae (3)

1. *Clinocardium uchidai* HABE

The shell is very similar to *Cl. californiense* in shape, but the shell is ovate, rather compressed, roundly ovate at the anterior part and somewhat elongate at the posterior end. Its surface is sculptured by more than 45 radial cords, divided by narrow and deep grooves. It is not marked by distinct concentric undulations. This is dull white, and covered by an ashy yellow periostracum. Distribution: only known from northeastern coasts of Hokkaidô, where it is common on sandy bottom.

2. *Clinocardium ciliatum* (FABRICIUS)

The shell is thin, fragile, inflated, circular, and a little more long than high. The surface sculpture consists of about 35 ridged radial ribs. The grayish yellow periostracum is ciliated along the ribs. Distribution: common on muddy bottom in northern seas, north of Hokkaidô. Young shells of this species are often found in stomachs of flatfish.

3. *Clinocardium californiense bulowi* (ROLLE)

This is a southern representative of this genus, and may be merely a small local form of the following species. The surface has about 36 radial ribs, with a few, distantly placed, concentric undulations formed by the temporary pauses of growth. A flexure on the posterior dorsal area runs from the umbo to the postero-ventral corner. The periostracum is grayish yellow. Distribution: Kyûshû to Honshû, uncommon on fine sandy bottom of bays.

4. *Clinocardium californiense* (DESHAYES)

This has a large but thin, circular shell covered with a dully brown periostracum. The radial ribs are rounded on their tops, and about 35–45 in number. Distribution: northern Honshû and northwards, commonly found on muddy bottom in shallow waters.

5. *Laevicardium biradiatum* (BRUGUIÈRE)

The shell is thin, inflated at the umbonal area, ovate in outline, and higher than long. The surface is rather smooth and polished, and obscurely ribbed at the middle. The ribs become more distinct toward both ends. The color is yellowish white and mottled with brown or orange-red. The inner margin is minutely crenulated. Distribution: widely distributed in tropical Pacific areas up to Amami Islands, rather common on shallow sandy bottom.

6. *Vepricardium sinense* (SOWERBY)

The shell is medium in size, solid, white, inflated and rounded. The surface is covered with distinct radial ridges, which are about 24 in number and granulated. The margin is strongly serrated. Distribution: from Formosa down to East Indies, in shallow waters.

7. *Vasticardium flavum* (LINNÉ)

This shell is ovate, rather thick, inflated and roundly curved at both anterior and posterior ends. The umbo is prominent above the hinge line and incurved. The sculpture consists of strong radial ribs, 27 in number, whose tops are flat and decorated with scales. The interspaces are deep and narrow. The periostracum is yellowish brown. Distribution: tropical Pacific areas up to Amami Islands, rather common on sandy bottom in offshore waters.

8. *Vasticardium alternatum* (SOWERBY)

The shell is white, oblique posteriorly, rather inflated, rounded at the front, and somewhat truncated. The scaly radial ribs are about 27 in number and carinated at the tops. The periostracum is thin and light yellow. Distribution: Amami Islands and southwards, uncommon on shallow sandy bottom.

9. *Vasticardium compunctum* KIRA

The shell is thick, solid, ovate, inflated and medium in size. The surface is marked by strongly scaly, radiating, elevated ribs, separated by very deep interspaces. The shell is characterized by large elongated blotches of dark brown on the posterior half of the surface covered with a yellowish periostracum. Distribution: Amami Islands

[PLATE 56]   Cardiidae, Tridacnidae

and the Ryûkyûs, rather common on shallow sandy bottom.

10. Vasticardium arenicola (REEVE)

The shell is rather thin, ovate, somewhat higher than long, narrowed toward the umbo, widened toward the ventral margin and considerably compressed. The sculpture consists of about 45 low radial ribs and narrow interspaces. The coloration is yellowish brown, mottled with purplish red. Distribution: south of central Honshû, very common on fine sandy bottom in shallow waters.

11. Vasticardium okinawaense KURODA

This species very closely resembles *V. enode* (Pl. 54), but the shell is smaller even in fully grown specimens and has somewhat more numerous radial ribs (42 in number). Distribution: Amami Islands to North Australia, common on sandy bottom of offshore waters.

12. Corculum impressum (SOLANDER)

This is a rather small species in this group of extraordinarily shaped shells. The shell is strongly compressed in posterior-anterior direction, and flatly heart-shaped in front view. The posterior side is a little more convex than the anterior side. The umbo is strongly incurved, from which a strong lateral keel runs to the middle of the ventral margin. This keel becomes thicker and spinous nodules on it are diminishing toward the ventral margin. The surface has low ribs, and maculated by light yellow on the semi-translucent white background. The margin is crenulated. Distribution: tropical Pacific areas up to Amami Islands, below the tide line.

13. Corculum monstrosum (GMELIN)

The shell is very similar to the following species, but the anterior side is more convex than the posterior. The medial lateral keel is somewhat curved frontwards. The radial ribs are less in number and granulated on the posterior side, while on the anterior convex side the ribs are more numerous and thinner. The shell is light yellow.

Distribution: tropical Pacific areas up to Amami Islands, in shallow waters.

14. Corculum cardissa (LINNÉ)

This is very close to *C. impressum,* but smaller in shell size. The shell is strongly compressed and heart-shaped having a strong lateral keel, on which a series of sharp prickles are sometimes arranged. The anterior as well as the posterior surface is slightly convex. The radial sculpture is more evident on the anterior surface than on the posterior. It is transparently white with light yellow tinge. Distribution: widely found in tropical Pacific areas, rather common on sandy bottom in submarine coral reef.

The above three species are grouped as follows :

The anterior and posterior sides nearly equally convex
    Shell exceeding 66 mm in height......
    ....*C. cardissa*
    Shell less than 22 mm in height ......
    .... *C. impressum*
The posterior side is rather flat ....
    ....*C. monstrosum*

Family Tridacnidae

The shells of this family are generally large, solid and heavy, and the largest of all shells are included here. The ligament is on the external side, and a large byssal gape opens on the anterior dorsal margin and its inner wall is crenulated. The surface is strongly folded by stout ribs often bearing scaly processes, and interspaces between them are sculptured by thinner radial ribs. The cardinal and posterior lateral teeth are present. The posterior muscle scar is placed at the center of the inner surface and the anterior muscle scar is absent.

15. Hippopus hippopus (LINNÉ)

This is a giant free-living tridacnid. The shell reaches about 300 mm in length, rather trigonal in shape with a wide, flat, posterior dorsal area. The sculpture consists of several large, broad and low radial ribs as well as several narrower ribs between them, whose tops are decorated with tubercular scales. The anterior gape is narrow. The ventral margin is strongly crenulated within. Distribution: Indo-Pacific areas south of Amami Islands, in shallow waters.

16. *Tridacna (Vulgodacna) noae* [RÖDING]

The shell is large, solid, heavy, and elongated oval in shape. The umbo is located rather posteriorly, so that the anterior dorsal margin is longer than the posterior margin, on which a large byssal gape opens. The surface has about 8 very strong, stout ribs, on which large scales are regularly and distantly placed. In addition, thinner radial ribs are found all over the surface, especially distinctly in younger stages. This was formerly known as *Tridacna elongata* LAMARCK. Distribution: this and the following two species are all widely distributed over tropical areas of the Indo-Pacific.

17. *Tridacna (Flodacna) squamosa* LAMARCK

This is an attractive shell having on its surface several very broad and stout radiating ribs, set with large distantly placed scales. Narrow radial ribs are seen between the large ribs. The umbo is situated near the middle of dorsal margin and there opens a large posterior gape. This is one of the common tridacnid species on the coral reef of the Ryukyus and Amami Islands.

18. *Tridacna (Chametrachea) crocea* (LAMARCK)

This is a rather small tridacnid species living buried in the coral. The umbo is located rather anteriorly, and the long posterior dorsal margin has a large byssal opening. The surface bears several stout ribs with narrow interspaces between them. The ribs usually have no scales, but are sometimes scaled near the margin.

[PLATE 57]   Veneridae

Family Veneridae (1)

These shells are usually trigonal ovate in shape, orbicular or elongated oval in some groups, equivalved, and tightly closed. The umbo is prominent and prosogyrate. The surface is smooth or sculptured by radial ribs and concentric lines. The ligament is external and embraces a resilium. On the cardinal plate, there are 3 diverging cardinal teeth with or without lateral teeth. The mantle line connecting the anterior and posterior muscle scars usually has a posterior sinuation. The inner margin is smooth or minutely crenulated. This is a large family to be divided into several subfamilies, such as Venerinae, Dosiniinae, Meretricinae, Sunettinae, Clementiinae etc.

1. Meretrix lusoria [Röding]

This is one of the economically important edible clams in Japan. This has been confused with the Philippine species, *Meretrix meretrix* (Linné), but the shell of this species is trigonal ovate, elongated posteriorly. The surface is covered with a thin, smooth and polished periostracum, and is colored white to chestnut-brown usually with broad radial rays. The coloration is, however, extremely variable. The interior is white and the mantle line has a small posterior sinus. The inner margin is smooth. Distribution: from Kyûshû up to Hokkaidô, China and Korea, common on fine sandy bottom in lower intertidal zone down to 5 fathoms depth.

2. Meretrix lamarckii Deshayes

Closely resembling the preceding species in shape, this has a thicker, less inflated trigonal shell with a shallower sinus on the mantle line. The shell size is also larger. Distribution: Formosa to Japan and Korea, on sandy bottom in shallow waters of the open sea.

3. Callista chinensis (Holten)

This medium-sized shell is ovate, accuminate on the back, and rounded at the front. The surface is covered with a smooth and polished periostracum, and colored in light brown with purplish rays.

The hinge plate bears 3 cardinal and 1 anterior lateral teeth. Distribution: south of central Japan to Korea and China, on shallow, fine sandy bottom.

4. Callista (Eocallista) brevisiphonata (Carpenter)

This resembles the preceding species in shape, but is larger exceeding 150 mm in length in fully grown specimens. The surface is marked by rough growth lines, and is covered with a smooth and polished periostracum, under which light purplish brown rays are seen on the yellowish background in young specimens. Distribution: northern Honshû, Hokkaidô and Siberia, common on fine sandy bottom in shallow waters.

5. Cyclina sinensis (Gmelin)

This has a circular and inflated shell, whose surface is covered with a vernicose yellowish brown periostracum except on the purplish marginal area, and sculptured by many weak striae and growth lines forming a reticulation. The beak is prominent and oblique anteriorly. The hinge plate is broad. The margin is minutely crenulated internally, corresponding to the outer radial striae. The name *C. orientalis* Sowerby has been applied for the Japanese specimens, but it seems to be only a form of this species. Distribution: from Formosa up to Honshû, China and Korea, commonly found on muddy bottom between tide marks in bays.

6. Dosinia (Phacosoma) troscheli Lischke

The shell is thick, compressed and circular. The lunule in front of the beak, which is strongly oblique forward, is cordate and deeply impressed. The surface is rayed with brown and marked by concentric lamellae. The mantle sinus is deep and triangular. Distribution: central Japan to Kyûshû, in shallow waters.

7. Dosinia (Phacosoma) japonica (Reeve)

The shell is white, without colored rays, solid and orbicular in shape. The surface is covered by concentric, thin, plate-like ridges along growth lines. Distribution: throughout Japan and Korea, very common on shallow, fine sandy bottom.

8. Dosinia (Dosinorbis) bilunulata (GRAY)

This is a large, compressed and orbicular shell, which is characterized by having the lunule surrounded by a larger area bordered by the lamellated keel. The surface bears distinct growth lines which are obsolete on the middle part and grow lamellate laterally. The shell is white, sometimes with brownish rays. Distribution: from Kyûshû up to Bôsô Peninsula of Honshû, uncommon on sandy bottom below the tide line.

9. Saxidomus purpuratus (SOWERBY)

This species is easily recognized by the deeply purpulish interior of the shell, which is solid, thick and squarish ovate in shape. The surface is ashy white and sculptured with roughly lamellate growth lines. In young specimens, the surface shows brownish radial rays and the interior is white. Distribution: from Kyûshû to Hokkaidô and Korea, very common on muddy bottom in shallow waters of bays.

10. Antigona lamellaris SCHUMACHER

This species is characterized by the strongly erect, frilled lamellae crossed by radial cords on the surface. The shell is very solid and trigonal ovate in shape. The lunule in front of the beak is very prominent and oblique, cordate and strongly impressed. It is yellowish brown outside, with broad, brownish rays, and is fleshy orange inside. The inner margin is crenulated. Distribution: central Japan and southwards, on shallow sandy bottom.

11. Periglypta (Tigammona) fischeri (RÉCLUZ)

The shell is rather large, solid and heavy, inflated, and roundly ovate in shape, resembling the following three species of this group. The surface is sculptured by concentric frilled lamellae, and is rayed with brownish shade. The interior is white, with no purple patch. Distribution: central Honshû and southwards, uncommon on shallow sandy bottom.

12. Periglypta puerpera (LINNÉ)

The shell is thick, inflated and round. The surface is reticulated with radial cords and growth lamellae. The outer surface is brownish with darker rays, while the interior is white with purplish posterior area. The ventral margin is crenulated within. Distribution: south of Amami Islands, commonly found on sandy bottom in shallow waters.

13. Periglypta reticulata (LINNÈ)

Strong radial ribs are crossed by concentric cords forming a coarse reticulation on the surface, which is spotted with white and lined with brown. The interior is yellowish except on the hinge plate, where it is stained fleshy orange. Distribution: central Honshû and southwards, common on sandy bottom of shallow waters.

14. Periglypta clathrata (DESHAYES)

This is the largest species in this group, exceeding 100 mm in length and is very close to P. puerpera in shape. The sculpture consists of regularly arranged concentric and radial narrow cords forming a reticulated network. The coloration is white with brownish radial rays. Distribution: south of central Honshû, common on shallow sandy bottom.

15. Venus (Ventricolaria) toreuma GOULD

The shell is solid and sphaerical when the valves are conjoined. The surface has beaded concentric cords and marked with brown rays and angular patches against the fawn background. The inner margin is minutely crenulated throughout. Distribution: south of central Honshû, rather common among pebbles between tide marks.

16. Venus (Ventricoloidea) foveolata SOWERBY

This is somewhat similar to the preceding species in shape, but the shell is less inflated, and the color is white, sometimes rayed with light brown. There are minute crenulations along the edge of the margin. The interior is white. Distribution: Hon-

[PLATE 57]   Veneridae

shû to Kyûshû, China and Korea, very common on muddy bottom at 5–100 fathoms depth.

17. Mercenaria stimpsoni (GOULD)

This northern species grows into very large size, attaining 100 mm in length. The shell is white, solid, rather compressed and trigonal ovate in shape. The umbo is at the anterior one third of dorsal margin. The surface is sculptured by lamellate growth lines, and the interspaces between them are crossed by radial riblets. Distribution: northern Honshû and northwards, on shallow, fine sandy bottom.

18. Protothaca jedoensis (LISCHKE)

This is a solid and inflated shell, with stout radial ribs on its surface. The interior is minutely crenulated on the ventral margin. Distribution: throughout Japan and Korea, abundant among pebbles in tidal zone down to a few fathoms depth.

19. Callithaca (Protocallithaca) adamsi (REEVE)

A large, moderately inflated and squarish ovate shell, whose brown surface is reticulated with lamellate concentric lines and numerous radial riblets. The interior is white and is crenulated on the ventral margin. Distribution: northern Honshû, Siberia and Korea, very common on shallow sandy bottom.

20. Gomphina (Macridiscus) veneriformis (LAMARCK)

This is a very solid, compressed and trigonal shell. The beak is situated at the middle of dorsal margin. The surface is rather smooth and polished, and varies from white to blue in color, usually with 3 radial rays. The hinge plate has 3 solid cardinal teeth without laterals. The ventral margin is smooth. As in *Tapes japonica*, the original bluish tone of fresh shells is lost, turning into brown, when they are boiled to remove their soft body. Distribution: central Japan and southwards, on fine sandy bottom of shallow waters.

21. Gomphina (Macridiscus) melanaegis ROEMER

This closely resembles the preceding species, but has an ovate shell, narrowing toward the posterior end and broadly rounded at the anterior margin, and with the gently curved ventral margin. Distribution: from Kyûshû to southern Hokkaidô, as a sandy bottom dweller in shallow waters.

22. Tapes (Amygdala) variegata (SOWERBY)

This shell hardly differs from the following species in shape, but the former has a smaller and less inflated shell, with weaker radial sculptures on its surface than that of the latter. Distribution: central Honshû and southwards, among pebbles between tide marks.

23. Tapes (Amygdala) japonica (DESHAYES)

This is also one of the economically important edible clams in Japan. The shell is somewhat elongate oval, moderately inflated and maculated with various bluish blotches and rays. Usually the coloration and pattern are different on both valves. The sculpture on the surface consists of radial ribs somewhat reticulated by growth lines. The interior is stained with purple on its posterior area. The ventral margin is smooth. This clam is favored by the inhabitants for food. Distribution: China, Japan, Korea and Siberia, abundant on sandy mud bottom between and below tide marks down to a few fathoms depth.

24. Paphia (Paratapes) undulata (BORN)

An elongate oval shell, whose surface is shiny and has weak growth lines and weak oblique grooves on the posterior part. This is light purple outside, and netted with brown divaricate lines. The hinge plate has cardinal teeth but no laterals. The interior is purplish. Distribution: south of central Honshû, commonly found on muddy bottom in bays.

25. Paphia euglypta (PHILIPPI)

This is also an elongate oval shell. The

PLATE **57**

PLATE 58

characteristic feature differing from the following three species is the strongly marked and rather distantly placed sulci on the surface. The exterior is brownish, rayed with 3–4 dark brown bands. Distribution: Kyûshû to Honshû, common on shallow sandy bottom.

26. Paphia schnelliana (DUNKER)

Though this resembles the preceding species, the shell grows larger, measuring about 100 mm in length, and is more inflated, and the umbo is more roundly prominent. The surface is densely grooved and the color is pale brown. Distribution: central Honshû to Kyûshû, on fine sandy bottom, 5–20 fathoms deep.

27. Paphia vernicosa (GOULD)

The shell is also very close to *P. euglypta* in shape and coloration. The characteristic feature of this species is the surface sculpture which tends to become obsolete on the middle part. Distribution: Kyûshû to Honshû, common on sandy bottom of shallow waters.

28. Paphia amabilis (PHILIPPI)

This is most closely allied to *P. euglypta*,

but differs from that species in that the sulci are more densely placed on the reddish brown surface. Distribution: central Honshû and southwards, found on fine sandy bottom in shallow waters.

29. Tapes platyptycha PILSBRY

This has a rather large, squarely oblong shell, which is compressed, rather smooth on the middle part of the surface, and is marked with shallow grooves on both anterior and posterior parts. The color pattern is variable, usually with scattering blackish spots and rays on the light yellowish brown ground color. Distribution: central Honshû and southwards, on sandy bottom below the tide line.

30. Tapes literata (LINNÉ)

This is a close ally of the preceding species, having a squarish oval and compressed shell. The color pattern is very characteristic; that is, the fawn-white surface is clearly reticulated by brownish black. But in some specimens, the marking consists of dots or bands of purplish brown. Distribution: widely distributed in the Indo-Pacific areas up to Amami Islands, common on shallow sandy bottom.

[PLATE 58]

Family Veneridae (2)

1. Lioconcha fastigiata (SOWERBY)

The shell is moderate in size, solid, and subangular cordate in front view. The umbo, elevated on the margin, is prominent

but oblique. The surface is smooth and polished, and is colored white to yellowish white with many triangular black markings. The ventral margin is smooth, and the mantle line is hardly sinuated. Distribution: Amami Islands and southwards, common on sandy bottom in shallow waters.

[PLATE 58]

Veneridae, Petricolidae, Mesodesmatidae

2. Lioconcha lorenziana (DILLWYN)

The shell is similar to the preceding species in shape, but the surface is colored yellowish brown with brownish rays and mottlings. Distribution: Amami Islands and southwards.

3. Lioconcha castrensis (LINNÉ)

This closely resembles *L. fastigiata* in shape and coloration, but the shell is more rounded in outline. The surface is marked by vivid blackish zigzag lines or angular markings on the cream-yellow surface. Distribution: south of Kyûshû, on sandy bottom in offshore waters.

4. Gafrarium pectinatum (LINNÉ)

The shell is oblong oval, solid, thick and rather compressed. The umbo is located at the anterior one third of the dorsal margin. The surface sculpture consists of nodulous stout ribs, which are bifurcate near the margin, and divaricating toward the posterior dorsal margin along a line, running from the umbo to the postero-ventral margin. The outside is whitish, with concentrically arranged blotches and dots of purplish brown. Distribution: widely distributed in the Indo-Pacific areas up to central Honshû, very common on shallow sandy bottom.

5. Gafrarium tumidum [RÖDING]

This is very closely allied to the preceding species in shape and sculpture, but the shell is rather inflated and more roundly ovate, and its surface bears nodulous radiating ribs which are bifurcate near the margin. The coloration is whitish, sometimes with purplish tone on the posterior area. Distribution: commonly and widely distributed in the Indo-Pacific areas up to Amami Islands.

6. Gafrarium divaricatum (GMELIN)

The shell is rounded ovate, solid and compressed. The surface is covered with numerous divaricating ribs and is stained in pale brown with darker brown blotches and mottlings which are more or less radially arranged. Distribution: central Hon-

shû and southwards, very common on sandy gravels between tide marks together with *Tapes japonica*.

7. Circe scripta (LINNÉ)

The shell is solid, and of compressed triangular shape with rounded ventral margin. The surface is concentrically sculptured by closely set ridges, and is colored yellowish white, with blackish brown wavy markings or dots as well as 2 darker brown broad radial bands. The mantle line is hardly sinuated, and the inner margin is smooth. Distribution: the Indo-Pacific areas up to central Honshû, very common on sand from tidal zone to a few fathoms depth.

8. Circe intermedia REEVE

This closely resembles the preceding species in shape and coloration, but can easily be distinguished in having the distinct divaricating sculpture, especially prominent on the umbonal area. Distribution: central Honshû and southwards, on sandy bottom in shallow waters.

9. Pitar (Pitarina) pellucidum (LAMARCK)

This shell is rather thin, swollen, trigonal ovate in shape. The umbo is prominent and oblique forwards, and usually colored brownish. The surface is rather smooth, and is light yellowish white with brownish radial rays and concentrically placed zigzag lines. The mantle line has a triangular sinus on its posterior part. Distribution: over tropical Pacific areas up to Amami Islands, rather common on fine sandy bottom in shallow waters.

10. Pitar (Pitarina) affine (GMELIN)

The shell is rather thin, somewhat transversely broad and trigonal ovate in outline. The surface is very characteristic in having the brownish radial rays on the light yellowish ground, which are crossed by concentric white bands. In some specimens, the coloration is plainly light yellow. Distribution: tropical Pacific areas up to Honshû, rather common on shallow, fine sandy bottom.

11. Pitar (Pitarina) subpellucidum (SOWERBY)

This closely resembles *P. pellucidum* in shape, but can be distinguished from the latter in having an inflated shell of which the surface is colored yellowish with brownish radial rays. Distribution: Amami Islands and southwards.

12. Pitar (Pitarina) striatum (GRAY)

The shell is strongly inflated, rather solid and roundly ovate in shape. The umbo is strongly prominent and oblique anteriorly. The surface is colored in yellow on the anterior half and brown on the posterior half, with thin calcareous sediments on the posterior and ventral parts. Distribution: the tropical Indo-Pacific areas up to Amami Islands, rather common.

13. Sunetta (Cyclosunetta) menstrualis (MENKE)

The shell is solid and thick, strongly compressed, rather circular and large in size. The surface is fairly smooth and polished, and pale purple with purplish brown rays and angularly zigzag lines. The escutcheon is deeply sunken between both valves, and the ligament is located behind the umbo at the bottom of escutcheon. The lunule is also excavated and smooth. The inner margin is minutely crenulated, and the mantle line is sinuated. Distribution: widely found in tropical Pacific areas up to Honshû, as a sand-dweller in shallow waters.

14. Sunetta (Cyclosunetta) concinna DUNKER

This is a small shell, thick, solid, compressed and trigonal ovate with the round ventral margin. The surface is smooth, polished, and is maculated with angularly zigzag, concentric lines and purplish radial rays on the background of pale yellowish to rosy. Distribution: central Honshû and southwards, rather common on shallow sandy bottom.

15. Sunetta (Sunettina) subquadrata (SOWERBY)

This is also a small species, but the shell is somewhat inflated, with a deeply sunken escutcheon on the posterior dorsal margin. Young shells of *S. menstrualis* is also closely similar to this shell in shape, but they have a more shallowly excavated escutcheon than that of this shell of the same size. Distribution: the Indo-Pacific areas up to central Honshû, not common on sandy bottom in shallow waters.

16. Anomalodiscus squamosus (LINNÉ)

The shell is rather small, but very solid and swollen, trigonal ovate, and acuminate posteriorly. The sculpture consists of closely set radial ribs latticed by somewhat scale-like growth ridges. The surface is colored in dull yellowish white. The inner margin is crenulated corresponding to the radial ribs on the surface. An obtuse ridge runs from the prominent umbo to the posterior end, forming a shallow groove in front of it. Distribution: widely distributed in the Indo-Pacific areas up to Honshû, very common on fine sandy bottom between tide marks.

17. Glycydonta marica japonica (KIRA)

This is also rather small, but thick and solid, and trigonal ovate in shape. The umbo is located almost at the middle of dorsal margin. Radial ribs on the surface are stouter than the concentric lamellate ridges and these form a latticed sculpture and series of leaf-like scales. The color is ashy white to light rose, with purplish brown blotches and diverging broad radial rays. The inner margin is crenulated. This form slightly differs from the following real form in having concentric ribs each composed of several weak growth ridges. Distribution: a sand-dweller between tide marks, ranging from Kyûshû to Honshû.

18. Glycydonta marica (LINNÉ)

This is somewhat larger in size, and simple concentric growth ridges are crossed by radial ribs on the surface, forming a latticed sculpture. Distribution: the Indo-Pacific areas up to Amami Islands, common on sandy bottom less than a few fathoms in depth.

[PLATE 58]

Veneridae, Petricolidae, Mesodesmatidae

19. Callanaits hiraseana KURODA

This is a lovely shell, similar to the Australian *C. disjecta* in shape and coloration. The shell is rather thin, subquadrately ovate, and cream in color. The surface is characteristically sculptured by distantly placed, thin but high frill-like concentric lamellae, on which 2 spinous processes are seen along the lines running from the umbo to the postero-ventral margin. The anterior dorsal margin is recurved, and the inner margin is minutely crenulated. Distribution: from Yakushima, south of Kyûshû, to central Honshû, rarely found at 20–150 fathoms depth.

20. Placamen tiara (DILLWYN)

This is also a small lovely shell, trigonal ovate in shape, with the rounded ventral margin. The umbo is strongly prominent and oblique forwards, situated behind the excavated anterior dorsal margin. The surface is white with 3–4 purplish brown rays, and is sculptured by very thick, erect, frill-like, concentric lamellae. Distribution: the Indo-Pacific areas up to Honshû, common on shallow sandy bottom.

21. Placamen isabellinum (PHILIPPI)

The shell is similar to the preceding species in shape, but this is larger, and its surface has distantly placed, lamellate growth ridges as well as thinner and lower lamellae between the ridges. The coloration is pale ashy white with pale purplish rays. Distribution: rather common in Formosa and southwards.

22. Anomalocardia (Cryptonemella) producta KURODA et HABE

This is very close to *A. squamosus* in shape, but the shell is larger than that species, and bears distinctly concentric ridges and weak radial riblets. The outer surface is light yellowish white with 2–3 brownish broad rays. The inner margin is crenulated. This was formerly known as *Cryptonema impressa* (ANTON). Distribution: not uncommon in Formosa.

23. Katelysia (Hemitapes) japonica (GMELIN)

The shell is ovate, somewhat acuminate toward the posterior end, rather solid and somewhat inflated. The umbo is located anteriorly to the long posterior dorsal margin. The surface is brown, sometimes rayed or dotted, and is sculptured by undulating growth ridges. The inner margin is smooth. Distribution: Amami Islands and southwards, below the tide line.

24. Notirus macrophyllus (DESHAYES)

The shell is small, oblong, irregular in shape owing to its nestling life in rock holes, rather thin but solid, and somewhat swollen. The umbo is located near the anterior end. The sculpture consists of distantly placed, very conspicuously lamellate, growth lines and weak radial threads, which become somewhat stronger on the posterior part. It is white and sometimes stained with pale brown near the posterior end. Distribution: uncommonly found in central Honshû and southwards.

25. Notirus ishibashianus (KURODA et HABE)

This is allied to the preceding species and irregular in shape, but usually rounded or oblong ovate and rather flattened. The surface has lamellate growth ridges, which are somewhat stronger on the posterior part. The coloration is dull white with brown radial rays on the posterior area. Distribution: from Kyûshû to Honshû, not common.

26. Notirus mitis (DESHAYES)

The shell is a little inflated and irregular in shape, but usually oblong ovate. Concentric frilled growth ridges on the outer surface become more pronounced posteriorly and reticulated throughout by radial ribs. This is white outside, but the interior is usually stained with violet on its posterior part. Distribution: south of central Honshû, very common in intertidal zone, nestling in holes bored by pholadid species into soft rock beds.

Family Petricolidae

The shells are small or medium in size, and irregular in shape owing to their boring life. The surface bears a reticulated sculpture consisting of growth lines and radial threads, but sometimes has divaricate radial sculptures. The hinge plate bears 2 cardinal teeth on the right valve and 3 on the left, without lateral teeth. The mantle line has a posterior sinus.

27. Petricolirus aequistriatus (SOWERBY)

The shell is transversely elongated, oval, narrowing posteriorly, solid, and white, but brownish on the posterior part. The surface is marked by coarse growth lines and radial threads, which are more prominent on the middle part. Distribution: from Kyûshû to Honshû, uncommon in tidal zone boring in mudstone.

28. Petriocola divergens (GMELIN)

The outline is roundly ovate, and very swollen. The surface is dull white, and bears divaricate sculptures, with radially arranged calcareous ridges on its posterior part. Distribution: found in the Indo-Pacific areas up to central Honshû, below the tide line down to 100 fathoms, boring in corals.

29. Claudiconcha japonica (DUNKER)

The larger right valve tightly embraces the smaller left valve with the calcareous deposits on its edge. The surface is white, with lamellate growth lines. The shell is irregular in shape, because of its burrowing life, but usually rounded ovate, and thick. Distribution: central Honshû to Kyûshû, burrowing rocks or among oyster colonies between tide marks.

30. Claudiconcha monstrosa (GMELIN)

This differs from the preceding species in having a reticulated sculpture on the surface. Distribution: central Honshû and southwards.

Family Mesodesmatidae

This family is represented in Japan by small- or medium-sized shells, solid and trigonally elongated ovate in shape. The ligament behind the umbo is external, but the resilium is internal and situated between 2 stout cardinal teeth. The mantle line has a sinus.

31. Davila munda (GOULD)

The shell is roundly trigonal ovate with the rounded ventral margin, rather compressed and solid. The anterior dorsal margin is shorter than the posterior dorsal margin. The umbo therefore is located posteriorly. The surface is rather smooth, and pale brown, with 2 somewhat darker radial rays on the umbonal area. This was formerly known as D. crassula (REEVE). Distribution: over the Indo-Pacific areas as far north to Amami Islands.

32. Caecella chinensis DESHAYES

The shell is ovate, rather compressed, and somewhat thin. The length is greater than height. The umbo is located almost at the middle of the dorsal margin. The surface is white, marked only by weak growth lines, and covered with a thick yellowish brown periostracum which is worn out on the umbonal area. The margin is smooth, and the mantle line is distinctly sinuated. Distribution: China, Korea and Japan south of Honshû, common among pebbles between tide marks.

33. Atactodea striata (GMELIN)

This is a very solid, rather compressed and trigonal shell, whose surface is white and shiny, wearing a thin yellowish periostracum. The surface is also sculptured by very conspicuously undulating ridges. The interior is white. The mantle line has a small sinus. Distribution: the Indo-Pacific areas up to central Honshû, as a sand-dweller between tide marks.

[PLATE 59]   Mactridae, Donacidae, Glauconomidae, Semelidae, Psammobiidae

Family Mactridae

The shells of this family are small to large, usually thin, inflated to flat, ovate to transversely elongated oval in outline, and sometimes gaping at their ends. The umbo is usually prominent and submedian. The surface is smooth or with concentric growth lines, and covered with a thin periostracum. The resilium is large and stout, and situated in a large chondrophore on the hinge plate behind the weak cardinal teeth. The lateral teeth are usually present. The mantle line has a posterior sinus. See also Plate 72.

1.   Raeta (Raetellops) pulchella (ADAMS et REEVE)

This is a thin, fragile, and inflated shell, with the white undulate surface. The anterior margin is rounded, while the posterior margin is rostrated and gaping. Distribution: throughout Japan, Korea and Siberia, very common on muddy bottom in sheltered waters.

2.   Mactra cuneata GMELIN

The shell is rather small, thin, trigonal ovate, and strongly inflated at the umbonal area. The surface is colored white to dull blue with brownish radial rays. Distribution: south of Kyûshû, rather common on sandy bottom in shallow waters.

3.   Mactra crossei DUNKER

The shell looks like young specimens of *M. chinensis*, but may be easily distinguished from the latter in having a rather solid compressed shell whose surface is marked by weak growth lines. The interior is usually purplish. Distribution: central and northern Honshû, rather common on shallow sandy bottom.

4.   Standella (Meropesta) nicobarica (GMELIN)

The shell is thin, white, somewhat inflated, transversely elongated oval in shape, rounded anteriorly and somewhat attenuating posteriorly, and gaping at both ends. The surface is covered by a thin light yellowish periostracum, and is sculptured by many radial cords. Distribution: widely distributed in the Indo-Pacific areas, northwards to central Honshû, common between tide marks on fine sandy bottom.

5.   Lutraria sieboldi REEVE

The shell is compressed, elongated ellipsoidal, slightly expanding toward the posterior margin and gaping at both ends. The umbo is located at the anterior one third of the dorsal margin. This is white, and covered by an olivaceous, thick periostracum. The hinge plate has a large projecting chondrophore. Distribution: central Honshû to Kyûshû and China, rather common on muddy bottom in shallow waters.

6.   Lutraria arcuata REEVE

This is closely related to the preceding species in shape, but the shell is more elongate and its dorsal margin is excavated and curved. Distribution: central Honshû to Kyûshû, as a muddy bottom dweller in shallow waters.

7.   Mactra ornata GRAY

The shell is thin, trigonal ovate and somewhat inflated. The surface is rather smooth, scattered by irregularly arranged red spots and sometimes with rays on the yellowish background. The periostracum is yellowish brown. The umbo at the middle of dorsal margin is stained in rosy orange. Distribution: central Honshû and southwards, uncommon on shallow sandy bottom.

8.   Oxyperas bernardi (PILSBRY)

This is a transversely broad, trigonal ovate, and rather inflated shell, marked on its surface by concentric sulci and scattered dark brown spots on the yellowish periostracum. Distribution: central Honshû to Kyûshû, as a sand-dweller at 3–30 fathoms depth.

9.   Tresus keenae (KURODA et HABE)

A large species exceeding 200 mm in shell length. The shell is thick, porcellaneous, somewhat inflated, ovate, and truncated and gaping at the posterior end. The surface is covered with a thick blackish periostracum, and bears rather coarse growth lines and an obtuse keel running from the umbo to the postero-ventral corner. The chondrophore on the hinge plate is very large and situated below the umbo. This is one of the edible clams in Japan, whose large siphons are mainly used for food. Distribution: Honshû to Kyûshû, rather common between the low tide mark and a few fathoms depth on muddy bottom.

10. Mactra chinensis PHILIPPI

This is also one of the important edible mussels in Japan and is commonly known as *Mactra sulcataria* REEVE, but the latter name is antedated by the former. The shell is rather thin, a little inflated and trigonal ovate in shape, and its surface is undulate near the margin and smooth around the umbo situated nearly at the middle of dorsal margin. The color varies from white to brown in younger stages and is dull white in the adult stage, sometimes with purplish brown rays. Distribution: throughout Japan, Korea and China, very common in tidal and subtidal zones in bays.

11. Caelomactra antiquata (SPENGLER)

A large shell exceeding 150 mm in length, rather thin, fragile and trigonal ovate in shape. The surface is colored purple, being darker around the umbo and paler toward the margin, and covered with a thin but distinct yellowish periostracum and with densely set weak growth lines. Distribution: central Honshû and southwards, as a fine sandy bottom dweller in offshore waters.

12. Mactra veneriformis REEVE

This is also one of the important edible mussels and is cultured in shallow waters of bays. The shell is thin, subtetragonal ovate and strongly inflated. The surface has distinctly marked growth lines, and is covered by a brownish gray periostracum with the purplish ventral margin. Distribution: central Honshû to Kyûshû, Korea and China, very common on muddy bottom between tide marks.

13. Spisula (Mactromeris) voyi GABB

The shell is large, attainning approxi-

mately 100 mm in length, rather flat, ovate and thick but fragile. The umbo is situated posteriorly to the middle of dorsal margin, the anterior dorsal margin being longer than the posterior. The surface is covered by a thick yellowish periostracum. Distribution: central Honshû and northwards, rather common on shallow sandy bottom.

Family Donacidae

The shells are rather small, thick and trigonal ovate. The anterior dorsal margin is longer than the posterior dorsal margin. The surface is smooth or sculptured. The hinge plate has 2 cardinal teeth and one lateral tooth on each side of them. The mantle line has a posterior sinuation. The inner ventral margin is smooth or crenulated.

14. Chion semigranosum (DUNKER)

The shell is small, thick, compressed and trigonal. The posterior half of the surface is decussate with growth lines crossing with radial ribs. The outside is white to purple, while the interior is usually purplish and is crenulated on the ventral margin. The animal migrates between the high and low tide marks with ebb and flow tides on sand beach. Distribution: central Honshû to Kyûshû, fairly common.

15. Latona cuneata (LINNÉ)

Resembling the preceding species in shape, the shell is somewhat large, and more rounded in outline. The interior side of the ventral margin is not crenulated. The habit is similar to that of the preceding species. Distribution: central Honshû and southwards.

Family Glauconomidae

This is a small family including only one genus and several species. The shell is thin, elongate oval, narrowing toward the posterior end and rounded at the anterior end. The surface is covered with a greenish periostracum. The hinge plate bears only 3 small cardinal teeth and the mantle line has a posterior sinus.

[PLATE 59]   Mactridae, Donacidae, Glauconomidae, Semelidae, Psammobiidae

16.   Glauconome chinensis CRAY

The features of the shell well agree with those of the family stated above. Distribution: central Hohshû to Kyûshû, Korea and China, known as a mud-dweller between tide marks in some bays as Tokyo Bay, Urado Bay, Ariake Bay and the Inland Sea of Japan.

Family Semelidae

The shell is small to fairly large, circular or ovate, rather compressed, thin or somewhat solid and usually whitish but sometimes tinted with red. The surface has a concentric or radial sculpture, but is sometimes smooth. The ligament is external with an internal resilium and situated in a oblique groove between the cardinal teeth. The mantle line has a deep sinus.

17.   Semele carnicolor (HANLEY)

The shell is circular, rather flat, somewhat thick and white to light orange in color. The surface is marked by lamellate growth lines and weak radial striae. Distribution: central Honshû to the Ryukyus and the Philippines, rather common on sandy bottom between tide marks.

18.   Semele cordiformis (HOLTEN)

This is a rather thin, circular shell, whose surface bears weak growth lines and radial threads, forming a fine reticulation. It is orange on the umbonal area and paler toward the margin. Distribution: central Honshû and southwards, uncommon on shallow, fine sandy bottom.

19.   Semele zebuensis (HANLEY)

Being close to S. carnicolor in shape and sculpture, the shell is larger in fully grown specimens. Its surface is sculptured by lamellate, erect and duplicate growth lines, and lacks any radial threads. The color is light yellowish white, with reddish orange rays. Distribution: south of central Honshû, common on shallow sandy bottom.

Family Psammobiidae (1)

This family includes a considerable number of species, whose shells are medium to large, thin or rather thick, orbicular to elongated oval, subtruncated and gaping at their posterior end. The surface is smooth or sculptured and covered with a thick periostracum. The hinge plate has the conspicuous nymph at the posterior part, the large external ligament and 2 cardinal teeth. No lateral teeth are present. The mantle line has a deep sinus at its posterior part.

20.   Azorinus minutus (DUNKER)

The shell is thin, strongly compressed, transversely ellipsoidal, and rounded and gaping at both ends. The umbo is located a little anteriorly to the middle of dorsal margin. The white surface is covered with a grayish thick periostracum, and a shallow groove runs from the umbo to the rather straight ventral margin. It seems to be a form of the following species. Distribution: central Honshû and southwards, on shallow muddy bottom.

21.   Azorinus abbreviatus (GOULD)

This is closely similar to the preceding species in shape, but the shell is larger in size. The umbo is located almost at the middle of dorsal margin. Distribution: Honshû to Kyûshû and China, common on muddy bottom in shallow waters.

22.   Solecurtus dunkeri KIRA

This is closely related to the following species, but may be distinguished from the latter in the transverse narrowness and thickness of the shell. Distribution: central Honshû to Kyûshû, uncommon on fine sandy bottom in shallow waters.

23.   Solecurtus divaricatus (LISCHKE)

The characteristic feature of this species is the divaricate sculpture on the surface of the razor-like shell, with both ends truncated and widely gaping. The surface is sculptured by incised lines divaricating along a line connecting the umbo with the postero-ventral corner and covered by calcareous deposits on the postero-dorsal area. Distribution: central Honshû and southwards, on sandy bottom near the low tide level.

169

PLATE 59

PLATE 60

Family Psammobiidae (2)

1. Gari gari (LINNÉ)

The shell is transversely elongate, compressed, truncated at the posterior end and stained in light purple. The beak is low and lies at the middle of the dorsal margin. The surface is marked by oblique lines, which begin anteriorly as regular incised lines and end abruptly along a line which is running from the umbo to the postero-ventral margin. The postero-dorsal area behind this line bears concentric lines. The species is easily distinguished from others in having this peculiar sculpture and has hitherto been called *G. truncata* (LINNÉ). Distribution: central Honshû and southwards, uncommon on fine sandy bottom in shallow waters.

2. Psammocola radiata (DUNKER)

The shell resembles the preceding species in shape, but the surface is smooth and marked by light brown rays against the purplish background. Distribution: south of central Honshû and southwards, uncommon on shallow, fine sandy bottom.

3. Psammotaea elongata (LAMARCK)

The shell is elongate but inflated, truncated and gaping at the posterior end. The surface is marked by rough growth lines, and colored light purple with paler rays under a thick brownish periostracum. Distribution: over the Indo-Pacific areas up to central Honshû, very common on muddy flats between the low tide mark and a few fathoms depth.

4. Asaphis dichotoma (ANTON)

Radial cords on the outer surface are characteristic of the shell, which is rather inflated and elongated oval in shape. Purplish rays radiates on the whitish background. The radial cords tend to have scaly processes crossing with growth lamellae on the posterior part of the surface. Distribution: central Honshû and farther south, very common on muddy and gravelly bottom near the low tide mark.

5. Psammocola kazusensis (YOKOYAMA)

This species has been confused with the American *Ps. californica* (CONRAD) by various authors for a long time. But this Japanese species differs from that species in lacking radial colored rays. The shell is white, flattish and transversely oval, and the posterior end is obliquely truncated and gaping. Distribution: northern Honshû and Hokkaidô, rather common on shallow muddy bottom.

6. Gari maculosa (LAMARCK)

The shell is elongate oval, compressed, rounded anteriorly, and subtruncated and gaping posteriorly. The surface color varies from white to yellow, brownish red or purplish black, with darker rays. It is marked by oblique incised lines except on the postero-ventral area bearing coarse growth lines. Distribution: widely distributed in the Indo-Pacific areas up to Honshû, common on sandy and gravelly bottom in shallow waters.

7. Psammotaea virescens (DESHAYES)

This small species has a transversely oval shell, which is thin and colored purplish. The surface is smooth and covered with a shiny olivaceous periostracum. The interior is also purplish, and the mantle line has a deep sinus. Distribution: south of Honshû, common on muddy bottom near the low tide mark in bays.

8. Psammotaea minor (DESHAYES)

This is very close to the preceding species in shape and color, but has purplish rays on the outer surface covered by a shiny yellowish periostracum. Distribution: central Honshû and southwards, common on fine sandy bottom between tide marks in bays.

9. Nuttallia olivacea (JAY)

The shell is thin, compressed and circular in shape, the right valve being flatter than the left one. The surface is smooth and polished, showing 2 whitish rays radiating from the umbo to the postero-ventral margin, and is covered by a vernicose periostracum. The interior is purplish and the mantle line has a deep posterior sinuation. Distribution:

[PLATE 60]　　　　　　　　　　　　　　　　　Psammobiidae, Tellinidae

Honshû to Kyûshû and Korea, common on shallow muddy bottom.

10.　Nuttallia solida KIRA

This shell resembles the preceding species in shape, but is more solid and somewhat elongated posteriorly. Both valves are nearly equally convex. Distribution: Shikoku and central Honshû, on sandy bottom of offshore waters.

11.　Soletellina diphos (LINNÉ)

The shell is large, thin, elongated elliptical in shape, rounded anteriorly, obliquely truncated and gaping posteriorly, and is colored purple. The surface is covered by a shiny olivaceous periostracum. Distribution: central Honshû and southwards, rather common on muddy bottom in shallow waters of bays.

12.　Soletellina boeddinghausi (LISCHKE)

This has a relatively shorter and higher shell than that of the preceding species, but other features are nearly the same in both species. Distribution: Honshû to Kyûshû, fairly common on fine sandy bottom in shallow waters.

Family Tellinidae (1)

These shells are small to large in size, usually ovate, sometimes circular or transversely elongated ovate, sharply or obtusely rostrated at the posterior end, rather compressed and thin to solid. The umbo is usually low, median or more or less posterior in its situation. The surface is smooth or concentrically sculptured. The ligament behind the umbo is external, and the resilium somewhat sinks between both valves. The hinge plate has 2 cardinal teeth, with or without lateral teeth. The mantle line has a deep sinus.

13.　Macoma (Psammacoma) awajiensis SOWERBY

The shell is thin, white, rather inflated, elongated oval, rounded and broadly produced anteriorly, and twisted and subtruncated posteriorly. The umbo is located at

about one third of the total shell width from the posterior end along the dorsal margin. The surface is smooth and polished. The hinge plate is narrow and has only 2 cardinal teeth. Distribution: Honshû to Kyûshû, Korea and China, commonly found on muddy bottom in bays.

14.　Arcopagia (Merisca) margaritina (LAMARCK)

The shell is thin but solid, compressed, ovate in shape, rounded anteriorly, narrowed posteriorly, and shortly truncated at the hind end. The surface is marked by concentric lamellate ridges and a fold running from the umbo to the postero-ventral corner. The exterior is light yellowish white, but the umbonal area tends to be light orange. The hinge plate has 2 cardinal teeth and one lateral tooth on each side of them. The posterior dorsal margin is rather straight. Distribution: over the Indo-Pacific areas up to Honshû, common on shallow muddy bottom. A. (M.) serricostata (TOKUNAGA) is a synonym.

15.　Clathrotellina carnicolor (HANLEY)

The shell is rather inflated, rounded ovate and white to light rose in color. The surface sculpture is characteristically reticulate due to narrow lamellae and radial narrow cords crossing together. The hinge plate is stained with yellow and has 2 cardinal and lateral teeth respectively. Distribution: central Honshû and southwards, uncommon on fine sandy bottom below the tide level.

16.　Macoma praetexta (VON MARTENS)

The shell is thin, compressed, ovate, the anterior part being larger than the posterior part, rounded anteriorly and subtruncated posteriorly, and white to rose in color. The hinge plate has only 2 cardinal teeth. This species looks similar to Tellinides ovalis (SOWERBY) in shape, but differs from the latter in lacking lateral teeth. Distribution: Honshû to Kyûshû, common on muddy bottom in shallow waters.

17.　Macalina bruguierei (HANLEY)

The shell is solid, roundly ovate and rather compressed. The cardinal teeth are very strong without laterals. The umbo is sowmewhat prominent and the posterior dorsal margin is slightly curved. The surface is rather smooth and dull white. Distribution: Amami Islands and southwards.

18. Macoma incongrua (VON MARTENS)

This has a thin, roundly ovate shell, which is rounded anteriorly, twisted and narrowed posteriorly and somewhat inflated. The right valve is flatter than the left one. The surface is smooth and white except the light orange umbo, and is covered by a thin periostracum. The anterior dorsal margin is slightly longer than the posterior dorsal margin. Distribution: throughout Japan, Korea and Alaska, very common on muddy bottom in inter- and subtidal zones.

19. Macoma tokyoensis MAKIYAMA

The species resembles *M. incongrua*, but can be distinguished from the above species in having a somewhat elongated oval shell with a rather straight posterior dorsal margin. The surface is white, and is covered by a thin periostracum. The mantle sinus almost reaches the anterior muscle scar in the left valve. Distribution: Honshû to Kyûshû, common on muddy bottom in shallow waters in bays.

20. Macoma contabulata (DESHAYES)

This also resembles the preceding two species in shape, but the shell is roundly ovate in shape, broadly rounded anteriorly, and narrowed but not twisted posteriorly. The surface is dull white under a rather thick brownish periostracum. The pallial sinus does not reach the anterior muscle scar. *Macoma anser* OYAMA is a synonym. Distribution: throughout Japan, Korea and North China, very common on muddy bottom between tide marks in bays.

21. Heteromacoma oyamai KIRA

The shell is dull white, inflated, thin but solid and roundly ovate, with a broadly rounded anterior margin. The ligament sinks between the posterior dorsal margins. The surface is rather smooth, bearing only growth lines. Distribution: northern Honshû, as a mud-dweller near the low tide mark.

22. Heteromacoma irus (HANLEY)

The shell is solid, and moderately com-
pressed, generally ovate in shape, rounded anteriorly, narrowed posteriorly and white to light yellow. The surface is marked by coarse growth lines. A keel runs from the umbo to the posterior end, delimiting a flat and narrow postero-dorsal area. The small but deeply excavated lunule is in front of the umbo, and the ligament lies between the deeply sunken escutcheons. The hinge plate is solid and rather broad with 2 cardinal teeth and no laterals. Distribution: throughout Japan and Korea, very common on muddy gravel bottom between tide marks.

According to Dr. A. M. Keen's critical study on the type specimen of *Macoma irus* HANLEY, so-called Japanese *Gastrana yantaiensis* (CROSSE et DEBEAUX) is more identical with the specimen rather than Chinese *G. yantaiensis* CROSSE et DEBEAUX. The scientific name for the Japanese form is, therefore, replaced by *Heteromacoma irus* (HANLEY) in use, and *Sinomacoma* YAMAMOTO et HABE 1959 should be synonymized with *Heteromacoma* HABE.

23. Scutarcopagia scobinata critia (GOULD)

The shell is circular, rather thick and solid, and moderately inflated. The surface is densely set with erect scales among growth lines, and with a flexure connecting the umbo with the postero-ventral corner. The color is yellowish white, with brown blotches. The hinge plate has 2 solid cardinal teeth and one lateral tooth on each side of them. Distribution: tropical Pacific areas up to Amami Islands, rather common on gravelly bottom below the tide level.

24. Scutarcopagia scobinata (LINNÉ)

Very closely resembling the preceding form in general features, this typical form has a more circular shell with larger scales and brownish radial rays on its outer surface. Distribution: south of Kyûshû.

25. Cyclotellina remies (LINNÉ)

The shell is circular, thick and solid, and slightly inflated. Undulated growth lines are seen on the white surface. The hinge plate has 2 solid cardinal teeth and one lateral tooth on each side of them. Distribution: Amami Islands and southwards.

[PLATE 61]   Tellinidae

Family Tellinidae (2)

1. Pinguitellina pinguis (HANLEY)

The shell is small, thin, ovate, rather inflated, milky white along the margin and light orange near the umbo. The umbo is located a little posteriorly to the middle of dorsal margin. A closely allied species, *P. robusta* (HANLEY), differs from this species in having a thicker shell whose interior is yellowish. Distribution: central Honshû and farther south, rather common on fine sandy bottom in shallow waters.

2. Jactellina obliquistriata (SOWERBY)

The shell is roundly ovate, and rather compressed. The surface is white, yellow or red in color. Besides growth lines, many oblique striae are characteristically marked over the exterior. Distribution: south of Kyûshû, rather common on sandy bottom in shallow waters.

3. Jactellina (Loxoglypta) transculpta (SOWERBY)

This shell is rather oblong ovate, compressed and orange in color. The umbo is placed rather posteriorly. The anterior end is rounded, while the posterior end is narrowly truncated. The sculpture consists of oblique striae covering the surface as in the preceding species. Distribution: Amami Islands and southwards, not uncommon on shallow sandy bottom.

4. Fabulina minuta (LISCHKE)

A small, thin, compressed and ovate shell, with the umbo situated at the posterior one third of the dorsal margin. The anterior margin is rounded and the posterior end is narrowed. The surface is smooth and is colored light rose or sometimes white. Distribution: throughout Japan, very common on shallow sandy bottom.

5. Moerella jedoensis (LISCHKE)

This is also a rather small tellinid shell, trigonal ovate in outline, compressed and colored rose, with radiating paler zones. Distribution: Kyûshû to Honshû, common on sandy bottom in shallow waters.

6. Fabulina iridella (VON MARTENS)

The shell is thin, semi-translucent, compressed, ovate in shape, rounded and produced anteriorly and somewhat narrowed posteriorly. The surface is smooth and polished, and is colored white, yellow or light rose, usually with 2 paler rays radiating from the umbo. Distribution: from Kyûshû to Honshû, also common on sandy bottom in shallow waters.

7. Fabulina nitidula (DUNKER)

This is flat ellipsoidal in shape, rounded and widely produced anteriorly, and slightly narrowed posteriorly. The surface is shiny and colored rose, and is marked only by growth lines on the left valve, while slightly oblique striae are crossing with growth lines on the right valve. Distribution: very common on fine sandy bottom in shallow waters throughout Japan.

8. Fabulina pallidula (LISCHKE)

Though this species is very closely similar to the preceding species in shape, the shell is more flattened and more produced anteriorly. The umbo is located at the posterior one third of the dorsal margin. The coloration is orange rose. This is a muddy bottom dweller in shallow waters of bays. Distribution: from Kyûshû to Honshû.

9. Moerella juvenilis (HANLEY)

This is a trigonal ovate shell, which is widely rounded anteriorly, attenuated posteriorly and rather inflated. The surface is smooth and polished, and is orange red, sometimes white or yellow. Distribution: China, Korea and Japan, abundant on fine sandy bottom between tide marks.

10. Jactellina (Loxoglypta) lauta (GOULD)

This is also a very flat and ovate shell, strongly produced and rounded anteriorly, and abruptly narrowed and obliquely truncated posteriorly. The umbo is located near the posterior end. The surface is sculptured all over by oblique striae as in *J. transculpta*, and is rayed by orange-red on the white ground color. Distribution: central

Honshû and southwards, rather common on shallow sandy bottom.

11. Tellinides ovalis (SOWERBY)

The shell is thin, shiny, flattened, transversely ellipsoidal in shape and rounded at both ends. The umbo is located almost at the middle of the dorsal margin. The surface bears weak growth lines. It is usually translucently white outside, with rosy rays. Distribution: over Pacific areas up to central Honshû, commonly found in shallow waters on sandy bottom.

12. Angulus vestalioides (YOKOYAMA)

This is somewhat similar to the preceding species in shape, but is more elongated oval, having the shorter posterior part and truncated posterior end. The umbo lies somewhat posteriorly to the middle of the dorsal margin. A groove runs from the umbo to the postero-ventral corner. Distribution: throughout Japan and East China Sea, common on muddy bottom, 10–100 fathoms in depth.

13. Pharaonella aurea (PERRY)

The shell is thin, transversely oblong oval, narrowed posteriorly forming a long rostration and rounded at the anterior end. The rostration is slightly bent toward the right side. The surface is smooth, polished and rather flat. Two ridges run from the umbo to the posterior truncation. The coloration is orange-red with a yellowish tinge at the base of the rostration, or plainly yellowish in some specimens. Distribution: central Honshû and southwards, uncommonly found on sandy bottom in shallow waters. This is called *Ph. rostrata* (LINNÉ) by some authors.

14. Pharaonella perrieri (BERTIN)

This resembles the last species, but the shell is comparatively higher than the last species and has a shorter posterior rostration. The color is usually rosy red. White specimens are also rarely found. Distribution: throughout Japan, south of Honshû, rather common on sands from the low tide mark down to a few fathoms depth. *Tellina consanguinea* SOWERBY is a synonym of this species.

15. Cadella lubrica (GOULD)

A small trigonal ovate shell, solid and compressed. The anterior dorsal margin is much longer than the posterior. The surface is marked by growth lines and several distinct undulations caused by occasional restings of shell growth. This is colored rose around the umbo and becomes whitish toward the margin. Distribution: Honshû and Hokkaidô, rare on shallow sandy bottom.

16. Tellinella pulcherrima (SOWERBY)

The shell is medium in size, compressed, oblong ovate, narrowed posteriorly and rounded anteriorly. The umbo is located almost at the middle of the dorsal margin. The sculpture consists of numerous small erect scales, which are distinct on both anterior and posterior areas but somewhat obcured on the middle part. The outer surface is purplish rose with narrow whitish rays. Distribution: widely found in Pacific areas up to central Honshû, uncommon on shallow sandy bottom.

17. Tellina spengleri (GMELIN)

The shell is white, narrowly trigonal and compressed, and has rather straight anterior and posterior dorsal margins. The umbo is located near the middle of the dorsal margin. The ventral margin is gently curved. Two or three dentate ridges run along the dorsal margin. Besides, the surface is sculptured by concentric lamellae. Distribution: south of Formosa, uncommon. *Tellinella rostrata* (LINNÉ) may be an older name for the same species.

18. Tellinides timorensis (LAMARCK)

This white shell is rather thin, somewhat convex, broadly ovate in shape and rounded at both ends or subtruncated at the posterior end. The surface is fairly smooth and polished, and an obtusely angled flexture runs from the umbo to the postero-ventral corner, slightly turning to the right side. Distribution: south of Amami Islands, uncommon.

19. Quidnipagus palatum IREDALE

The shell is ovate in shape, rather thick, somewhat convex, white to light yellow,

[PLATE 61]   Tellinidae

rounded anteriorly and narrowed toward the posterior. The surface is roughened all over with undulating thick broken wrinkles, and an obtuse ridge runs from the umbo to the posterior truncation on the left valve forming a flexure turning to the right side. Distribution: central Honshû and southwards, rather common on sandy bottom in shallow waters.

20.   Scutarcopagia linguafelis (LINNÉ)

The shell is moderately thick, somewhat inflated, rounded ovate in shape and widely produced anteriorly. The umbo is thus located rather posteriorly to the middle of the dorsal margin. A rather strong rib runs from the umbo to the postero-ventral corner, forming a distinct flexure turning rightward. The surface is roughened all over with small triangular spines, and is marked by narrow rosy rays on the whitish background. Distribution: south of Amami Islands, uncommon.

21.   Tellinella philippii (ANTON)

This is a rather small species, whose shell is oblong ovate with the antero-dorsal margin longer than the postero-dorsal margin. The posterior rostration is truncated at the distal end. The surface has distinct growth lines, and is colored rose with rays. Distribution: south of Amami Islands.

22.   Laciolina chloroleuca (LAMARCK)

Fully grown specimens are fairly large, thick, rather compressed, widely rounded anteriorly and shortly beaked toward the posterior end. The surface is smooth and polished. The color is white to orange with rosy rays. Distribution: south of Amami Islands, uncommon.

23.   Pharaonella perna (SPENGLER)

The shell is transversely elongate, rather thin, somewhat convex, rounded anteriorly, narrowly rostrated toward the posterior and obliquely truncated at the distal end, with a constriction at the base of the posterior part of ventral margin. A flexure runs from the umbo to the postero-ventral corner, turning rightward. The surface is smooth and polished and is white or light rose. The

interior surface is light yellow. Distribution: over Pacific areas up to central Honshû, uncommon on sandy bottom in shallow waters.

24.   Tellinella staurella (LAMARCK)

This is rather solid, somewhat convex, elongated ovate, rounded anteriorly, narrowed posteriorly and obliquely truncated at the distal end. The surface is marked by concentric growth ridges and a distinct fold running from the umbo to the postero-ventral corner, the area behind the fold being narrow and bent to the right side. The shell is white to light yellow outside, with 2 short red rays on the umbonal area and many purplish rays radiating from the umbo to the margin. The interior is light yellow in the umbonal cavity. Distribution: widely found in the Indo-Pacific areas as far north to Amami Islands, not uncommon on sandy bottom of offshore waters.

25.   Arcopagia (Merisca) diaphana (DESHAYES)

The shell is very flat, solid, ovate in shape, with a straight posterior dorsal margin, rounded anteriorly and very acuminated toward the posterior end. The sculpture on the chalky white surface consists of concentric wrinkles, thin slightly undulate ridges and very fine radiating threads. Besides, an angular fold runs from the umbo to the postero-ventral corner, and divides the serrated postero-dorsal area turning rightward from the main part. This is an intertidal bivalve on muddy bottom. Distribution: from Honshû to Formosa.

26.   Macoma (Rexithaerus) sectior OYAMA

This shell is thin, rather convex, ovate in shape, widely rounded and produced anteriorly, and broadly truncated posteriorly, forming a winged postero-dorsal area separated by an obtuse rib. The umbo lies rather posteriorly to the middle of the dorsal margin. The right valve is less convex than the left. The surface is rather smooth and white. This species had been confused with American M.(R.) secta (CONRAD). Distribution: throughout Japan, Korea and Formosa, rather common on muddy bottom in shallow waters.

PLATE 61

1   × 1 ⅕

2   × 1 ⅕

3   × ⅘

4   × 1 ⅕

5   × 1 ⅕

6   × ⅘

7   × ⅘

8   × 1 ⅕

9   × ⅘

10   × ⅘

11   × 1

12   × ⅗

13   × ⁷⁄₁₀

14   × ⁷⁄₁₀

15   × 1

16   × ⅘

17   × ⅘

18   × 1

19   × ⅘

20   × 1

21   × ⅘

22   × ⅘

23   × ⅘

24   × ⅘

25   × ⅘

26   × 1

27   × ⅘

28   × ⁷⁄₁₀

29   × ⅘

PLATE 62

1 × 4/5

2 × 3/5

3 × 3/5

4 × 3/5

5 × 3/5

6 × 3/5

7 × 3/5

8 × 3/5

9 × 3/5

10 × 3/5

11 × 3/5

12 × 3/5

13 × 3/5

14 × 3/5

a,

b,

c,

18 × 3/5

19 × 3/5

20 × 3/5

21 × 3/5

15 × 3/5

16 × 4/5

22 × 3/5

23 × 3/5

24 × 3/5

17 × 4/5

27. *Tellinella virgata* (LINNÉ)

The shell is rather solid, somewhat inflated, ovate, rounded anteriorly, and acuminated posteriorly forming a short truncation. The surface is sculptured by concentric and dense growth ridges, and bears a flexure running from the umbo to the postero-ventral corner, behind which the narrow postero-ventral area is slightly bent toward the right side. The color is white to yellow, with purplish rays. This is closely similar to *T. staurella* in shape and coloration, but is larger in size and proportionally higher than long. Distribution: Amami Islands and southwards, not uncommon on shallow sandy bottom.

28. *Pharaonella tongana* (QUOY et GAIMARD)

The shell is oblong ovate, roundly produced anteriorly and attenuated posteriorly forming a rather short rostrum, rather thin and somewhat convex. The surface is smooth and polished, and is colored white with rosy rays on the umbo. Two or three folds run on the postero-dorsal area from the umbo to the margin. The ventral margin is gently curved with a weak constriction on its posterior part. This species differs from *Ph. perna* in having the shortly rostrated shell and red-colored umbo. Distribution: over Pacific areas up to Amami Islands, uncommon on shallow, fine sandy bottom.

29. *Peronidia venulosa* (SCHRENCK)

The shell is solid, compressed, elongated ovate, and large in size, exceeding 100 mm in length. The whitish surface is marked by growth lines of moderate strength, distantly placed undulations and a weak fold running from the umbo to the postero-ventral corner. The interior is bright orange in color. Distribution: northern Honshû to Siberia and Alaska, rather common on fine sandy bottom in shallow offshore waters.

[PLATE 62]

Family Solenidae

The razor shells are elongate, almost parallel-sided, and usually truncated, gaping and sometimes rounded at both anterior and posterior ends. The umbo is low and situated at or near the anterior end of shell. The surface is smooth and polished, and covered with a thin periostracum. The ligament behind the umbo is external. These bivalves dwell in the slanting pit bored in sand, and are collected for their edible flesh. Although they may be enticed out of the pit by a pinch of salt that appears to irritate the animal, the collector must be very quick to grab it.

1. Solen (Solenarius) luzonicus (DUNKER)

This is a small razor shell inhabiting the deep bottom around Japan. The shell is thin, elongate, about 45 mm in length and slightly curved dorsally. It is obliquely truncated at the anterior end and vertically truncated at the posterior. The surface is stained in rose and white alternately along growth lines. Distribution: from Honshû to the Philippines, near 50 fathoms depth.

2. Solen intermedius KOCH

The shell is very narrow, long and straight, obliquely truncated at the anterior end and vertically truncated at the posterior end. The surface is alternately colored in rose and white as in the preceding species. Distribution: central Honshû and southwards, uncommonly collected from sandy bottom in shallow waters.

3. Solen (Solenarius) krusensterni SCHRENCK

The shell is elongate, feebly curved dorsally, arcuate and constricted at the anterior end and sharply truncated at the posterior end. The surface is covered with a smooth yellowish periostracum. Distribution: Honshû to Sakhalin and Korea, common on shallow sandy bottom.

4. Solen (Solenarius) roseomaculatus PILSBRY

This small razor shell closely resembles S. luzonicus, but is more strongly curved and maculated with rose on the white background. Distribution: widely distributed in the Indo-Pacific, north to central Honshû, rather common on shallow sandy bottom.

5. Solen sloani GRAY

This is quite similar to the preceding species in coloration, but the shell is larger and straight. Distribution: Amami Islands and southwards, rather common on sandy bottom in shallow waters.

6. Ensiculus philippianus (DUNKER)

The shell is thin, elongate, compressed, curved dorsally, and rounded and gaping at both ends. The surface is smooth and shiny, and maculated with brownish purple. Distribution: central Honshû and farther south, rather common on fine sandy bottom between tide marks.

7. Solen strictus GOULD

This razor shell is widely known as S. gouldi CONRAD, but it seems to be a synonym antedated by this name. The shell is very narrow and long, obliquely truncated at the anterior and vertically truncated at the posterior end, and with a straight dorsal margin. The surface is covered with a smooth, polished and yellowish periostracum. Distribution: throughout Japan and Korea, common on sand-flats near the low tide mark.

8. Solen grandis DUNKER

This is the largest of this group in Japan, attaining about 150 mm in length and 35 mm in height. The shell is straight, rather solid, and truncated at both ends. The surface is smooth and polished, and covered with a yellowish brown periostracum, under which the shell is rosy. Distribution: central Honshû and southwards, uncommon on fine sandy bottom near the low tide mark.

9. Solen gordonis YOKOYAMA

This is very close to the preceding species in shape, but differs in the smaller size of fully grown shell, which is mottled with rosy purple and vertically truncated anteriorly. This razor shell is commonly collected by fishermen with S. strictus from sandy bottom in shallow waters. Distribution: central Honshû to Kyûshû.

10. Sinonovacula constricta (LAMARCK)

The shell is elongate, compressed, gaping at the rounded anterior and posterior ends, and slightly constricted at the middle of the surface. The periostracum is thick and yellowish. The umbo is low and lies at the anterior one third of the dorsal margin. The interior is white. Distribution: only found in Kojima Bay of central Honshû and Ariake Bay of Kyûshû in Japan, and also in China, in deep pits burrowed by the animal in muds near the low tide mark.

11. Culterensis attenuatus (DUNKER)

This shell is characterized by the elongate shape, posterior attenuation, straight dorsal margin, and rounded and gaped anterior end. The surface is covered with a yellowish smooth periostracum except the white dorso-anterior area. Distribution: central Honshû to Kyûshû and China, common on fine sandy bottom in shallow waters.

12. Siliqua japonica (DUNKER)

This is a small, thin shell whose surface is rayed by white on the purplish background. A white internal fold running vertically from the umbo to the ventral margin is seen through the shell from the outside. Distribution: central Honshû down to the Philippines, uncommon on shallow sandy bottom.

13. Siliqua pulchella (DUNKER)

This closely allied species differs from the above species in having a more elongate shell of purple color. Other features are nearly the same. Distribution: central Honshû to Kyûshû, not uncommon.

14. Siliqua alta (BRODERIP et SOWERBY)

This is a large species, exceeding 120 mm in length and 65 mm in height. The shell is thick, compressed and gaping at both ends. In young specimens, the surface is covered with a vernicosely brownish periostracum, which is, however, worn out in fully grown specimens. This genus is characterized by an internal rib running from the umbo to the ventral margin as stated in the preceding two small species. Distribution: Hokkaidô and northwards, very common on sandy bottom in shallow waters.

Family Hiatellidae

These shells are small to large, white, often

irregular in shape and gaping at both ends, and is covered with a deciduous periostracum. The ligament is external and the teeth on the hinge plate are small and obsolete. Mantle line is usually discontinuous or with a deep sinus.

15. Hiatella flaccida GOULD

The shell is usually small, white and irregular in shape owing to its adherent life. The surface is covered with a thick yellowish periostracum. A small tooth occurs on the hinge plate below the umbo. The mantle line is discontinuous. In young specimens, spiny keels run from the umbo toward the postero-ventral corner. This was formerly known as *Hiatella orientalis* (YOKOYAMA). Distribution: throughout Japan, Korea and China, common among roots of seaweeds and in rock crevices in shallow waters.

16. Panopea japonica (A. ADAMS)

The shell is thin and fragile, white, transversely elongate and widely gaping at both ends. The surface is rough, with distantly placed undulations. The mantle line on the inner surface is continuous and has a wide posterior sinus. Distribution: throughout Japan, Korea and northwards, collected from sandy bottom of shallow waters.

17. Panomya ampla DALL

Being close to the above species in outline, this shell has the discontinuous mantle line which distinguishes it from the former. The shell varies in shape but generally squarish ovate, thick but fragile, and broadly truncated and gaping at the posterior margin. The surface is ashy white, roughly wrinkled and covered by a thick brown periostracum. Distribution: northern Honshû and northwards, rather commonly collected from muddy bottom in shallow waters. This is a representative of the cold current elements.

Family Corbulidae

The shells are usually small, solid, trigonal ovate and inequivalved, the right valve being larger than the left. The posterior end is usually rostrated. The ligament and resilium are internal. The right valve has a single large tooth below the umbo with a deep resilifer pit behind it, and the left valve with a projecting chondrophore. The mantle line is entire.

18.   Potamocorbula amurensis (SCHRENCK)

The shell is thick and solid, white, ovate and covered with a thick and rough periostracum. The ventral margin of the right valve overlaps that of the left. This is known only from brackish water lagoons in northern Honshû and Hokkaidô, but there are evidences that it was widely distributed over Japan in the Pleistocene Period. Distribution: besides Japan, Korea, China and Siberia.

19.   Solidicorbula erythrodon (LAMARCK)

This shell is very solid, heavy, inflated and ovate. The right valve tightly embraces the left by the overlapping ventral margin and deposits a calcareous matter on the posterior rostration. The surface is sparsely marked by growth lines, and lacks a distinct periostracum. The inner margin is stained with purplish rose. Distribution: south of central Honshû, common on shallow sandy bottom.

Family Lyonsiidae

The shells of this small family are thin and fragile, nacreous, small to large in size, ovate to elongated oval, sometimes irregular in shape and rostrated and gaping posteriorly. Both valves are connected by the resilium, enforced by the shelly lithodesma. The interior is pearly and the mantle line has a shallow sinus.

20.   Entodesma navicula ADAMS et REEVE

The shell is thin, nacreously white, irregular in shape but usually oval, and broadly truncated and gaping at the posterior margin. The surface is covered with a thin brownish periostracum. Distribution: southern Hokkaidô to Kyûshû, among roots of seaweeds.

21.   Entodesma naviculoides YOKOYAMA

This closely resembles the preceding species in its young stage, but grows to a larger size, attaining approximately 70 mm in length. The shell is covered with a thick, rough and brown periostracum which easily flakes off when dry. The interior is brownish white and pearly. Distribution: north of Hokkaidô, in subtidal zone.

Family Myidae

The shells are small to large, white, porcellaneous, ovate, and gaping at the posterior end. The left valve has a large horizontally projected chondrophore below the umbo. The resilium is internal and attaches to the chondrophore of the left valve connected with the resilier pit of the right. The mantle line deeply sinuates at the posterior part.

22.   Mya (Arenomya) arenaria (?) oonogai MAKIYAMA

The shell is rather thin, fragile, ovate, rounded anteriorly and attenuated toward the gaping posterior end. The surface is rather smooth under a thin periostracum. This is often confused with *Mya japonica* JAY by Japanese authors, but the latter has a thick shell covered with a rough brownish periostracum, showing a close relation to *Mya truncata*. Distribution: Honshû to Kyûshû and Korea, common on muddy bottom between tide marks in sheltered waters.

Family Pandoridae

These shells are thin, pearly white, compressed and inequivalved, the slightly inflated right valve being larger than the flat left. The posterior dorsal margin is longer than the anterior one and rather straight. The resilium is internal and the interior is pearly.

23.   Pandora (Kennerlia) wardiana A. ADAMS

This is a large shell for this group. The shell is thick, nacreous and semicircular in shape, with the long straight posterior dorsal margin and a short anterior rostrum. Distribution: northern Honshû to Hokkaidô and Siberia, uncommon on muddy bottom at 30–100 fathoms depth.

Family Thraciidae

The shells are small to large, thin, porcellaneous, white and inequivalved, the slightly inflated right valve being larger than the flat left. The posterior end of the shell is truncated and gaping. The surface is covered with minute granules all over. The mantle line has a sinuation on its posterior portion.

24. *Thracia kakumana* Yokoyama

The shell is large for this group, dully white, compressed and roundly ovate, with a wide posterior truncation. The ligament is external, while the resilium is internal enforced by a lithodesma. Distribution: northern Honshû to Sakhalin and Korea, not uncommon on muddy bottom in shallow waters.

Family Cuspidariidae

The shells of this deep-sea family are usually white, thin and inequivalved, the right valve being a little smaller than the left. They are also inequilateral, globose ovate, rounded anteriorly and rostrated or elongated posteriorly. The surface is smooth or sculptured with undulate growth lines or radial ribs, and is covered by a thin periostracum. The hinge plate has a projecting chondrophore to which the resilium attaches, and usually has cardinal and lateral teeth. Lithodesma is present. The mantle sinus is not seen.

1. Myonera fluctuosa Kuroda

The shell is thin, milky white, and transversely oblong ovate in shape, with a narrow but short posterior rostration. The surface is strongly undulating. This is very close to the species of the genus *Cuspidaria* in shape, but has no lateral teeth on the right valve. Distribution: off Pacific coasts of Japan, uncommon at 50–100 fathoms depth.

2. Cuspidaria suganumai Nomura

This is especially characterized by a narrowly elongated beak behind the globosely ovate shell. The surface is smooth. Distribution: very common on deep muddy bottom of Japan, at 50–100 fathoms depth.

3. Cuspidaria japonica Kuroda

The shell is white, globose and ovate, with a rather short rostrum attenuated toward the truncated distal end. The surface is marked by growth lines and is covered with a thin periostracum. The lateral teeth are present. Distribution: central Honshû to Kyûshû, uncommon on muddy bottom, 50–100 fathoms in depth.

4. Cuspidaria hindsiana (A. Adams)

The shell is thin, white, elongate and ovate, ventricose and has a posterior rostration with a weak constriction at its base. The surface is undulate. This species somewhat resembles *M. fluctuosa* in shape, but differs from the latter in having the anterior and posterior lateral teeth on the right valve,

and dense undulations on the surface. Distribution: uncommonly collected from deep seas 50–100 fathoms in depth, south of central Honshû.

5. Cuspidaria hirasei Kuroda

This is a rather large shell for the family. It is white, rather thick, inflated and globose, and has a very narrow and long posterior beak projecting obliquely. Distribution: from Honshû to Kyûshû at 50–100 fathoms depth.

6. Cuspidaria nobilis (A. Adams)

This shell is also large, attaining approximately 50 mm in length, and is markedly characterized by the posterior rostration covered with an orange-red colored periostracum. The shell is ovate, inflated and sculptured by undulating growth lines on its surface. The posterior lateral tooth on the right valve is strong. Distribution: Honshû to Kyûshû, 50–100 fathoms in depth.

Family Poromyidae

These shells are thin, ovate or trigonal, inflated, globose and somewhat rostrated and truncated at the gaping posterior end. The surface is smooth or granulated externally, and the interior is pearly. The ligament is external and lies behind the umbo, while the resilium is internal with a small lithodesma. The mantle line is simple.

7. Poromya flexuosa Yokoyama

The shell is rather thick, trigonal ovate in shape, rounded at the anterior end and truncated and gaping at the posterior. The surface is covered by radially arranged minute granules, and is also covered with a yellowish periostracum. A flexure runs from the umbo to the postero-ventral corner. Distribution: Honshû to Kyûshû, rather common on fine sandy bottom at 10–150 fathoms depth.

8. Cetoconcha eximia intermedia Habe

The shell is very thin and fragile, semi-translucent, nacreous, largely inflated, globose and a little rostrated posteriorly. This is a local form of *C. eximia* Prashad collected from East Indies. Distribution: from Honshû to Kyûshû, 50–100 fathoms in depth.

Family Verticordiidae

The shells are thin to solid, white in color, circular or elongated ovate in shape, and usually inflated. The surface is covered by granules arranged in dense radial lines and more or less conspicuous radial ribs. The hinge has a cardinal knob below the umbo. The interior is pearly and the mantle line is usually simple.

9. Euciroa (Acreuciroa) teramachii KURODA

This is a large species for the family exceeding 60 mm in length. The shell is rather thick, a little inflated, ovate in shape, broadly rounded anteriorly and attenuated toward the posterior end, forming a short rostrum. The surface has radial ribs bearing numerous fine granules. This may be a form of *E. rostrata* JACKEL et THIELE. Distribution: only known from Tosa Bay, Shikoku, 150–200 fathoms deep.

Family Laternulidae

These shells are thin, oblong, somewhat rostrated and gaping at the posterior end, semi-translucent and pearly. The umbo is fissured, supported internally by an oblique plate. The surface is wholly covered by minute granules. The chondrophore is spoon-shaped, projecting from the hinge line to behind the umbo. The resilium connecting both valves is enforced with a lithodesma which is absent in some species. The mantle line has a posterior sinus.

10. Laternula rostrata (SOWERBY)

This shell is easily distinguished from other Japanese species of the same genus in the presence of the broadly gaping truncation at the posterior end. It is very thin and nacreous, inflated and transversely elongated triangular in shape. The surface is wholly covered with minute granules. The valves are connected with a lithodesma and the resilium is under the umbo. Distribution: Amami Islands and southwards, in shallow waters.

11. Laternula (Laternulina) flexuosa (REEVE)

The shell is thin, semi-translucently nacreous, ellipsoidal in shape, rounded anteriorly and broadly and roundly rostrated posteriorly. The subgeneric name, *Laternulina* HABE 1952, was proposed based on the lack of lithodesma. This was known as *L. japonica* (LISCHKE). Distribution: Honshû to Kyûshû and Korea, on sandy mud bottom not deeper than a few fathoms.

12. Laternula limicola (REEVE)

This is closely similar to the preceding species in shape, but is covered by a dirty white periostracum and is not upwardly rostrated at the posterior end. This has a lithodesma. Distribution: very common on muddy bottom between tide marks in bays, all over Japan.

Family Gastrochaenidae

The shells range from small to medium size, ovate or narrowly elongate, and live either free or enclosed in a calcareous tube, or burrowing in corals or other shells. They are white, rather thin, inflated and widely gaping ventrally. The umbo is located anteriorly. The ligament is external. The surface bears concentric, rough or smooth lines. The hinge has an obsolete tooth or is edentulous. The interior is white and has the widely sinuated mantle line.

13. Spengleria mytuloides (LAMARCK)

This shell is rather thin, narrowed anteriorly and widely truncated posteriorly. The surface is covered with a thin yellowish periostracum and is divided by a flexure, running from the umbo to the postero-ventral corner, into the whitish antero-ventral area and the postero-dorsal area on which the periostracum is thick. Distribution: over the Indo-Pacific areas up to central Honshû, burrowing in calcareous rocks in shallow waters.

14. Rocellaria cuneiformis (SPENGLER)

The shell is yellowish white, ovate, sharply attenuated toward the anterior end, rounded posteriorly, rather solid, inflated and widely

182

gaping in front. Numerous growth lamellae are more spaced on the posterior than on the anterior part of the surface. The umbo is scarcely prominent and situated near the anterior end. This is a borer in coral rocks which secretes a luminous mucus within its mantle cavity. Distribution: over the Indo-Pacific areas up to central Honshû.

Family Pholadidae

These rock- or wood-borers are white, circular to elongate oval in shape, inflated and thin to thick. The anterior surface is sculptured by concentric toothed ridges, which disappear on the smooth posterior part. The anterior gape is wide and filled up with the callus attached to each valve in some groups, and the posterior end is narrowly gaping. There are no ligament and no hinge teeth. A narrow spoon-like blade or a pophysis protrudes into the interior from below the umbo. The shells have various, anterior, dorsal and ventral accessory plates and various calcareous processes at the posterior end.

15. Jouannetia (Pholadopsis) globulosa (QUOY et GAIMARD)

The shell is globose, white and sphaerical. The anterior gape is wide but is usually closed by a white callus on the right valve in the resting stage. The posterior process on the right valve is shortly rostated and armed by a series of spines on its edge. The surface is divided into two parts by a groove; the anterior part bears a rasp-like sculpture and the posterior area is marked only by growth lines. Distribution: widely found in the Indo-Pacific areas up to central Honshû, burrowing in coral rocks between tide marks.

16. Martesia striata (LINNÉ)

The shell is elongated oval, rounded anteriorly and narrowed toward the gaping posterior end. The anterior gape is wide but closed by a callus in the resting stage. The surface is divided into two distinct parts by a narrow groove, the anterior part is rasped, and the posterior part is covered by a rough yellowish periostracum and marked by somewhat lamellate growth lines. Over

the umbo, there is a subquadrate accessory plate or protoplax. An elongate accessory plate is present on the dorsal and ventral margins respectively. The Japanese form, called M. cupula (YOKOYAMA), hardly differs from this Atlantic species. Distribution: over tropical and subtropical areas in the world, boring in submerged timber.

17. Jouannetia cumingii (SOWERBY)

This species closely resembles J. globulosa in general features, but the shell has no spines on the posterior process of the right valve. Distribution: the Indo-Pacific areas up to central Honshû, boring in coral rocks.

18. Pholadidea (Penitella) kamakurensis (YOKOYAMA)

The shell is ovate, rounded anteriorly and narrowed posteriorly, white, rather thick and inflated. The antero-ventral gape is closed with a callus in the resting stage. The surface is divided into two parts by a narrow median groove. The anterior part is rasped, while the posterior part bears growth lamellae only. The posterior end is narrowly gaping. A protoplax sits on the middle of the dorsal margin. Distribution: from Kyûshû up to southern Hokkaidô, commonly found boring in soft rocks.

19. Parapholas quadrizonata (SPENGLER)

This is somewhat similar to the preceding species in shape, but has a pair of accessory plates on the dorsal margin. The postero-dorsal part of the outer surface is covered with a very thick, foliaceous, yellowish periostracum. Distribution: central Honshû and southwards, burrowing in soft rocks.

20. Aspidopholas yoshimurai KURODA et TERAMACHI

The shell is very close to Martesia striata in shape, but lives in a calcareous tube built for itself. The shell is elongated oval, rounded anteriorly and narrowed posteriorly, and has several accessory plates, such as proto-, meso-, meta- and hypoplaxes. Distribution: central Honshû to Kyûshû, boring in soft rocks.

PLATE 63

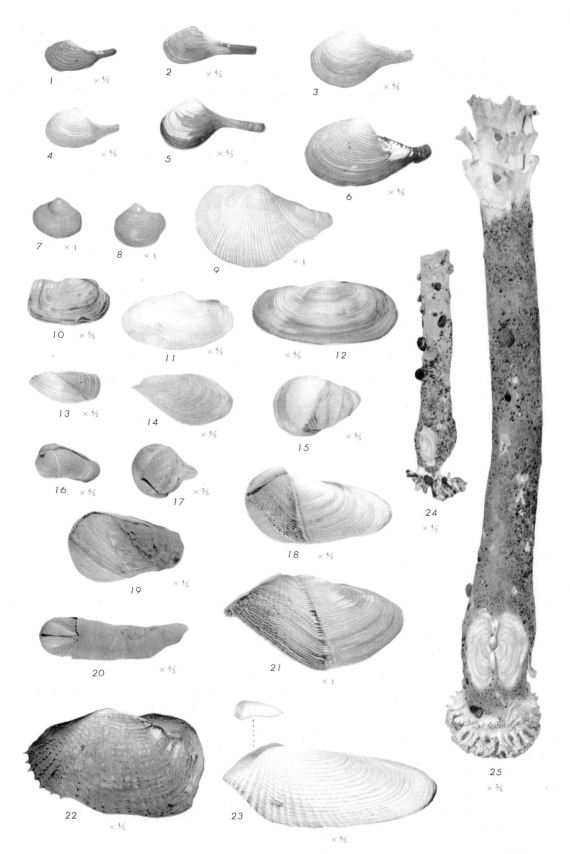

PLATE 64

21. Zirfaea subconstricta (YOKOYAMA)

The shell is ovate, inflated and widely gaping antero-dorsally, but without a closing callus. The surface is divided into two parts by a narrow groove. The anterior part bears a rasp-like sculpture, while the posterior part has only growth lines under a thin periostracum. The small chitinous protoplax rides over the umbo on the reflexed anterior margin. Distribution: from Kyûshû up to Hokkaidô, commonly found boring in soft rocks between tide marks.

22. Barnea (Umitakea) dilatata japonica (YOKOYAMA)

This is a white, large but thin shell, which is narrowed anteriorly and widely truncated and gaping posteriorly. The surface bears growth lamellae and radial cords, forming spines at their intersections on the anterior part, and is covered with a brownish periostracum. The protoplax is white, large, and lanceolate in shape. The large siphon tastes very delicious and collected by fishermen. Distribution: Honshû to Kyûshû, especially abundant in Ariake Bay of Kyûshû, as a mud-dweller below the low tide mark.

23. Barnea (Anchomasa) manilensis (PHILIPPI)

The shell is elongate, thin, fragile, white and inflated, gaping widely at the anterior and narrowly at the posterior end. The surface is rather distantly and regularly marked by concentric lamellae. Radial striae are stronger anteriorly and weaker posteriorly, and carry spines at the points of intersection with the lamellae. A shelly, lanceolate, accessory plate or protoplax is over the hinge area. The internal blade or apophysis under the beak is long and narrow. A small

form from Japan, locally named as *inornata* PILSBRY, is connected with this species by the existence of all kinds of transitional forms. Distribution: over tropical Pacific areas as far north to Hokkaidô, very common boring in clay or soft rocks in intertidal zone.

Family Clavagellidae

These peculiar bivalves are adapted for burrowing life on the sea bottom, and live in a long calcareous tube which the animals secreted outside their own shell. The tube is attached with root-like calcareous tubercles at its anterior end. The shells themselves are degenerate, thin and small, white, and are free when young, but in adults one or both valves are merged with the tube far larger than the shell. The ligament is external and the mantle line is sinuate.

24. Clavagella (Stirpulina) ramosa DUNKER

This has a narrow but long tube about 80 mm long and 12 mm wide, to which the left valve is cemented, while the right one is free within the tube, and sand grains or pebbles are adhered on its surface. Distribution: south of central Honshû, living on sea bottom, 20–100 fathoms deep, with its posterior end exposed.

25. Penicillus (Foegia) giganteus (SOWERBY)

This resembles the preceding species in shape, but the calcareous tube is much more larger and longer, reaching 300 mm × 30 mm in approximate size. Both valves are merged with the anterior portion of the tube. The mouth of the tube is armed by several folded or expanded fringes. Distribution: Honshû to Kyûshû, uncommon at 5–20 fathoms.

[PLATE 64]

Freshwater Molluscs

Since big rivers and extensive lakes are scarce on the islands of the Japanese Archipelago, the freshwater molluscan fauna of

this country is rather poor, comprising about one hundred species and varieties. But their local distribution and variations are especially interesting from the standpoints of biogeography, historical geology, and other sciences. They are also closely connected with the life of the Japanese, offering important foods, as the mother shell of freshwater pearl, as intermediate hosts of human parasites, and so forth. It is noteworthy that the fauna is now being enriched by foreign species, imported into this country with other aquatic plants and animals for ornamental use. *Physa acuta* BRAPARNAUD, now widely spread in southern parts of Japan, offers a good example.

Class Gastropoda

Family Pleuroceridae

These snails are usually turreted with about 10 whorls, and covered by a yellowish olive periostracum on its surface, always coated with black dust. Earlier whorls are, however, generally eroded away. The body whorl is rather large. The aperture is ovate in shape, and its columellar margin is simple. The operculum is thin, ovate, paucispiral, brown and stained by black dust. The animal is oviparous or ovoviviparous, and the male has no sign of the penis.

1. *Semisulcospira niponica* (SMITH)

This is an endemic species in the Lake Biwa. The shell is elongated ovate, with only about 5 remaining whorls in grown specimens, earlier whorls being decapitated. The surface of whorls is decorated by brown spiral bands, and covered by a blackish brown periostracum. Strongly granulated spiral cords, 3 in number, are seen on each whorl, and 2 additional cords are encircling the base of body whorl. The reproduction is ovoviviparous.

2. *Semisulcospira bensoni* (PHILIPPI)

The shell is subulate, with about 12 whorls in perfect specimens, but generally only 5–7 of them are remaining in larger shells. The surface is covered with an olive yellow periostracum stained by black dust, ornamented by 3 brown bands on the body whorl and sculptured by densely set spiral cords. In some forms, longitudinal ribs also occur on earlier whorls. The aperture is ovate, and its outer margin is not thickened. The operculum is also ovate, closing the aperture.

The animal is ovoviviparous, and the female has small brown young shells in her brood pouch, which measure about 2 mm in height and are more than 200 in their number per pouch. This is usually known as *S. libertina* (GOULD), and is an intermediate host of the lung fluke. Distribution: very common on pebbles in streams, throughout Japan.

Family Thiaridae

The shells are very close to the members of the preceding family in shape, but the reproduction is parthenogenetic. Therefore no male is present.

3. *Stenomelania loebbeckii* (BROT)

The shell is rather large and turreted, with 5–7 remaining whorls. The surface is smooth and polished under the cover of a brown periostracum, but some forms have weak spiral threads below the suture and several spiral grooves on the base of body whorl. Distribution: rather common in brackish waters from central Honshû to Kyûshû.

Family Lymnaeidae

These shells are thin and usually dextral, and its spire is small as compared with the large body whorl. The aperture is wide, and its outer margin is thin and acute. The columellar margin is twisted, forming an arc. The animal is hermaphrodite, as a member of the basommatophoran pulmonates. The operculum is absent.

4. *Lymnaea (Radix) japonica* (JAY)

The shell is thin and globular, with a small spire and a large body whorl. The aperture is large and slighly expanded at the outer margin. The upper end of columellar margin is twisted. This is hardly separable from the European *L. auricularia* (LINNÉ) in the shape of the shell, whereas the chromosome number is different in the two species (18 in *japonica* versus 17 in *auricularia*, in haploid numbers). This is well known as an intermediate host of the fluke, *Fasciola hepatica* (LINNÉ). Distribution: all over Japan.

185

Family Viviparidae

The snails are ovate and conical, with about 6 roundly convex whorls. The surface is smooth or spirally corded, coated by a greenish or olivaceous periostracum and decorated by brownish bands in some species. The aperture is roundly ovate, and its margin is simple. The operculum is horny, and has concentric lines, with a nucleus situated subcentrally. The animal is ovoviviparous, and the male uses his curved right tentacle as a penis.

5. Sinotaia quadrata (BENSON)

The shell is pyramidally conical and thin, with about 6 whorls, whose surface is covered by a greenish olive periostracum. Each whorl is rather weakly convex, with 2–3 spiral threads forming weak keels, and the body whorl bears an obtuse angle at the base. The operculum is brown in color. This is commonly known as *S. histrica* (GOULD) in Japan. Distribution: widely found in China, Korea and Japan.

6. Cipangopaludina chinensis malleata (REEVE)

This mud snail is globosely conical, with very strongly inflated whorls, and covered over its surface by a smooth and polished, olivaceous periostracum. The body whorl is very large and quite rounded at the periphery. The operculum is corneous and brown in color. Distribution: this is very common in paddy rice fields throughout Japan, and the farmers collect this snail for food.

7. Cipangopaludina (Heterogen) longispira (SMITH)

This is characterized by the large embryos in the brood pouch, exceeding 15 mm in height. The shell has the tall spire, composed of about 7 whorls which have a flattish belt below the suture. The surface is smooth, polished and covered with a yellowish periostracum. Distribution: endemic in the Lake Biwa.

8. Cipangopaludina japonica (VON MARTENS)

The shell is large and ovate, with a conical spire. The whorls are not so strongly convex as in *C. chinensis malleata*. This dwells in ponds and streams throughout Japan, and the northern form of this species bears an angular periphery on the body whorl as in young specimens of the southern form, named *C. j. iwakawa* (PILSBRY).

Class Pelecypoda

Family Corbiculidae

The shells are medium in size, and triangularly ovate in shape. The surface is sculptured by concentric growth ridges, and covered by a yellowish brown periostracum. The hinge plate has 3 cardinal teeth and a long lateral tooth on each side of them. The ligamant is external. The interior is purplish, and the mantle line is entire. They live in fresh or brackish waters, and their flesh is favored by the Japanese.

9. Corbicula sandai REINHARDT

The shell is trigonally ovate in shape, and has distinctly undulating growth ridges on the shiny surface covered by a vernicose periostracum. The umbo is large, and strongly elevated beyond the hinge line. This is oviparous. This species is endemic in the Lake Biwa, and is collected for food by the inhabitants.

10. Corbicula japanica PRIME

·This closely resembles the preceding species in shape, but the umbo is not so strongly elevated as in that species. This is also edible. Distribution: on sandy bottom in brackish waters in Japan, Korea and Sakhalin.

11. Corbicula (Corbiculina) leana PRIME

This is also close to the preceding species in shape, but the shell is ovate, with a low umbo and the surface is covered by a yellowish periostracum, bearing large or small scattered spots, instead of brownish black rays in the preceding species. This is ovoviviparous, incubating many minute embryos in the brood gill chamber. Distribution: on sandy bottom of streams throughout Japan, except Hokkaidô.

Family Unionidae

These bivalves are usually large or very large, often exceeding 200 mm in length, ovate, and sometimes lanceolate in shape. The surface is smooth or sculptured and covered by a thick periostracum. The ligament is external. The hinge plate is with or without teeth. The interior is conspicuously nacreous. The animals are ovoviviparous, incubating minute grochidia, which is the larval name of this group, in the brood gill chamber.

12. Margaritifera margaritifera (Linné)

This is a famous pearl mussel in Europe. The shell is elongate oval in shape, rather thick and wears a very dark brown periostracum. The umbo is situated rather anteriorly. The hinge plate has a cardinal tooth and a long posterior lateral tooth on the right valve. Distribution: Hokkaidô and the Japan Sea side of Honshû, in clear streams.

13. Pseudodon (Obovalis) omiensis (Heimburg)

The shell is ovate and rather thin, and the surface is sculptured by divaricating, furcate ribs on its posterior half. The hinge plate bears a spoon-like, projected, cardinal tooth and a very weak posterior lateral tooth on the right valve. Distribution: fairly common in the Lake Biwa, but rather rare in other parts of Honshû and Kyûshû.

14. Inversidens japonensis (Lea)

This is rather small for the family, ovate and thick. The surface is marked by a divaricating sculpture all over or on the umbonal area, forming many granules. The hinge plate has a solid cardinal tooth and a posterior lateral tooth on the right valve. Distribution: very common in streams throughout Japan.

15. Lanceolaria oxyrhyncha (von Martens)

The shell is lanceolate and thick. The umbo is located near the anterior end, and the posterior end is rather pointed. A rib runs from the umbo to the posterior end. The hinge teeth consist of a cardinal and a posterior lateral tooth on the right valve. This very closely resembles the Chinese species, L. grayanus (Lea), in shape. Distribution: endemic in the Lake Biwa.

16. Anodonta woodiana lauta (von Martens)

This is hardly distinguishable from the Chinese A. woodiana (Lea) in shell features, and may be a local form of the latter species. The shell is large, thin, and rather inflated. The hinge plate bears no teeth. The interior is pearly. Distribution: common in ponds throughout Japan and Korea.

17. Unio douglasiae nipponense (von Martens)

This is rather small for the family, but thick and solid, and ovate in shape tapering to the posterior end. The umbo is situated rather anteriorly on the dorsal margin, from which divaricating sculptures expand toward the margin. The hinge plate has one rather flat cardinal tooth and one posterior lateral tooth on the right valve. This is connected with the real form U. douglasiae by various intermediate forms. Distribution: commonly found in streams throughout Japan.

18. Lanceolaria oxyrhyncha cuspidata Kira

This closely resembles L. oxyrhyncha in shape, but is more sharply attenuated toward the posterior end. There are various kinds of intermediate forms between this and the real form. Distribution: Honshû and Shikoku.

19. Anodonta japonica (Clessin)

This is similar to A. woodiana in shape, but has a more elongate and less inflated shell. Distribution: on muddy bottom of streams in Honshû and Shikoku.

20.   *Cristaria plicata spatiosa* (CLESSIN)

This is a very large mussel, reaching approximately 250 mm in the length of fully grown specimens. The shell is ovate, with a straight dorsal margin in larger specimens, thin, and moderately inflated. In young specimens, a very flat wing-like projection is attached to the straight dorsal margin. The umbo is situated anteriorly. The surface is rather smooth, except the wavy postero-dorsal area, and covered by a dark yellowish brown periostracum. The interior is pearly, and the hinge plate has a posterior lateral tooth on the right valve. This form hardly differs from the typical form in China and Korea. Distribution: throughout Japan, in lakes and marshes.

This group superficially resembles the *Anodonta* group in shape, but can at once be distinguished from *Anodonta* in having the posterior lateral tooth on the hinge plate.

Land Snails

Class Gastropoda

In sharp contrast to freshwater molluscs, the land shell fauna is very rich in Japan and its adjacent islands. In addition to the prevailing warm and moist climate that favors land snails' life, the geographical isolation by such natural barriers as channels and complicated mountain ranges caused the differentiation of many species and local forms. In his comprehensive study, Dr. Kuroda enumerated 888 species and 374 subspecies native to the Japanese Archipelago, including Fomosa, the Ryukyus, Bonin Islands, Japan proper, the Kuriles and southern half of Sakhalin. Only a small number of representative species are, however, illustrated here, with the exception of the genus *Euhadra*, the most familiar group of large-sized land snail in Japan, of which the greater part of species are presented in Plate 66 and 67.

Family Helicinidae

These shells are small or medium in size, thick and solid, with a low spire composed of about 5 whorls. The body whorl is very large. The aperture is semilunate in shape, and its outer margin is very thick forming a varix, and the parietal wall is covered by a shiny enamelled callus. The inner whorls are reduced away, forming one large chamber as in the sea snail family Neritidae. The operculum, enough closing the aperture, is semilunate and calcareous.

1. Waldemaria japonica (A. ADAMS)

The shell is rather small, thick and solid, with a low spire. The whorls are 5 in number. The aperture is semilunate, and its outer margin is very thick forming a strong varix. Its color is yellow to reddish brown. The calcareous semilunate operculum is reddish brown in color. This varies locally in size and coloration. The figured specimen is called *W. j. reinii* (KOBELT), which is a larger yellowish form. Distribution: common in Honshû, Shikoku and northern parts of Kyûshû.

Family Cyclophoridae

This family includes a large number of species, whose shells range from very minute to large size, and are usually thick and solid, with a low or high spire. The whorls are round with deep sutures. The aperture is circular and thickened at the margin, sometimes with a tubular siphon for breath, used when the operculum closes it. The operculum is corneous or calcareous, and multispiral with a centric nucleus.

2. Pupinella (Pupinopsis) rufa (SOWERBY)

The shell is pupoid in shape, consists of 6.5 whorls, and is reddish brown in color. The aperture is circular and surrounded by the thickened whitish margin which has both anterior and posterior canals. The operculum is thin, brownish and horny. Distribution: central Honshû to Kyûshû and southern Korea, very common among pebbles and decaying logs.

3. Spirostoma japonicum (A. ADAMS)

The shell is planorboid with an almost flat spire. The whorls are 5 in number and round with deep sutures. The surface is smooth, polished and covered with a yellowish periostracum. The aperture is circular and its margin is slightly thickened. The brown, horny operculum is very characteristic in being spirally conical just like the pupa of a certain fly. The umbilicus is very wide. Distribution: the same with *P. rufa*, very common on the forest floor.

4. Chamalycaeus hirasei (PILSBRY)

The shell is very small, solid, and whitish rose, with a low spire of 5 rounded whorls. The aperture is circular, with somewhat thickened lips. A small breathing tube turning backwards is formed along the suture near the aperture. This is the characteristic feature of this group. The surface has distinct growth plicae. The operculum is circular, horny, multispiral and concave at the center. Distribution: chiefly occurs in Kinki District of central Honshû.

189

5. Diplommatina (Sinica) collarifera SCHMACKER et BÖTTGER

The shell is minute and pupoid in shape, with about 7 whorls. Each whorl is rounded with a deep suture, and the penultimate whorl is the largest in diameter, while the body whorl is somewhat constricted. The surface is reddish orange in color, and sculptured by growth lines. The aperture is circular, with an obtusely angular corner at the distal end of columellar margin which bears a distinct tooth. A short palatal plica occurs on the inner wall of body whorl. Distribution: widely found in Honshû except its northern part, northern Shikoku and northern Kyûshû.

6. Cyclotus (Procyclotus) campanulatus VON MARTENS

This is a rather small, thick and solid shell, with a somewhat elevated spire. The whorls are very round with deep sutures, and are 5 in number. The surface is smooth and polished, and bears brown spots on the yellowish brown periostracum. The aperture is circular, thickened at the margin, and closed by a thick calcareous operculum. The umbilicus is perforated. Distribution: rather common from Honshû to Kyûshû and southern Korea.

7. Cyclophorus herklotsi VON MARTENS

The shell is medium in size, thick and solid, with a moderately elevated spire and a very large body whorl. The whorls are 5 in number, and entirely rounded with deep sutures. The periostracum is brown in color, sometimes with a chestnut spiral band and dark spots. The aperture is circular, and somewhat thickened at the margin. The umbilicus is deeply perforated. The operculum is circular, brown, horny and slightly concave toward the center. Distribution: widely and commonly distributed from Honshû to Kyûshû and southern Korea.

Family Succineidae

The snails are thin and fragile, with a small spire and a very large body whorl. The aperture is also very wide, and its margin is thin. This shell is very similar to the pond snail *Lymnaea* in shape, but the animal of this family has a pair of tentacles, bearing eyes on their tops as in the garden snail.

8. Succinea lauta GOULD

The shell is rather large for this group, thin and fragile, and transparently brownish yellow, with a very large body whorl. *S. hirasei* PILSBRY is another Japanese species distributed in Honshû and northern Kyûshû, and has a narrower shell than this species. Distribution: very common among grasses near streams in Hokkaidô and northern Honshû.

Family Helicarionidae

The shells are minute to medium in size, usually yellow to brown in color, thin, fragile, and semi-transparent. The axis is seen through the shell. The spire is low or somewhat elevated, with 5–7 whorls. The animals have a very narrowly elongated foot, which bears a small tail-like process on its posterior end. The mantle is extended over the shell. They are usually the inhabitants among litters on the forest floor, and are carnivorous.

9. Bekkochlamys microglypta (PILSBRY)

This is a large shell for this group, reaching 10 mm in diameter, thin, polished, and ivory brown, with a rather flat spire composed of 5 whorls. The aperture is wide, and its margin is thin and sharp. The umbilicus is minutely perforated. Distribution: widely distributed from Honshû to Kyûshû.

Family Bradybaenidae (1)

These shells are small to large, including so-called garden snails. The spire is usually elevated, with 5–7 whorls. The body whorl is large. The surface is covered by a smooth or hairy periostracum. The aperture has the thickened and somewhat expanded margin in fully grown specimens, with a few exceptions. The shells closely resemble those of the family Camaenidae, but these 2 families are easily distinguished from each other by the features of genitalia. The genital organ of this family has a dart sac

190

with several mucus glands, with or without a flagellum on the penis and unexceptionally without an appendix of the penis.

10.   Trishoplita goodwini (SMITH)

The shell is white, thin and fragile. The spire is moderately tall, with 5 whorls. The aperture margin is slightly thickened and expanded. The umbilicus is narrowly and deeply perforated. Distribution: common on leaves of shrubs in central Honshû.

11.   Trishoplita hilgendorfi (KOBELT)

This is very close to the preceding species in shape, but the shell is rather thick and colored in shiny brown, and has 6.5 whorls. Distribution: this is an endemic species in the Ibuki limestone hills of central Honshû.

12.   Bradybaena similaris (FÉRUSSAC)

The shell is rather small, thin and fragile, with a low spire. The whorls are 5.5 in number, and rather rapidly increase their width toward the aperture, whose margin is slightly thickened and expanded. The body whorl is large and rounded at the periphery. It is yellow or light reddish brown, with or without a dark brown peripheral band. The umbilicus is narrowly perforated. This species is widely spread over tropical and subtropical areas in the world, including Japan.

13.   Aegista tumida cavata (PILSBRY)

The shell is flat and disc-like, with a low spire. The whorls are rounded, with deep sutures, and are 6 in number. The surface is covered with a velvety thick epiderm. The aperture is circular, and its margin is white and very thickened. The umbilicus is wide. This form occurs in southern parts of Kinki District, while A. tumida GUDE is rather common in western Honshû.

14.   Trishoplita pallens JACOBI

The shell is large for the Trishoplita group, and has a low spire, comprising 5.5 whorls. Each whorl is rounded, with the deep suture. The coloration is white, but some forms have broad, brown, basal band. The aperture margin is slightly thickened

and expanded. The umbilicus is rather wide. Distribution: Shikoku.

15.   Aegista (Plectotropis) vatheleti (MABILLE)

The shell is rather large, flat, solid and thick, with a low spire. The whorls are 7 in number, and the body whorl is surrounded by the acutely angular periphery. The surface bears a velvety periostracum with a series of hairs along the periphery. The margin of aperture is thickened and expanded. The umbilicus is very wide. Distribution: common in Honshû and Shikoku with some local forms. This was formerly known by the name, A.(P.) vulgivaga (SCHMACKER et BÖTTGER).

Family Enidae

The shells are dextral and elongated pupoid in shape, with 8–10 whorls. The aperture is ovate, and its margin is thickened and flatly expanded, without any lamellae.

16.   Mirus reiniana (KOBELT)

The shell is cylindrical pupiform in shape and light yellow to yellowish brown, with 7.5–9.5 whorls. The margin of aperture is white, thickened and expanded. Distribution: southern Hokkaidô to Kyûshû, with some local forms.

Family Camaenidae

This family is hardly separable from the family Bradybaenidae in shell features, but the genital organ is without the dart sac near its opening.

17.   Satsuma myomphala (VON MARTENS)

The shell is large, thin, and with 6.5 whorls forming a rather low spire. The surface is smooth, and covered with a thin yellowish periostracum encircled by a dark brown, narrow band on the periphery. The aperture is rather large, and its margin is thick and expanded. The umbilicus is closed or narrowly perforated. Distribution: widely distributed from Honshû to Kyûshû, with several local forms.

18. *Satsuma japonica* (PFEIFFER)

The shell is usually medium but very variable in size, and light yellow to brown, with a tall spire consisting of about 8 whorls. The aperture is oblique downwards, with the thickened and expanded margin. The umbilicus is closed or narrowed by the columellar margin. Distribution: Honshû and Shikoku, with several local forms.

19. *Satsuma (Coniglobus) oshimae* (PILSBRY)

The shell is large and thick, with a low spire. The whorls are 6 in number, and rapidly increase their width toward the aperture. The surface is covered by a yellowish brown periostracum with a dark brown band at the periphery. The aperture margin is thickened and somewhat expanded. The umbilicus is narrow but deep. This is very close to a form of *S. (C.) mercatoria* (PFEIFFER) from the Ryukyus. Distribution: rather common in Amami Islands.

Family Bradybaenidae (2)

20. *Fruticicola (Acusta) despecta sieboldiana* (PFEIFFER)

The shell is globular, thin and yellow to brown without any color bands, and has a slightly elevated spire of 5 whorls. The aperture is large, and its margin is thin. This form hardly differs from the real *A. despecta* (SOWERBY) found in the Ryukyus. Distribution: throughout Japan, very abundant in cultivated fields and villages.

21. *Bradybaena (Phaeohelix) submandarina* (PILSBRY)

The shell is medium in size, rather solid, and yellowish brown to brown, with a dark brown narrow band on the periphery. The spire is low or rather high, with 6.5 whorls. The margin of aperture is thickened and somewhat reflexed. The umbilicus is small but deep. Distribution: rather common under fallen leaves in bushes, ranging from Satanomisaki, the southernmost cape of Kyûshû, to Tokara Islands.

22. *Fruticicola (Ezohelix) gainesi* (PILSBRY)

The shell is globular and thin, with a low spire of about 5 whorls. The surface is covered with a yellowish or reddish brown periostracum, sometimes encircled by 1 or 2 reddish brown bands. The aperture is very large, slightly thickened and feebly expanded at its outer margin in adult shells. Distribution; Hokkaidô and northern Honshû.

Family Clausiliidae

The shells are sinistral and fusiform, with about 10 whorls. The aperture is pyriform and its margin is thickened and reflexed, containing the superior, inferior and subcolumellar lamellae. The inner wall of body whorl bears the principal and palatal plicae transversely, and a longitudinally placed lunella. The white tongue-like calcareous plate called the clausilium closes the aperture at the lunella within the aperture when the animal is withdrawn into the shell, just like the operculum of the prosobranchiate snails. It is ovoviviparous, containing several embryos in the oviduct of the female genital organ.

23. *Stereophaedusa japonica* (CROSSE)

The shell is elongated fusiform, reaching about 30 mm in height, and yellowish brown to blackish brown in color. The spire is very tall consisting of about 11 whorls. The aperture has a distinct superior and inferior lamellae. Distribution: from Honshû to Kyûshû, common.

24. *Megalophaedusa martensii* (VON MARTERNS)

The shell is the largest of this family in Japan, reaching approximately 50 mm in height. The whorls are 9 in number. The color is usually brown to purplish brown, and sometimes light yellow. The aperture has the solid superior and rather weak inferior lamellae. A long principal and many small palatal plicae arranged along the growth line are seen on the inner wall of body whorl. Distribution: central Honshû and eastern Shikoku, with several local forms.

[PLATE 66]   Genus Euhadra

Genus *Euhadra* (1)

This group comprises the largest and most familiar garden snails of Japan, distributed from southern Hokkaidô to Yaku-shima and Tanegashima, south of Kyûshû. The shells have a rather low spire containing about 6 whorls, which gradually increase their width toward the aperture. The aperture is rather wide and slightly oblique downwards, and its margin is thickened and reflexed in adult shells. The umbilicus is narrowly but deeply perforated. The animals have a dart sac with mucus glands, and the penis is attached with a flagellum and without an appendix. These are the characteristic features of this group to separate it from the superficially allied *Satsuma*-group belonging to Camaenidae.

Four spiral color bands on the surface of body whorl are also characteristic of this genus, and are variously combined into several kinds of common design. The bands in full set consist of the subsutural, (1), peripheral (2) and basal (3) bands and the umbilical patch (4). This design is called the *sandai*-pattern (Textfig. 1). The subsutural band frequently drops as shown in Textfig. 2, resulting in the *callizona*-pattern. When the subsutural and basal bands are both lacking, the design is called the *eoa*-pattern. Another common design is the *herklotsi*-pattern (Textfig. 4), in which the subsutural and basal bands are wide and fading toward the suture and the umbilicus respectively. Textfig. 5 is the bandless form, and Textfig. 6 is the *nimbosa*-pattern consisting of oblique, golden yellow streaks. The last pattern may be superposed upon any other patterns. Other patterns than these, such as 1030, 0030, 0004, etc. are rather exceptional. A single population of the same species usually includes a few or more of these different combinations of color bands.

Certain species of this genus as *E. callizona*, *E. congenita*, *E. dixoni*, etc. are mainly arboreal in their life, and have thin, whitish shells, while others are terrestrial, having thick and dark-colored shells, as in *E. sandai*, *E. eoa*, *E. senckenbergiana*, etc. Species of the latter group generally include two races which are connected by various transitional forms. One is the hill race that has larger, dark brown-colored shell, and

contains many-banded individuals (*sandai-*, *herklotsi-*, *nimbosa*-pattern, etc.) in high percentages. Another is the lowland race that has smaller, light-colored shells, especially rich in *eoa*-patterns. The two races of the same species are so widely different in appearance that the identification of species is sometimes extremely difficult without the anatomical examination of genital organs.

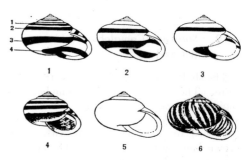

sandai-pattern   *callizona*-pattern   *eoa*-pattern
   (1234)   (0234)   (0204)

herklotsi-pattern   bandless-pattern   *nimbosa*-pattern
                        (0000)

Color band patterns in *Euhadra* (after Pilsbry)

1. Euhadra latispira tsurugensis (COCKERELL)

This is found in western Hokuriku District along the Japan Sea. This large snail usually has 4 bands of *sandai*-pattern on the yellowish ground, of which the subsutural and basal bands tend to fade away a little before the aperture. *E. latispira* PILSBRY et HIRASE is the hill race of this species, distributed around Mt. Hakusan.

2. Euhadra latispira yagurai KURODA et HABE

This is another lowland race of the same species found in the Japan Sea side of Chûgoku District, and is characterized by the depressed shell smaller than that of the preceding race. Most of the shells of this race have no colored bands on the yellowish surface.

3. Euhadra senckenbergiana (KOBELT)

This and *E. awaensis* are the largest land snails in Japan exceeding 60 mm in diameter. This beautiful hill race has the

PLATE 65

PLATE 66

blackish *herklotsi*-pattern and golden *nimbosa*-pattern on the brown ground. The aperture is wide. This chiefly occurs on central highlands of Chûbu District.

4. Euhadra senckenbergiana notoensis KURODA et TERAMACHI

This is a lowland race of the above species, mostly with 4 narrow bands on the yellowish ground. It occurs in Hokuriku District, and is replaced by *E. s. aomoriensis* PILSBRY et GULICK in Tôhoku District.

5. Euhadra senckenbergiana minoensis PILSBRY

A small lowland race, showing the *eoa*-pattern on the yellowish brown ground. The whorls rather rapidly increase their width toward the aperture. It is connected with the real *senckenbergiana* through an intermediate form, *E. s. ibukicola*. This race is restricted to a narrow area east of Lake Biwa.

6. Euhadra nachicola KURODA

This is an endemic species in a southern part of Kii Peninsula. The shell is large and colored in olivaceous brown with the vague *herklotsi*-pattern but without any radial streaks.

7. Euhadra awaensis PILSBRY

This is the largest land snail of Japan, occuring on mountains in eastern Shikoku. The surface is mallate, and covered by a velvety dark brown periostracum with the *herklotsi*-pattern. The umbilicus is deep with the steep wall. The specimen illustrated here, collected in Tokushima Prefecture, measures 64 mm in maximum diameter. *E. a. vortex* PILSBRY is a smaller race in southwestern Shikokû.

8. Euhadra awaensis idzumonis (PILSBRY et GULICK)

Another large race of the preceding species, found in Chûgoku District. The shells of lowlands show the *eoa*-pattern on the yellowish ground, but those collected from the Chûgoku Range have larger, reddish brown shells with *herklotsi*-pattern.

9. Euhadra eoa gulicki PILSBRY

This is a hill race of this species distributed in Kinki District. The mallate surface, with the *herklotsi*-pattern, is covered by a dark brown velvety periostracum and the umbilicus is wide.

10. Euhadra eoa communisiformis KANAMARU

A small lowland race of *E. eoa*, mainly distributed in southeastern part of Kinki and around Nagoya. The shell is covered by a slightly yellowish velvety periostracum and bears a very narrow blackish peripheral band and a small umbilical patch. This is superficially very close to *E. sandai communis* in the shell features, but differs from the latter in its mallate surface and narrow peripheral band. Moreover, the animal lacks a black band on its dorsal hump, which is always found in *E. sandai*. The race in the Kii Peninsula is called *E. e. shigeonis* KURODA.

11. Euhadra herklotsi (VON MARTENS)

This is widely distributed throughout Kyûshû. The typical form bears the *herklotsi*- or *eoa*-pattern on the yellowish ground, sometimes with 0230-pattern that is rather commonly found in the species of the genus *Nesiohelix*, which may be an ancestral form of the genus *Euhadra*. The lowland race in southern Kyûshû is named *E. h. nesiotica* PILSBRY, and the hill race is represented by *E. h. hyugana* KURODA, whose shell is colored dark brown with the blackish *herklotsi*-pattern.

12. Euhadra decorata (PILSBRY et HIRASE)

This sinistral snail occurs in the northeastern parts of Honshû. The shell is brownish yellow, usually with the *herklotsi*- or *eoa*-pattern and yellowish streaks along the coarse growth lines. It is a lowland race of this species.

13. Euhadra decorata tobai S. HIRASE

This is the only one hill race of this species, having the large shell with the *herklotsi*-pattern and splendid golden yellow streaks. This is collected among mountains in Tôhoku District.

[PLATE 66]   Genus Euhadra

14. *Euhadra decorata iwadensis* TOBA et KURODA

The shell bears the *eoa*-pattern on the yellowish, rather smooth surface. This may be a race of this species related to *E. grata* to a certain extent. This is rather rarely found in Tôhoku District.

Genus *Euhadra* (2)

1. Euhadra sadoensis (PILSBRY et HIRASE)

This is an endemic species on Sado Island in the Japan Sea. The shell is rather small and moderately elevated conical, and decorated with the *herklotsi*-pattern on the light yellowish ground.

2. Euhadra callizona amaliae (KOBELT)

This is the commonnest tree snail of central Japan. This neat shell bears black bands on the white ground usually in the *callizona*-pattern. This race is also very characteristic in having the rosy aperture, and differs from the typical form in its larger and lower shell. This occurs in Kinki and western parts of Chûbu District.

3. Euhadra callizona (CROSSE)

A lovely small shell found on Hakone and Amagi Ranges, southeast of Mt. Fuji. The black bands on the white ground are narrower in this race than those of the preceding race and the aperture margin is not stained in rose.

4. Euhadra dixoni (PILSBRY)

This tree snail is distributed in Chûgoku and Shikoku Districts. It differs from the preceding species in having the higher conical spire and entirely black basal stain combinating the basal band with the umbilical patch. But sometimes wholly bandless specimens also occur. *E. d. okicola* PILSBRY is a small island form known from Oki Islands, and *E. d. montivaga* PILSBRY et HIRASE is a form found in Shikoku.

5. Euhadra congenita hickonis (KOBELT)

This is a common tree snail in Chûgoku, Shikoku and eastern parts of Kyûshû. This shell bears the *callizona*- or *eoa*-pattern on the whitish or purplish brown ground, more or less accompanied with the rose or whitish *nimbosa*-pattern.

6. Euhadra congenita (SMITH)

A local form only seen in Kôbe and its vicinity. The shell is characterized by coarse growth lines on the surface.

7. Euhadra sandai (KOBELT)

This is a beautiful snail that bears the typical *sandai*-pattern in black, together with the golden *nimbosa*-pattern. The spire is very low. This is rather common in western hills of Chûbu District.

8. Euhadra sandai kuramana KURODA et TARAMACHI

This is a rather large, beautiful snail, being the intermediate race between *E. sandai* and *E. s. daisenica* KURODA. This hill race chiefly occurs in northern Kinki District.

9. Euhadra sandai daisenica KURODA

This is a large hill race seen on Chûgoku Range. The shell has a somewhat elevated spire, with golden streaks along the growth lines.

10. Euhadra sandai communis PILSBRY

A common lowland race of this species, distributed over Kinki District except the southern part of Kii Peninsula. The shell is rather small and low, and has a yellowish periostracum with the *eoa*-pattern, and rarely with the *sandai*-pattern. The *nimbosa*-pattern on the surface is very weak.

11. Euhadra peliomphala (PFEIFFER)

This is the commonnest snail in Kantô and eastern parts of Chûbu District. The shell is of medium size, and has a rather low spire. The surface bears 3 narrow black bands and an umbilical patch in the *sandai*-pattern, or has the *eoa*-pattern. But color bands are occasionally missing.

12. Euhadra peliomphala simodae (JAY)

This is only a race of the preceding species found in lowlands of Izu Peninsula. The shell usually has the *eoa*-pattern, together with the *nimbosa*-pattern. In some specimens, one or two color bands are missing.

[PLATE 67]   Genus Euhadra

13. Euhadra peliomphala nimbosa (CROSSE)

This is a beautiful hill race of this species, collected from Amagi and Hakone Ranges. The shell is rather small and colored in purplish brown, with the golden *nimbosa*-pattern.

14. Euhadra brandti sapporo (IJIMA)

This is the only known species of this genus in Hokkaidô, restricted to its southwestern part. The shell bears the *callizona*-pattern on the whitish ground. But this species differs from *E. callizona* in having a very broad periphral band, and is closely related to *E. brandti* being a northern form of this species connected with the latter by various transitional forms.

15. Euhadra brandti roseoapicalis KIRA

In this hill race, the shell has the pretty *nimbosa*-pattern, together with the *callizona*-pattern on the purplish brown ground. Though this is apparently close to *E. p. nimbosa*, the animal has broad black band on its dosal hump, while a narrow brown band is seen on the latter. *E. brandti* (KOBELT) is a lowland race of this species. This hill race is found in northern parts of Kantô and Chûbu Districts, and the lowland race in northern Kantô District.

16. Euhadra grata emurai KURODA

This small sinistral snail is smooth and polished on its surface and colored greenish yellow, mostly with the *eoa*-pattern. This race is found in the northern part of Niigata Prefecture. *E. grata* (GUDE) differs from this race in having the elevated whitish shell with various band patterns, and is collected from Yamagata Prefecture.

17. Euhadra grata gratoides KIRA

This local race in the northwestern part of Tôhoku District hardly differs from the real *E. grata* in shape and coloration, but is somewhat smaller in size.

18. Euhadra scaevola interioris PILSBRY

This is distributed in hilly areas of Chûbu and northern Kinki Districts, and differs from the real *E. scaevola* (MARTENS) in its larger and lower shell, which is colored in brown and marked by coarse growth lines on the surface. *E. s. mikawa* AMANO is characterized by the angular periphery on the body whorl, and is endemic on limestone hills of Aichi Prefecture, east of Nagoya.

19. Euhadra quaesita (DESHAYES)

This is a very common sinistral snail in northern half of Honshû. The shell is rather large, and marked by the *eoa*-pattern on the yellowish surface. The specimens collected from Hegura Island off Noto Peninsula represent a small, globular, insular race named *E. q. heguraensis* KURODA et TAN.

20. Euhadra quaesita montium (MARTENS)

This is a hill race of the preceding species, and has a dark brown shell with the *herklotsi*-pattern. This is also widely distributed in northern half of Honshû.

PLATE 67

PLATE 68

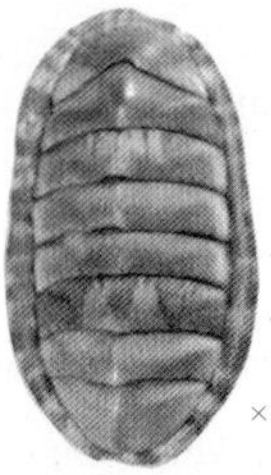

× 1⅕

1

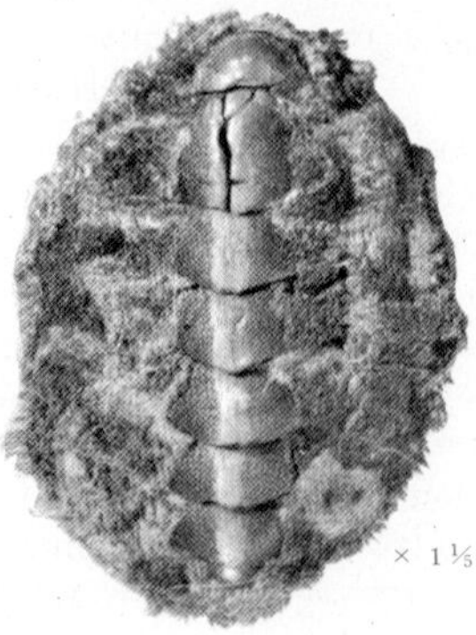

× 1⅕

4

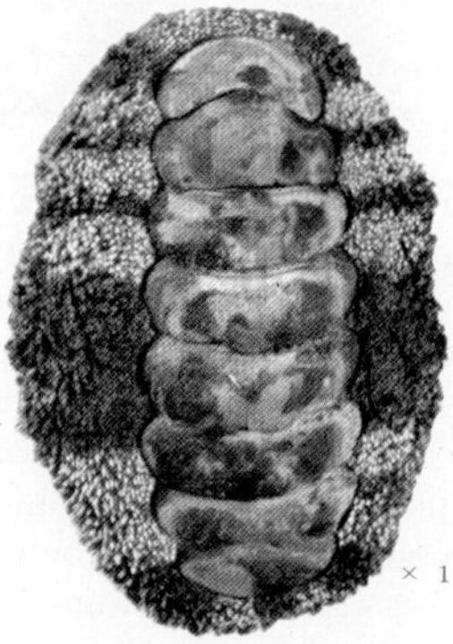

× 1⅕

5

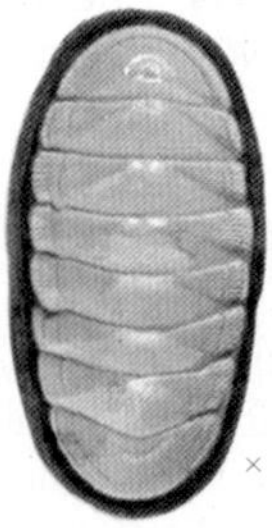

× 1⅕

2

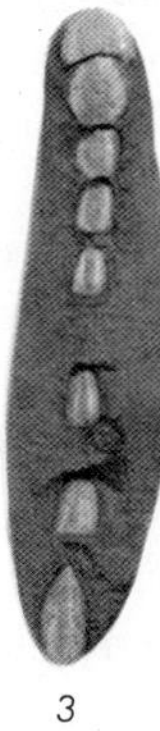

× 1⅕

3

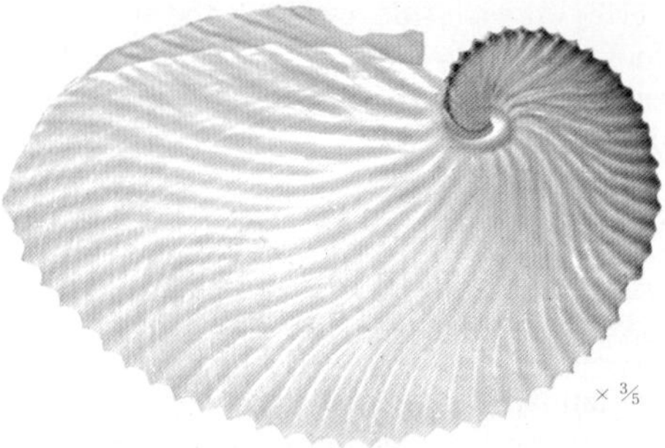

× ⅗

6

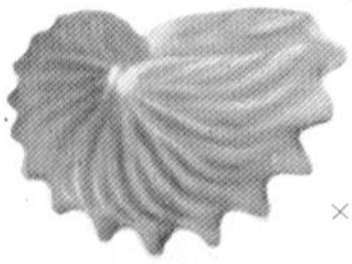

× ⅘

7

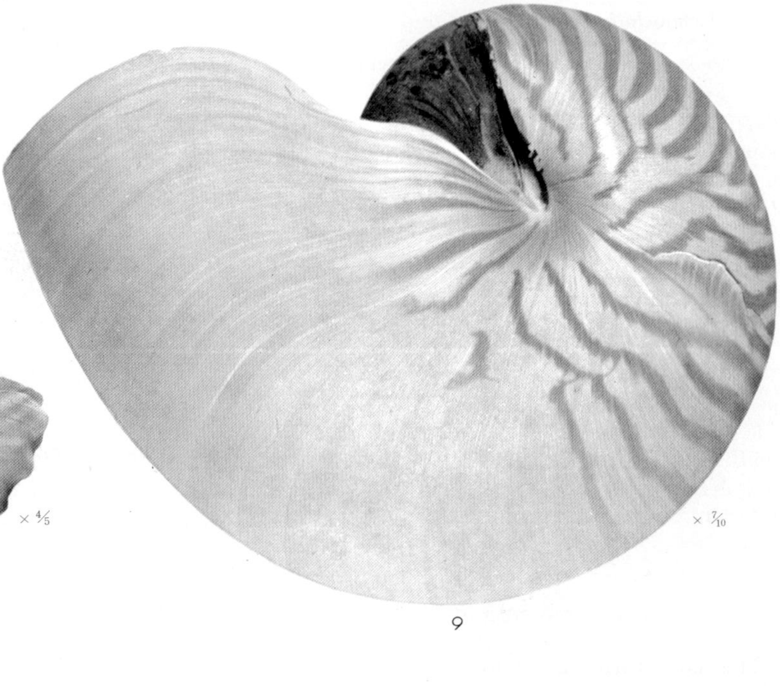

× 7/10

9

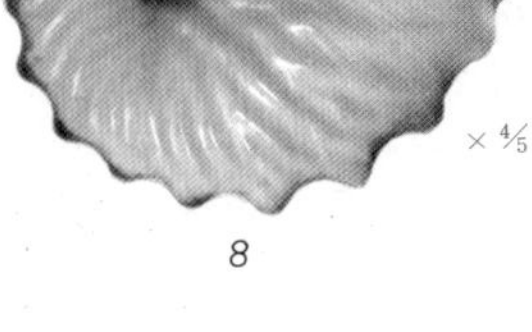

× ⅘

8

Class Polyplacophora

This is a rather small group well known as Loricata or Amphineura (including A-placophora) and is mostly the inhabitant of intertidal rocky shores throughout the world, but some are deep sea dwellers. This is quite unique in having the multivalved shells composed of 8 overlapping plates. These valves are surrounded by the leathery girdle forming an oval ring. The valves are usually sculptured by longitudinal ribs and other structures, and the girdle is often scaly or spiny. On the ventral side, the body has a large adhesive foot. The mantle encircles the body, and the fringed gills are arranged in a series on each side between the mantle and foot. The head is small, and bears no tentacles, no eyes, but only a mouth containing the radula. The sexes are separate, and the female lays eggs in ropes or clusters.

Family Ischnochitonidae

This family is characterized by scales covering the girdle and the insertion plates on the anterior and posterior valves which are not scalloped.

1. Ischnochiton comptus (GOULD)

A very common chiton on gravely shores. The animal is elongate and ellipsoidal in shape, and the shell is surrounded by a rather narrow scaly girdle. The valves are very broad, but narrow in height. The color of the shell varies from white to yellow, red or purplish black. Distribution: throughout Japan.

2. Ischnochiton boninensis (BERGENHAYN)

This closely resembles the preceding species, but the animal is narrow and long. The girdle is also narrow, and covered with small scales. The coloration is similar to that of the preceding species. Distribution: common on gravely shores throughout Japan.

Family Cryptoplacidae

This is a worm-like chiton whose animal is long, and bears small and separately placed valves on a very large spiny girdle. The insertion plate on the anterior valve has 3 slits.

3. Cryptoplax japonicus PILSBRY

The animal has a very large girdle on its upper side, when alive. The anterior 5 valves are overlapping, while the posterior 3 are separate each other. Distribution: not uncommon on rocks between tide marks throughout Japan, except Hokkaidô.

Family Acanthochitonidae

The animals are rounded, with a broad girdle covered all over with conspicuous tufts of siliceous spicules on both sides of rather small valves, arranged along the middle line. The anterior valve has 5 slits on its insertion plate, and other valves also bear 5 slits.

4. Acanthochiton defilippii (TAPPARONE-CANEFRI)

This is the largest species of this group. The girdle is covered by densely set, rather coarse spicules, with conspicuous sutural tufts of longer spicules on both sides of valves. Distribution: common on rocks between tide marks from central Honshû to Kyûshû.

Family Chitinidae

The characteristic features of this family are the spiny or scaly calcareous girdle constricted between each two valves and the finely pectinated teeth on the insertion plates on the anterior and posterior valves.

5. Liolophura japonica (LISCHKE)

This is a rather large species. The girdle surrounding the valves is covered with densely set, stout, calcareous spines, and is alternately banded with blackish brown and white. Distribution: very common on upper surfaces and in crevices of rocks between tide marks from Honshû to Kyûshû.

Class Cephalopoda

This class includes the octopus, squid, cuttlefish and pearly nautilus. They live only in the sea. The animal has the naked body, as the shell is reduced internally or is absent, but the shell of some *Nautilus* and *Spirula* is coiled externally or subexternally. The cephalopods except *Nautilus* have 8 or 10 arms, on which disc-shaped suckers are arranged. One or more arms in male cephalopods form a copulatory organ known as the hectocotylus. The eyes are very large and highly specialized. The large mantle wholly covers the large visceral mass. The mouth within the circle of arms has the upper and lower jaws, forming a parrot-like beak, and a ribbon of radula for their carnivorous life.

Family Argonautidae

The female of the family is distinctly larger than the male, and constructs a very thin and delicate shell in which she dwells and lays her eggs. The third pair arms of the male is highly specialized, and become hectocotylus. The upper pair of arms in female turn into broad membranes at their extremities which secrete the shell.

6. *Argonauta argo* LINNÉ

The shell is rather roundly coiled, large, growing into 200 mm or more in length, thin and fragile, white, tinged in pale black on the tubercles on the early spire, and compressed laterally with somewhat tuberculated keels at the margin. The surface is sculptured with numerous bifurcating wavy ridges. Distribution: over the Indo-Pacific areas.

7. *Argonauta boettgeri* MALTZAN

This is very closely similar to the following species, but has more numerous bifurcating ribs on the smaller, light brownish yellow shell. The tubercles on the keels of the shell are very prominent. Distribution: the same with the above species.

8. *Argonauta hians* SOLANDER

This is a rather small, round shell, with coarse bifurcating ribs terminating in tubercles on the keels. The mouth is rather wide. The color is cream to pale gray. Distribution: the same with the preceding 2 species.

Family Nautilidae

This family is an only living representative, or a living fossil, of the four-gilled cephalopods, many species of which are known as fossils, including ammonites.

9. *Nautilus pompilius* LINNÉ

This is a large and thick shell, more than 150 mm in diameter, whose surface is smooth, polished and marked by reddish brown wavy lines against the creamy background, but the parietal wall in the aperture is colored black. The animal lives in the large external shell described above, whose interior is crossed by septa separating the individual chambers. The last one is large and contains the animal. The numerous filament-like arms have no suckers. It has no ink sack. This dwells among coral rocks on the sea bottom, eating crabs. This is occasionally washed ashore in southern Japan, but has never been found alive there. Distribution: the Indo-Pacific areas.

Cross-section of the shell of *N. pompilius*
(after Yagura)

Family Ellobiidae

The shells are rather solid, ovate with an elevated spire on the large body whorl, and usually brown in color. The surface is smooth or sculptured. The aperture is like an ear in shape, and is armed with the teeth inside the thickened margin. The operculum is absent. They inhabit salt-water marshes in tropical and subtropical areas.

1. Cassidula plecotrematoides japonica MÖLLENDORFF

The shell is oval and its spire is small, but the body whorl is very large. The smooth, purplish brown surface is marginated by a groove below the suture. The aperture has 2 teeth on the thick columellar margin and also a notch on the thick, expanded outer margin. Distribution: from Amami Islands to Honshû, rather common among gravels on slimy and muddy bottom in bays.

2. Melampus nuxcastanea (KURODA)

The shell is solid, ovate, narrowed anteriorly and the greatest in diameter at the shoulder of body whorl. The surface is smooth, polished and colored brown. The spire is low. The aperture is narrow and bears 2 folds on the columellar margin and a series of small teeth on the inner wall of outer lip. This was formerly confused with *M. coffeus* distributed along Atlantic coasts of America. Distribution: Honshû to the Ryukyus, common among intertidal gravels in bays.

3. Pythia cecillei (PHILIPPI)

This is characterized by the somewhat dorso-ventrally flattened shell with an elevated spire. The color is brown, with a darker brown band below the suture and numerous scattered blotches. The aperture has the expanded outer margin and is armed with a series of strong teeth blocking the aperture. Distribution: Amami Islands and Kyûshû, rather common.

4. Melampus fasciatus (DESHAYES)

This resembles *M. nuxcastanea* in shape,

but is larger and ornamented by transverse white zones on the brown surface. Distribution: over the Indo-Pacific areas up to Amami Islands.

5. Cassidula mustelina (DESHAYES)

This is an ear-shaped shell, large for the group, which is very thick, smooth and polished, and oval in shape having a low spire. The coloration is purplish brown with whitish transverse zones. The margin of aperture is very thick, expanded and is carved as in *C. plecotrematoides japonica*. Distribution: tropical Pacific areas up to Formosa, very common among roots of mangroves.

6. Pythia pantherina A. ADAMS

This is larger than *P. cecillei*, but very similar to the latter in shape and coloration. There are many longitudinal threads on the upper part of body whorl, which are weakened on the lower part. *P. scarabaea* (LINNÉ) is a closely allied species. Distribution: Formosa and the Ryukyus, not uncommon.

7. Ellobium chinense (PFEIFFER)

A thick, elongate oval shell. The surface is covered by a brown periostracum and is weakly decussate on the upper part of the large body whorl occupying about 4/5 of the shell length. The aperture is ear-shaped and light yellowish white, with 2 folds on the columellar margin. Distribution: central Honshû to China, on slimy mud of reed swamps in bays.

Family Siphonariidae

They are the limpet-like, air-breathing shells, commonly attaching to rocks between

Comparison of the inner sides of *Siphonaria sirius* (Siphonariidae) (left) and *Cellana dorfsuosa* (Patellidae) (right).

[PLATE 69]   Ellobiidae, Siphonariidae, Pyramidellidae

tide marks. The shells are depressed and ribbed on its outer surface. The inner surface bears a horseshoe-shaped muscle scar, opening on the right side of the inverted shell and connected with a siphonal groove. This is a distinguishing feature of this family (see textfigure).

8. Siphonaria (Sacculosiphonaria) japonica (DONOVAN)

This is a thin, low conical limpet shell whose surface is sculptured by many radial ribs of different thickness. It is covered by a yellowish periostracum and dotted with brown between the ribs. The interior has a purplish chocolate-brown spatula alternately marginated by white and black dots. Distribution: from Hokkaidô to Kyûshû and Korea, very common on rocks between tide marks.

9. Siphonaria (Patellops) acmaeoides PILSBRY

The shell is low conical, oval and sculptured by about 15 primary ribs and several fine riblets between these ribs. The coloration is ashy white, with white radial rays on the ribs and blackish tinge in the interspaces. The inside is yellowish white, bearing rather radially arranged blackish blotches. The siphonal ridge is indistinct. Distribution: from Honshû to the Ryukyus, uncommon in tide pools on rocky shores.

10. Siphonaria (Mestasiphon) subatra PILSBRY

The shell is flat conical, with many radial ribs on its outer surface. The siphonal ridge consists of 2 conjoint ribs and distinctly projects beyond the margin. This is white on ribs and purplish black on their intervals on the outer surface, while the inner surface is blackish brown with pale spots on its margin corresponding with the exterior ribs. Distribution: Amami Islands and southwards, common.

11. Siphonaria laciniosa (LINNÉ)

This shell is rather solid and conical, with a pointed apex and rather straight sides. The surface has stout primary ribs

and several riblets between them, and is covered by a yellowish periostracum except on the white strong ribs. The interior bears a brownish spatula alternately marginated by white and brown radial bars. Distribution: very common in tropical Pacific areas up to central Honshû.

12. Siphonaria (Mestasiphon) sirius PILSBRY

The shell is medium in size and low conical. The surface bears 7–9 white, very strong, radial ribs and 2–3 riblets between the ribs. The interspaces are colored in black. The interior has a whitish spatula and radial streaks corresponding with the ribs on the outer surface. Distribution: from Honshû to Kyûshû; very common on rocks between tide marks.

Family Pyramidellidae

This family is more closely related to the cephalaspid opisthobranchiate molluscs rather than to the aglossate prosobranchia to which it has been formerly considered to belong. These species are ectoparasitic on polychaete worms and molluscs, and suck the hosts' blood by means of a buccal pump. They are hermaphrodite as in opisthobranchs. The shell is turreted or oval with many whorls. The larval shell is sinistral, while the adult shell is dextral. The surface is smooth or sculptured by axial and/or spiral ribs. The aperture has 1 or 3 folds on the columellar margin and is closed by the thin paucispiral operculum.

13. Agatha virgo A. ADAMS

This is a rather small, thin and elongated oval shell, whose surface is smooth, polished and semi-transparently white. The aperture contains a distinct fold at the upper end of columellar margin. Distribution: central Honshû to Kyûshû, rather common.

14. Syrnola brunnea (A. ADAMS)

The shell is solid and turreted with about 15 whorls, each whorl being marginated by a canaliculate sutural groove. The surface is smooth, polished and brown-colored. The body whorl is rather small and has an obtuse basal angle. Two folds occur on the straight columellar margin, the upper one being stronger than the lower one. Distribution: central Honshû to Kyûshû and China, uncommon on shallow sandy bottom.

15. Tiberia pulchella (A. ADAMS)

A rather thin but solid shell, highly pyramidal in shape and composed of about 12 whorls. The body whorl has a peripheral band and a periumbilical band of black on the light yellowish brown ground. Other upper whorls only show a black peripheral band above the suture. The surface is smooth and polished. The aperture has 2 distinct folds on the white columellar margin. The umbilicus is narrowly perforated. Distribution: Honshû to Kyûshû, rather common on sandy bottom between and below tide marks.

16. Actaeopyramis eximia (LISCHKE)

The shell is rather thin but solid, and elongated oval in shape, with about 12 whorls. The embryonic whorls are smooth, polished and white, while succeeding whorls are sculptured by spiral grooves punctured with growth cords, and is covered with a thin blackish periostracum. The aperture lacks teeth on the columellar margin. Distribution: from Honshû to Kyûshû, not uncommon.

17. Leucotina gigantea (DUNKER)

The shell is the largest of the group, yellowish white, oval in shape and has about 10 whorls. Each whorl is rather convex and sculptured by spiral grooves, the upper 2 of which are strong forming canaliculated sutural and subsutural grooves. The body whorl is rather large, occupying more than one half of the shell length. The aperture has a thickened and reflexed columellar margin, bearing an indistinct fold on its upper end. The umbilicus is narrowed by the dilation of the columellar margin. *L. dianae* (A. ADAMS) is a smaller allied species characterized by the round ovate shell. Distribution: central Honshû to Kyûshû, uncommonly collected from fine sandy bottom in shallow waters.

18. Otopleura (Aphalista) mitralis (A. ADAMS)

The shell is very solid and cylindrical ovate, with the large body whorl and conical spire. The sculpture consists of many strong axial ribs without any spiral threads. The aperture is semicircular, and its columellar margin has 3 folds, the upper one being larger than the others. The surface color is white to cream, with irregular dark brown patches. Distribution: widely found in the tropical Indo-Pacific areas up to Amami Islands, not uncommonly washed ashore.

19. Otopleura auriscati (HOLTEN)

This closely resembles the preceding species in shape. The shell is cylindrically elongated with a rather high spire and very solid. The surface is longitudinally ribbed, and the interstices of ribs are crossed by spiral beady cords below the suture. It is colored cream or white, being banded and spotted with chestnut-brown. The aperture has 3 folds on the columellar margin and basal fasciole. There is no umbilicus. Distribution: over the Indo-Pacific areas up to Amami Islands, not uncommon.

20. Pyramidella (Milda) ventricosa GUÉRIN

The shell is ovate, widely inflated at the body whorl and has a conical spire. The surface is smooth, polished, colored white and spotted with dark brown or marked by 3 bands. Of the 3 columellar folds, the upper one is larger than other two. There is a basal fasciole, and the umbilicus is closed. Distribution: Amami Islands and farther south over the Indo-Pacific areas, uncommon.

21. Pyramidella sulcata A. ADAMS

The shell is solid and highly turreted with about 15 whorls. Each whorl is slightly convex. The surface is smooth and rather polished, and bears 1–2 series of dark brown spiral patches crossed by pale brown streaks. The columellar margin of aperture has 3 folds. The umbilicus is closed. Distribution: the Indo-Pacific areas up to Amami Islands, uncommon.

[PLATE 69]   Ellobiidae, Siphonariidae, Pyramidellidae

22. *Pyramidella terebelloides* (A. ADAMS)

The shell is thin but solid, and elongated oval with a high conical spire. The surface of the large body whorl has 3 brown, narrow, spiral bands on its white ground, but earlier whorls have only 2. The umbilicus is narrowly and deeply perforated. Distribution: widely distributed in the Indo-Pacific areas up to central Honshû. *P. terebellum* (MÜLLER) has broad bands on the surface of its shell.

23. *Pyramidella (Voluspa) acus* (GMELIN)

This is large for the family, highly turreted with more than 20 whorls, smooth and polished. Each whorl is rather convex and the suture is somewhat canaliculated. The color is creamy white with chestnut-brown spots and regularly arranged 4–5 spiral bands. The aperture has 3 folds on the columellar margin. Distribution: the same with the preceding species in the geographical range, not common on shallow, fine sandy bottom.

PLATE 69

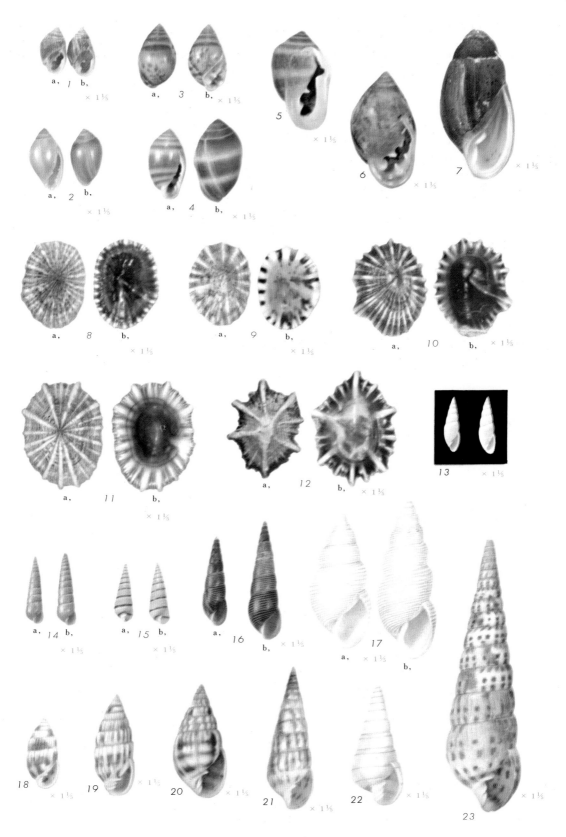

PLATE 70

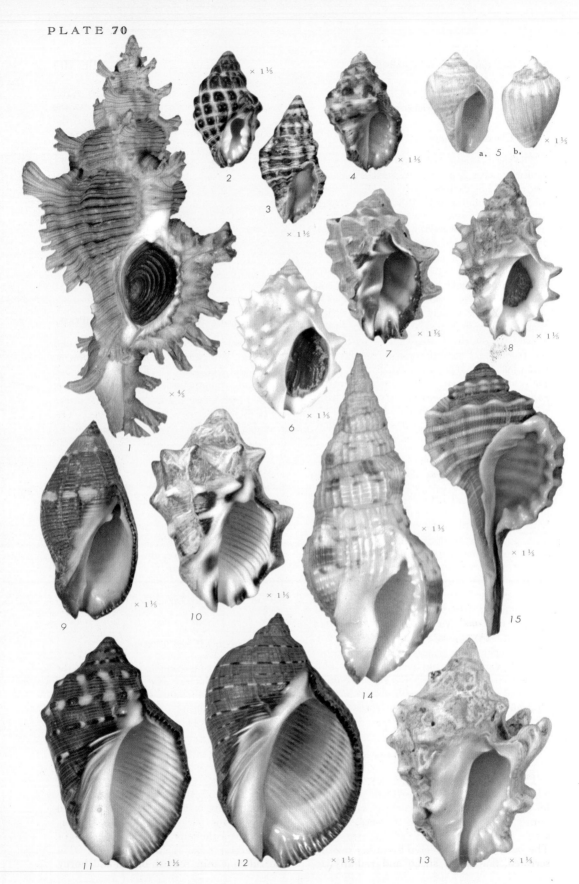

2   × 1⅕

3   × 1⅕

4   × 1⅕

a, 5 b,   × 1⅕

6   × 1⅕

7   × 1⅕

8   × 1⅕

1   × ⅘

9   × 1⅕

10   × 1⅕

14   × 1⅕

15   × 1⅕

11   × 1⅕

12   × 1⅕

13   × 1⅕

Family Muricidae (4)

1. *Chicoreus saulii* (SOWERBY)

The shell is large, solid and very elongately fusiform, with 3 prominent varices on each whorl. The varices are set with erect, foliaceously muricated, rather large fronds, intervening a small one. The surface is transversely sculptured by fine cords and delicate striae. The aperture is rather small and oval. The outer lip is rather thick and finely crenulated, while the parietal lip is feebly callused and has a small knob. The columellar lip is simple and smooth. The anterior canal is widely elongated and deeply channeled, and recurved. The coloration is pale yellowish brown, stained with pink; the fronds and the aperture are edged with rose-pink, and the spiral cords and striae are chestnut-brown. This differs from *M. rosarius* and *M. torrefactus* in having a rose-tinged and finely striated shell. Distribution: southern Honshû to the tropical Indo-Pacific areas, in shallow waters.

2. *Drupa granulata* (DUCLOS)

This drupe shell is small, solid and fusiform. The spire has 5 whorls, each marked with 2 series of blackish brown granules. The body whorl is spirally sculptured by 6 rows of somewhat squarish, radially arranged and blackish brown granules. The interspaces are faintly and spirally striated. The aperture is rather narrow and elongate, the outer lip being thick and with a few denticulated nodules within it when fully matured. The interior is grayish in color. The anterior canal is short and wide, the posterior canal being narrowly notched. This species is easily recognized by its regularly arranged knobs. Distribution: central Honshû and southwards, on rocks below the low tide mark.

3. *Drupa margariticola* (BRODERIP)

The shell is small, rather thick and somewhat fusiform. The 6 whorls are sculptured by finely serrated spiral striae, which are faintly lamellated by growth lines, with a series of small granules at the shoulder. The body whorl is covered by rather densely serrated, fine spiral striae and radially arranged furrows, which are crossed by spiral striae forming 3 series of granules at the crossing points, the upper series on the shoulder being the largest. The aperture is elongate fusiform, the outer lip being thick and somewhat denticulated within. The coloration is blackish brown with 4 spiral white bands on the body whorl. The interior is white and the margin of aperture is pale reddish brown. This is somewhat like the next species, but differs in having a more elongate shell and finely serrated sculpture. Distribution: central Honshû and southwards, on rocks below the tide mark.

4. *Purpura (Mancinella) squamosa* (PEASE)

The shell is small, solid and rhomboidal fusiform. The spire consists of 3 whorls. The body whorl is large, and sculptured by broad, roundly elevated, radial furrows which form 4 series of granules at the crossing points with squamous spiral striae. The granules are stained by dark brown, and the interspaces are white and are also finely striated. The aperture is large and semicircular. The outer lip is rather thin and slightly denticulated on the inner margin. The interior is grayish white and the margin is dark brown in color.

This differs from the preceding species in its compressed shell shape and broad, rounded, radial furrows, and also differs from *P. clavigera* in having finely serrated spiral striae. Distribution: Kyûshû and southwards, on rocks below the low tide mark.

5. *Pinaxia citrina* (KURODA)

The shell is small and somewhat like the cone shell in shape. The spire is low, and has 4 whorls. The body whorl is very large, occupying four-fifths of the shell length. The surface is rather smooth, with only faint spiral threads, and is covered by a velvety, light yellowish periostracum. The aperture is large and feebly notched posteriorly, the interior being orange-red in color and ribbed with 13–15 reddish brown lirae. The outer lip is simple and the edge is sharp, and the parietal lip is somewhat concave. The columella is somewhat straight. The anterior canal is short and wide. The operculum is thin, reddish brown and horny.

[PLATE 70]   Muricidae, Colubrariidae, Cymatiidae

The genus *Conothais* was once established for this species on its distinctive shell shape, but is now synonymized with this genus. Distribution: from central Honshû to Kyûshû, common on rocks below the low tide mark.

6. Purpura (Mancinella) siro (KURODA)

The shell is medium in size, solid and rather rounded in shape. The spire is conical, has 4 whorls and has a series of tubercles at the shoulder. The body whorl is sculptured by 4 spiral rows of tubercles which are stout and somewhat pointed, the upper one being the largest. The aperture is large, rather ovate in shape and the outer lip is thin and bears 4 notches and numerous crenations. The interior is spirally and finely striated, and the columella is stout with a feeble torsion. The coloration is pure white. This species differs from *P. echinata* in its white color, smoothly striated surface and less erected spines. Distribution: south of central Honshû, in shallow waters.

7. Purpura (Mancinella) distinguenda DUNKER et ZELEBOR

The shell is medium in size, rather thick and nearly oval. The spire has 4 whorls. Earlier whorls are armed with a series of erect and pointed, spirally arranged nodules. The body whorl is large, about 3/4 as long as the shell, and sculptured by 4 rows of large, erect, pointed granules which are spirally and radially arranged. The aperture is large and semi-circular, the outer lip being rather thin and finely crenulated at the margin. The interior has 4 small denticles and the columellar lip is straight and somewhat callused. It is light brownish on the surface, while the interior is grayish white, the margin is stained with dark chocolate, and the columellar lip is reddish brown. This species somewhat resembles *P. tuberosa*, but differs in its smaller shell and the lack of orange colored striae inside the aperture. Distribution: southern Kyûshû and southwards, on rocks below the tide level.

8. Purpura (Mancinella) echinata BLAINVILLE

The body whorl is encircled by 4 series of pointed, erect granules which are radially arranged and of nearly equal size. In addition, it is covered by numerous, irregular, somewhat minutely serrated, fine, spiral striae. The aperture is somewhat large, the outer lip being thin, finely striated and crenulated within. The columellar lip is rather straight and thickly callused. The shell is pale brown outside, and white inside. This species is distinguished from the preceding one by the equal-sized granules and serrated striae, and also differs in its shell shape. Distribution: central Honshû and southwards, in shallow waters.

9. Nassa francolinus (BRUGUIÈRE)

The shell is medium to rather large in size, solid, thick and fusiform. The spire is accuminate and has 5 whorls, the body whorl being 3/4 as long as the total shell length. The surface is sculptured by irregularly elevated, fine, spiral cords and minute growth lines. The aperture is rather large, the outer lip being thin and with numerous, fine crenulations. The parietal lip has a rather large fold on its upper part, and the columella is somewhat recurved and heavily callused. The anterior canal is broad, rather short, and deeply channeled, while the posterior canal is narrowly notched. The coloration of outer surface is reddish brown, and irregularly stained with white maculations and zigzag striae. The interior is cinnamon-brown and the outer edge of aperture is alternately stained with dark brown and white. Distribution: southern Honshû and farther south, in shallow waters.

10. Purpura (Mancinella) tuberosa [RÖDING]

This medium-sized snail is solid, heavy and nearly oval. The spire is conical, and has 5 whorls, each of which bears a series of tubercles at the shoulder. The body whorl is large, and sculptured by 3 series of radially arranged tubercles, the upper one being extremely large and sharply pointed. The interspaces are finely and spirally striated. The aperture is large, and the outer lip is rather thin and finely denticulated. The interior is finely striated with orange-red color bands, and the margin is alternately stained with white and blackish brown. This species is closely related to *P. distinguenda*, but differs in having a larger shell and 3 series of tubercles in consrast to 4 series in that species. Distribution: south of Amami Islands, on rocks below the low tide mark.

11. Purpura rudolphi (LAMARCK)

The shell is medium in size, thick and solid. The spire is rather small, comprising 3 whorls. Each whorl has a series of small, blackish brown nodules at the shoulder, and is also slightly angulated and finely striated. The body whorls is extremely large, and sculptured by broad, spiral ribs which are set with large and low nodules, the interspaces being marked with regular, broad but low, spiral cords. Its surface is also roughly rippled with rugose growth lines. The aperture is large and semi-circular, and the outer lip is thin and finely crenulated within. The columellar lip is somewhat wide and callused. The coloration is blackish brown and spotted with white on the granulated ribs. The aperture is white with pale brown hue. This species closely resembles the next one, but differs in having a smaller and granulated shell. Distribution: central Honshû and southwards, on rocks below the low tide mark.

12. Purpura persica (LINNÉ)

This is similar to the above species in general features of the shell. The body whorl is sculptured by narrow and low, roughly and finely nodosed, spiral ribs, 7 or 8 in number, and the interspaces are marked with numerous, fine striae. The outer lip is rather thin and somewhat deeply rippled at the margin. The interior is marked with reddish brown striae on the porcellaneously white background. The columellar wall is reddish orange, broad, convex and thickly callused. This differs from *P. rudolphi* in lacking the granulated sculpture and having a wider anterior canal. It is also distinct in its large-sized and finely sculptured shell. Distribution: southern Kyûshû and southwards, below the low tide mark.

13. Purpura (Mancinella) armigera (LINK)

The shell is rather large, thick, solid and somewhat inflated fusiform. The spire is conical, and has 6 whorls, each bearing a series of large, blunt nodules. The body whorl is large and marked on its surface by 3 series of large, blunt, erect, finger-like granules, of which the upper one is extremely large. The surface is also sculptured by broad but low spiral cords, and mostly covered with thick calcareous deposits. The outer lip is rather thin and denticulated within, and the columellar wall has 2 or 3 weak folds at the center. The coloration is reddish brown and the granules are mostly white. This species is distinct in its large size and extremely large granules. Distribution: Tanegashima and southwards, on rocks below the tide mark.

Family Colubrariidae

14. Colubraria maculosa (GMELIN)

The shell is rather solid, thick, oblongly turreted, and large in size, exceeding 95 mm in length. The spire is obtusely acuminate, including 12 or 13 whorls. The whorls bear 3 roundly elevated, broad varices, which are not continuous from one whorl to the next. The surface is closely and coarsely latticed by rather prominent, radial ridges and fine spiral cords, and strongly granulated at their crossing points. The interstices are finely cancellated with somewhat raised striae. The body whorl is rather large, about half as long as the shell, and sculptured in the same way as the earlier whorls. The aperture is narrow and fusiform, the outer lip being denticulated and callused within. The columellar callus layer widely spreads over the body whorl. The anterior canal is very short but wide, and somewhat recurved. The exterior is light brown and variously stained and maculated with brown and light orange-brown spots. This species differs from *C. castanea* in having a larger and light-colored shell, and also from *C. cumingi* (DOHRN) in having a large, coarsely sculptured and finely maculated shell. Distribution: south of the Ryukyus, in shallow waters.

[PLATE 70]

Muricidae, Colubrariidae, Cymatiidae

Family Cymatiidae (2)

15. Cymatium caudatum (GMELIN)

The shell is medium in size, rather solid, club-shaped and ventricose. The spire is rather short and has 4 post-nuclear whorls, which are covered by a brownish periostracum. The suture is deeply canaliculated. The body whorl is extremely large and its surface is marked with roundly elevated, broad varices on both sides, and sculptured by broad but low, rounded, radial furrows and thick, roundly elevated, spiral ribs which are 7 in number and overriding the varices. These furrows and ribs form roundly topped granules at their crossing points. Moreover the surface is finely reticulated by delicate, radial and spiral threads. The aperture is large, and the outer lip is rugosely and roughly denticulated within. The columella is strongly wrinkled at its upper part. The anterior canal is prominently long, and rather smooth and deeply channeled. It is purplish brown outside with reddish orange tinge, and reddish orange inside the aperture. This species is closely related to *C. gutturnium*, but the latter is white in color and the suture is not canaliculated. Distribution: Kyûshû and southwards, in shallow waters.

Family Olividae (2)

1. Baryspira hilgendorfi (VON MARTENS)

The shell is solid, fusiform in shape and medium in size. The surface is smooth and highly polished. The spire is elevated, but is wholly covered with a thick brown callus except the mammilated apex. It is brown with a broad pale brown band on the body whorl, which is marginated by a whitish shallow groove at its lower edge. The aperture is elongate ovate, with the twisted, callused, columellar margin. The operculum is the same with that of *B. albocallosa*. Distribution: Suruga and Sagami Bays, rarely collected from 80–150 fathoms depth.

Family Terebridae (2)

2. Decorihastula affinis (GRAY)

The shell is subulate with about 18 whorls, and is closely and longitudinally ribbed on the outer surface. A subsutural groove and narrow spiral grooves are also marked forming a mosaic sculpture. It is blotched with brown on the carnelian red ground. Distribution: central Honshû and southwards, uncommon on shallow sandy bottom.

3. Hastula verreauxi (DESHAYES)

The shell is acutely subulate. The surface is rather smooth and polished, with longitudinal, densely set plicae all over. The exterior is ashy yellow to light brown, with a pale zone containing dark brown dots below the suture. Distribution: the Indo-Pacific areas up to Amami Islands, common on sandy bottom in shallow waters.

4. Cinguloterebra serotina (ADAMS et REEVE)

The shell is highly turreted with about 30 whorls. Each whorl is sculptured by 2 distinct subsutural grooves bearing granulated cords. The rest of the surface is reticulately grooved. The color is light brown with large dark brown blotches. Distribution: from central Honshû to China, common on sandy bottom, 10–50 fathoms deep.

5. Clathroterebra fortunei (DESHAYES) var.

The whorls are about 25 in number, and are rather convex. The surface has many axial ribs, crossed by spiral narrow cords producing the reticulated appearance. It is light yellow, with a light brown broad zone on the lower half of each whorl. The base of the body whorl is whitish. The aperture is small and rather narrowly canaliculated downwards. This varietal form may be confused with *Cl. fortunei*, but can easily be distinguished from the latter by the absence of a distinct subsutural groove on the convex whorls and by the finer reticulated sculpture. Therefore a new name should be given to this species. Distribution: off Tosa Bay, about 50 fathoms in depth.

6. Impagus confusa (SMITH)

This is a small subulate shell whose surface is smooth and polished, bearing weak growth lines, and is colored purplish brown, with a white zone on the periphery and whitish patches below the suture. The aperture is rather wide. Distribution: Bonin Islands, on shallow sandy bottom.

7. Hastulina solida (DESHAYES)

The shell is cylindrically oblong, solid and stout, with about 12 whorls. The surface is smooth and polished and is tesselated with light yellowish brown on the whitish ground. Distribution: the Indo-Pacific areas up to Amami Islands, very common on sandy bottom in shallow waters.

8. Hastulopsis gotoensis (SMITH)

This subulate shell is rather small, with about 12 whorls and is smooth on later whorls, while earlier whorls are longitudinally plicate. The color is purplish brown, yellow and dark brown spots are alternately arranged below the suture, and a narrow yellowish band encircles the obtusely angulated periphery. This may belong to the same species with *H. melanacme* (SMITH). Distribution: from central Honshû to Kyûshû, rather rare on shallow sandy bottom.

[PLATE 71]   Olividae, Terebridae

9. Hastulina casta (HINDS)

The shell is cylindrically elongated with about 14 whorls, smooth and polished except many axial grooves below the suture. The surface is white with light brown blotches, or half white and half black on the upper and lower parts of each whorl respectively. Distribution: the Indo-Pacific areas up to central Honshû.

10. Brevimyurella lischkeana awajiensis (PILSBRY)

This is closely similar to *B. lischkeana* (Pl. 39) in shape and coloration, but the shell is more stout, having comparatively larger diameter on the body whorl, which is sculptured with axial costae without any spiral threads. Distribution: central Honshû to Kyûshû, rather common on sandy bottom in shallow waters.

11. Noditerebra (Diplomeriza) evoluta kirai OYAMA

This is subulate with about 20 whorls, ashy brown, with a whitish zone on the periphery. Each whorl is slightly convex and is sculptured by axial ribs and a strongly constricted subsutural groove below the suture. The spiral threads are very weak. This form is collected from deep bottom of 20–50 fathoms off Honshû and Shikoku. The original form of this species is rather common on sandy bottom between tide marks and 5 fathoms depth, in areas from Kyûshû to central Honshû and Korea.

12. Triplostephanus lima (DESHAYES)

This closely resembles *C. serotina* in shape and coloration, but is larger and has a more densely reticulated sculpture on the surface. Distribution: central Honshû to Kyûshû and China, rather common on fine sandy bottom in shallow waters.

13. Abretiella cerithina (LAMARCK)

The shell is cylindrically subulate, rather stout and solid. The whorls are slightly convex, and are sculptured by plicae at the suture on earlier whorls, while later whorls are smooth and has a shallow sub-sutural groove. The exterior is yellowish white, and stained and streaked with orange-yellow. Distribution: Shikoku and farther south over the Indo-Pacific areas, very common on shallow sandy bottom.

14. Dimidiacus cingulifera (LAMARCK)

The shell consists of about 20 whorls, and is light brown in color. The surface is rather smooth and polished, with distantly placed, punctured, spiral grooves between the periphery and crenulated sutural girdle. Distribution: the Indo-Pacific areas up to Shikoku, common on shallow sandy bottom.

15. Subula argus (HINDS)

The shell is rather large in size and elongated subulate with about 18 whorls. Earlier whorls have a narrow subsutural groove, but the groove tends to disappear on lower whorls. Four encircling rows of somewhat squarish pale yellow spots are marked on the white ground. These coloration is very regular and characteristic. Distribution: the Indo-Pacific areas up to Amami Islands, uncommon on shallow sandy bottom.

16. Subula (Oxymeris) felina (DILLWYN)

The shell is large, conically subulate and rather solid, with about 15 whorls. The smooth surface bears a narrow subsutural groove, and is colored white with 2 encircling rows of reddish chestnut spots. The necklace of spots above the suture is very characteristic. Distribution: the same with the preceding species.

17. Subula (Oxymeris) chlorata (LAMARCK)

This shell is large, solid and conically subulate, and resembles the preceding species in shape, but the coloration is quite different. It is decorated on the milky white surface of whorls by 2 spiral rows of purplish brown flames divided by a narrow subsutural groove. Two additional rows of purplish spots are also encircling on the base of body whorl. Distribution: the Indo-Pacific areas up to Amami Islands, uncommon on shallow sandy bottom.

PLATE **71**

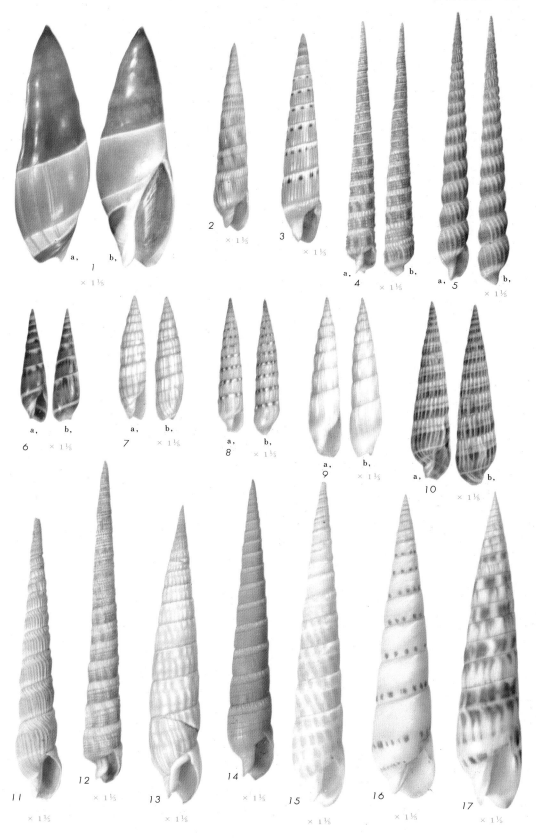

a,   b,
1
× 1⅕

2
× 1⅕

3
× 1⅕

a,   b,
4   × 1⅕

a,   5   b,
× 1⅕

a,   b,
6   × 1⅕

a,   b,
7   × 1⅕

a,   b,
8   × 1⅕

a,   b,
9   × 1⅕

a,   b,
10
× 1⅕

11
× 1⅕

12
× 1⅕

13
× 1⅕

14
× 1⅕

15
× 1⅕

16
× 1⅕

17
× 1⅕

PLATE **72**

1 × ⅘

2 × ⅘

3 × 1⅕

4 × ⁷⁄₁₀

5 × 1⅕

6 × 1⅕

7 × ⅘

8 × 1⅕

9 × ½

10 a,   b,   × 1⅓

1. *Amusium japonicum* (GMELIN)
—Pectinidae—

The shell is large, exceeding 100 mm in length in fully grown specimens, compressed, orbicular in shape with small ears and gaping at both ends. The left valve is reddish, and the right yellowish white in color. Radiating internal ribs reach the edge, becoming obsolete toward the umbo. *A. pleuronectes* (Pl. 49) is an ally of this species, but the former has a smaller shell of different coloration. The number of the internal ribs on the left valve is about 40 in *A. japonicum* instead of about 25 in *A. pleuronectes*. *Capulus dilatata* (Pl. 14) frequently attaches to the surface of the left valve and bores a hole through the shell. Distribution : central Honshû and southwards. This is one of the edible mussels in Japan, rather common on shallow, fine sandy bottom.

A left valve of *Amusium japonicum* with a scar and perforation made by a parasitic *Capulus dilatata* shown on the right side.

2. *Fulvia mutica* (REEVE) —Cardiidae—

The shell is large, about 100 mm long and much inflated, but thin and fragile, and internally rose in color. The surface is rayed with numerous erect hirsute series on the yellowish periostracum, corresponding to the linear grooves. The mantle line is entire. This is also one of the important edible mussels in Japan. Distribution : throughout Japan, Korea and China, occasionally abundant on muddy bottom of sheltered waters.

3. *Meiocardia moltkiana sanguinomacu-lata* DUNKER —Glossidae—

This is a very unique shell. The beak is strongly inclined forwardly. Its surface bears distantly placed coarse concentric ribs and a strongly angular rib running from the beak to the sharply pointed postero-ventral corner. The color of blotches on the light yellowish background is reddish brown. Distribution : tropical Pacific seas up to central Honshû, uncommonly collected from sandy bottom in shallow waters.

4. *Spisula (Pseudocardium) sachalinensis* (SCHRENCK) —Mactridae—

An important edible mussel in northern Japan. The shell reaches a very large size, exceeding 100 mm in length, and is solid and heavy in fully grown specimens. The surface is covered by a rough and yellowish brown periostracum. The hinge plate has a large pit, rather small cardinal teeth, and a stout lateral tooth on each side of the cardinals. The mantle line is deeply sinuated. Distribution ; northern Honshû and northwards, common on sandy bottom in shallow waters.

5. *Solemya (Petrasma) pervernicosa* (KURODA) —Solemyidae—

The shell is rather large, elongated and rounded, gaping at both ends. The surface is covered with a horny periostracum which is smooth, polished, and yellowish brown, extending like the fringe far beyond the margins of both valves. Distribution : Japan Sea and Pacific coasts of northern Honshû, uncommon on muddy bottom of 70–100 fathoms depth.

6. *Pterelectroma zebra* (REEVE)
—Pteriidae—

A small triangular species having a thin and fragile shell. The left valve is somewhat inflated, while the right is flat. The surface is smooth, polished, striped with dark brown bands, extending obliquely from the umbo to the margin. This attaches by the byssus to a certain hydroid species on rocks in shallow waters. Distribution : widely distributed in the Pacific up to central Honshû. The specimen shown here is named *Pt. zebra tomlini* (PRASHAD) as a varietal form.

[PLATE 72]

7. *Annachlamys reevei* (ADAMS et REEVE)
—Pectinidae—

The shell is medium-sized, and circular in shape, with almost equal ears. The left valve is rather flat, while the right valve is somewhat convex. Broad but low ribs regularly radiate on the surface, and the interspaces are narrowly grooved, crossed by slightly lamellate growth lines. The color is very pretty golden orange with white blotches. The radial ribs are about 18 in number. Distribution: central Honshû and southwards, rather rare on shallow, fine sandy bottom.

8. *Curvemysella paula* (A. ADAMS)
—Montacutidae—

This is characterized by a curved shell adapted to the symbiotic life with the helmet crab. The shell is thin but solid and white, covered by a light yellowish periostracum. The hinge teeth are weak. Distribution: widely distributed in the Indo-Pacific, northward to central Honshû.

9. *Pteria (Magnavicula) penguin* [RÖDING]
—Pteriidae—

This is a very large pteriid species, reaching 300 mm in height. The height is greater than the length. This has a rather long, winged posterior process. The hinge line is long and straight. The shell is dark bluish brown outside, and the inner surface is very brilliantly nacreous, with a deep black marginal area. This attaches by the byssus to rocks in shallow waters, and is occasionally used as the mother shell of cultured pearl. Distribution: south of Amami Islands.

10. *Anomia chinensis* PHILIPPI
—Anomiidae—

This pearly saddle oyster is a sessile form, adhering to the substratum by the calcareous byssus through a large foramen on the right valve. The left valve has 3 scars inside at the center, and no holes. The color is white to brown, without striped bands. Distribution: throughout Japan, Korea, China and Indonesia.

Index to Latin Names